ENGINEERING
MECHANICS

ENGINEERING MECHANICS

By

SEIBERT FAIRMAN

LATE PROFESSOR OF ENGINEERING MECHANICS
PURDUE UNIVERSITY

AND

CHESTER S. CUTSHALL

PROFESSOR OF ENGINEERING MECHANICS
PURDUE UNIVERSITY

SECOND EDITION

NEW YORK: JOHN WILEY & SONS, INC.
LONDON · SYDNEY

PREFACE TO SECOND EDITION

In the preparation of this edition, no radical departures from the original textbook were contemplated. The only addition of consequence is a chapter on product of inertia and moments of inertia about principal axes, which is added primarily for the benefit of students in aeronautical engineering for use in connection with unsymmetrical bending. The data of many problems have been altered, and new problems have been inserted throughout. In recognition of the desires of a number of teachers, answers for some problems have been omitted.

SEIBERT FAIRMAN
C. S. CUTSHALL

May, 1946

PREFACE

In view of the fact that several good textbooks are already available in the field of elementary engineering mechanics, the authors realize that some explanation may be due for introducing a new volume on this subject. Books in this field differ from one another principally in the amount of material covered, the arrangement, and the manner of presentation. It is intended that this book shall differ from others in one or more of these aspects.

The time available for a basic course in mechanics in many institutions is limited by other curricular requirements. Therefore, instead of planning a comprehensive treatise on the subject, the authors have attempted to plan a textbook which can be covered in the time usually allotted to the subject without the necessity of omitting large sections, thus destroying the continuity. To accomplish this purpose, it is necessary to avoid much repetition of topics previously covered in prerequisite courses, and to eliminate topics which may properly be deferred to more advanced courses. Accordingly, proofs of certain propositions such as the parallelogram law and Varignon's theorem, usually demonstrated in the general physics course, are here omitted. Likewise, topics such as product of inertia which may properly be considered in advanced strength of materials, certain parts of kinematics, and balancing of reciprocating parts of mechanisms are also omitted. Other topics are included, particularly in kinetics, which may conveniently be omitted if time limitations make it necessary. In recognition of the growing importance of dimensional analysis and its applications, a very brief introduction to this subject has been made at the beginning of that part of the book dealing with kinetics, and the dimensional formula is given for each new quantity taken up thereafter.

In arranging the material, the authors were guided by the belief that a task may be accomplished with greater facility if all the necessary tools are available at the beginning. Hence, the various processes for resolving forces into components, combining into resultants, and determining moments are explained for all types of force systems before entering into the discussion of static equilibrium. In kinetics, the relations between work and kinetic energy are developed at an early

vii

point so as to be available for use in the dynamics of rotating bodies.

In the presentation of the material, the authors have endeavored to avoid making the subject appear more complex than necessary. A knowledge of integral calculus is assumed, and this branch of mathematics is employed as the occasion requires; however, the use of calculus is not indicated when simple algebra is sufficient. A liberal number of solved examples are supplied to illustrate and explain further the topics under discussion and to arouse the student's interest. These are followed by numerous problems for the student to solve. The answers are given for all such problems because the authors feel that the student acquires a greater confidence in his progress if he has a check on his results. Most of the answers have been determined by slide-rule computation to the nearest third significant digit. Instructors who prefer that answers not be given may make changes in the data. Although the authors have endeavored to furnish problems of a practical engineering character whenever possible, they maintain that at times problems of the so-called academic type have a definite teaching value and so have not hesitated to insert them at strategic points.

The authors wish to acknowledge their indebtedness to Dean R. G. Dukes for reading the manuscript and offering valuable suggestions; to Professor A. P. Poorman, who has been a guiding influence through many years of personal and professional association; and to Professor W. B. Sanders, who has generously devoted considerable time in checking the solutions of all examples and problems.

Acknowledgment is also made of the use for reference purposes of books on mechanics by Poorman, Seely and Ensign, Dodge and Thompson, Boyd, and others.

SEIBERT FAIRMAN
C. S. CUTSHALL

PURDUE UNIVERSITY
June, 1938

CONTENTS

PART I—STATICS

CHAPTER I

INTRODUCTION; GENERAL PRINCIPLES

CHAPTER II

EQUILIBRIUM OF COPLANAR FORCES

CHAPTER III

STRESSES AND REACTIONS IN SIMPLE STRUCTURES

CHAPTER IV

EQUILIBRIUM OF FORCES IN SPACE

CHAPTER V

FRICTION

CHAPTER VI

CENTROIDS AND CENTER OF GRAVITY

CHAPTER VII

MOMENT OF INERTIA OF AREA

CHAPTER VIII

PRODUCT OF INERTIA OF AREA; MAXIMUM AND MINIMUM
MOMENTS OF INERTIA

CHAPTER IX

MOMENT OF INERTIA OF MASS

PART II—KINETICS

CHAPTER X

RECTILINEAR MOTION

CHAPTER XI

CURVILINEAR MOTION AND ROTATION

CHAPTER XII

Work, Energy, and Power

CHAPTER XIII

Dynamics of Rotating Bodies

CHAPTER XIV

Plane Motion

CHAPTER XV

Impulse, Momentum, and Impact

PART I—STATICS

CHAPTER I

INTRODUCTION; GENERAL PRINCIPLES

Art. 1. The Relation of Mechanics to Engineering. *Mechanics* is that branch of the general science of physics which treats of the action of forces on material bodies. It is usually divided into two parts, *statics* and *kinetics*. *Statics* treats of the relations between forces acting on bodies at rest. *Kinetics* treats of the relations between forces acting on bodies in motion and includes the subject of *kinematics*, which deals with pure motion.

Engineering mechanics or *applied mechanics* is the study of the principles of mechanics as applied to problems of engineering. Since the engineer constantly faces problems involving the control of forces and their application to useful purposes, the study of the effects and relations of forces necessarily constitutes an essential part of his preparation. Consequently the subject of mechanics is a basic part of the engineering curriculum and must precede such technical subjects as machine design and structural design.

The study of mechanics is customarily preceded by a course in general physics. A knowledge of the laws, definitions, and principles taken up in the mechanics branch of physics will be assumed throughout this book. Although these fundamental physical concepts will be restated as they arise in the course of the subject, reference should be made to a textbook in general physics if a more detailed discussion is desired. A knowledge of the various branches of mathematics, including elementary integral calculus, and the ability to use them are also assumed.

Art. 2. Force. *Force* may be defined as that which changes, or tends to change, the state of motion of a body. This conception of force is involved in the laws of motion as formulated by Sir Isaac Newton. These laws are stated as follows:

1. A body at rest tends to remain at rest, and a body in motion tends to remain in motion with the same speed in a straight-line path, unless acted upon externally by some unbalanced force. This law is the basis of the statics part of mechanics.

1

2. If a body is acted upon externally by an unbalanced force, there will result in the motion of the body an acceleration proportional to the force and inversely proportional to the mass of the body. This law is the basis of the kinetics part of mechanics.

3. For every force there is an equal, opposite, and collinear reaction; that is, a single force cannot exist alone, or a body cannot exert a force on another without receiving an equal force in return.

The *resultant* of a system of forces is a single force, or a force couple, which acting alone will produce the same effect as the system. (The force couple will be explained in Art. 6.) The *equilibrant* of a system of forces is a single force, or a force couple, which if added to the system will balance or neutralize the system. It follows that the resultant and equilibrant are equal in magnitude but opposite in direction or sense; also, when the resultant and equilibrant are each single forces, they must be collinear.

The *components* of a force are two or more forces which, acting together, have an effect identical to that of the given force. Hence, a force is the resultant of its components.

The *moment* of a force is the measure of its turning or twisting effect about a given axis and is determined by the product of the force and its perpendicular distance from the axis.

A *vector* is a physical quantity which involves a sense of direction as well as magnitude. Any vector may be represented graphically by a straight line whose length represents to some chosen scale the magnitude of the vector and which has an arrowhead at one end to designate the direction. A force is not completely specified without giving both its magnitude and direction and is therefore a vector quantity. Other examples of vector quantities are displacement, velocity, acceleration, and momentum.

A physical quantity which involves magnitude but no sense of direction is known as a *scalar* quantity. Time, for instance, does not have direction and is therefore a scalar quantity. Other examples of scalar quantities are mass, work, and energy.

Art. 3. Fundamental Laws Governing Forces. The following laws are developed in general physics and are briefly restated here without further proof.

The Parallelogram Law. If two coplanar, concurrent forces are laid out vectorially with both forces pointing toward or both away from their point of intersection and the parallelogram is completed upon the forces as sides, the diagonal of the parallelogram, drawn from the point of intersection, represents completely the resultant of the forces. In Fig. 1, *A* and *B* represent the two forces upon which the parallelogram is constructed. The diagonal R is the resultant of the forces. This process, which can be applied to any vector quantities, is known as geometric or vectorial addition.

The Triangle Law. If two coplanar, concurrent forces are laid out vectorially with the beginning of the second at the end of the

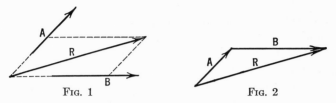

FIG. 1   FIG. 2

first, the vector extending from the beginning of the first to the end of the second, thus forming the third side of a triangle, represents completely the resultant of the forces. In Fig. 2 are shown the same forces A and B of Fig. 1, laid out with their resultant R to form a triangle. By a comparison of the two figures it is readily seen that the triangle of Fig. 2 is in reality a portion of the parallelogram of Fig. 1. The triangle law is thus a corollary of the parallelogram law.

The Polygon Law. When it is desired to obtain the resultant of more than two coplanar, concurrent forces, either the parallelogram or triangle law may be applied, any two of the forces being combined into their resultant, which is in turn combined with a third force, and so on until all the forces have been included. From such use of the triangle law the polygon law is derived: If the forces of a system of any number of coplanar, concurrent forces are laid off consecutively as vectors with the beginning of each vector at the end of the preceding one, the vector extending from the beginning of the first force to the end of the last, thus forming the closing side of a polygon, represents completely the resultant of the system. In Fig. 3 are shown four forces

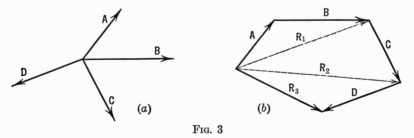

FIG. 3

A, B, C, and D. The resultant R_1 of forces A and B is obtained by means of the triangle law. Force C and resultant R_1 are similarly combined into their resultant R_2. Finally, force D and resultant R_2 combine to give R_3, which is the resultant of the entire system. It is now obvious that the intermediate resultants R_1 and R_2 are unnecessary. If they are removed from the figure, a polygon remains. It should be noted that in this polygon the forces follow each other in direction around the polygon, whereas their resultant points in the opposite direction. If the vector representing the resultant were reversed in direction so as to follow the forces, it would then represent the *equilibrant* of the system.

According to the law of *transmissibility of forces*, a force may be transmitted any distance along its line of action without changing its effect. However, a force cannot be shifted out of its line of action without altering its effect.

Art. 4. Resolution of a Force. A force may be resolved into two components by applying the principles stated in Art. 3. Application of the principle may be made by graphical, trigonometric, or algebraic methods.

a. Graphical Method. This method involves laying out forces vectorially to a suitable scale and constructing geometric figures. For instance, to determine the components of a force, the given force may be laid out as a vector and a parallelogram constructed with this vector as a diagonal. The sides of the parallelogram then represent the required components. It is obvious that an infinite number of parallelograms may be constructed with a given line as a diagonal. It is therefore necessary to specify the lines of action of the components desired.

Example 1

The force F in Fig. 4 is 400 lb. and is to be resolved into two components whose action lines make angles of 30° and 105°, respectively, with F. Determine the components.

Solution: The force F is laid out to some convenient scale as shown in Fig. 4. Through one end of F, lines are drawn at 30° and 105° with F. Parallel lines

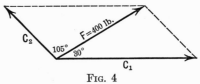

Fig. 4

are drawn through the other end of F so as to complete a parallelogram with F as the diagonal. The sides C_1 and C_2 constitute the required components and scale 546 lb. and 283 lb., respectively.

If the action lines of the desired components are to be at right angles with each other, the parallelogram becomes a rectangle and the components are known as rectangular components. Since it is possible to construct an infinite number of rectangles upon a given diagonal, it becomes necessary to specify the direction of such components. The graphical construction is then similar to that in Ex. 1 above.

b. Trigonometric Method. In the trigonometric method of resolving a force into its components, the parallelogram or triangle may be sketched free-hand and the laws of trigonometry then applied to determine the components.

Example 2

Solve Ex. 1 by the trigonometric method.

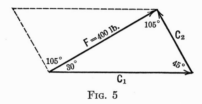

Fig. 5

Solution: The triangle, consisting of F and its components C_1 and C_2, is sketched and the angles are indicated as shown in Fig. 5. By the sine law:

$$\frac{C_1}{\sin 105°} = \frac{400}{\sin 45°} \quad \text{and} \quad \frac{C_2}{\sin 30°} = \frac{400}{\sin 45°}$$

whence $C_1 = 546$ lb. and $C_2 = 283$ lb.

It should be noted that in this method of solution it is not necessary to draw forces to scale or to lay out the angles exactly.

Example 3

The force F in Fig. 6 is to be resolved into its vertical and horizontal components, F_V and F_H.

Solution: From the trigonometry of the right-angle triangle of Fig. 6,

$$F_V = 500 \sin 35° = 287 \text{ lb.}$$

$$F_H = 500 \cos 35° = 410 \text{ lb.}$$

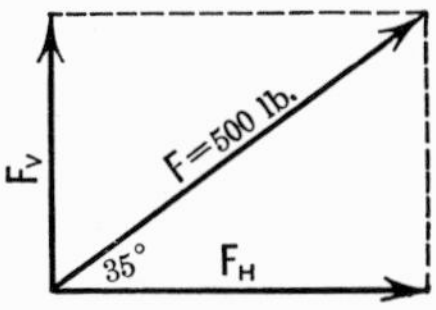

Fig. 6

Example 4

The line of action of force F in Fig. 7 passes through points O and A, as shown. Determine the vertical and horizontal components of this force.

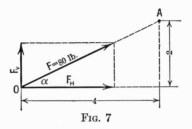

Fig. 7

Solution: The distance OA is first computed.

$$OA = \sqrt{(4)^2 + (2)^2} = 4.47$$

Then, by trigonometry,

$$F_V = 80 \sin \alpha = 80 \times \frac{2}{4.47} = 35.8 \text{ lb.}$$

$$F_H = 80 \cos \alpha = 80 \times \frac{4}{4.47} = 71.6 \text{ lb.}$$

It should be noted in this case that it is not necessary to determine the value of angle α.

Problems

(The following problems should be solved trigonometrically and checked graphically.)

1. Resolve a 2000-lb. force acting at $15°$ with the horizontal into its vertical and horizontal components.   *Ans. $F_V = 518$ lb.; $F_H = 1930$ lb.*

2. Resolve a 700-lb. force into components acting at $20°$ and $40°$ with the force.   *Ans. $C_1 = 520$ lb.; $C_2 = 276$ lb.*

3. A force of 900 lb. acts through the origin and a point whose coordinates are $x = 12$, $y = 5$. Determine the x and y components of the force.   *Ans. $F_x = 831$ lb.; $F_y = 346$ lb.*

4. A force of 3000 lb. acts at an angle of $60°$ with the x axis. Resolve this force into components acting at $105°$ and $330°$, respectively, with the x axis.   *Ans. $C_1 = 4240$ lb.; $C_2 = 3000$ lb.*

5. A force of 10,000 lb. has two components, $C_1 = 6000$ lb. and $C_2 = 12,000$ lb. Determine the angle which C_1 makes with the 10,000-lb. force.   *Ans. $93.8°$.*

Art. 5. Composition of Coplanar, Concurrent Forces. The resultant of a system of coplanar, concurrent forces may be determined by graphical, trigonometric, or algebraic methods.

a. Graphical Method. The principle of this method has already been explained in Art. 3. If only two forces are to be combined, either the parallelogram or triangle law may be used. If more than two forces are to be combined, the application of either parallelogram or triangle laws may prove to be unnecessarily tedious, and the polygon law may then be used to advantage. In laying out the polygon, the forces may be taken in any order.

Example 1

Determine the magnitude of the resultant of the four forces shown in Fig. 8 (a) and its angle θ_H with the horizontal.

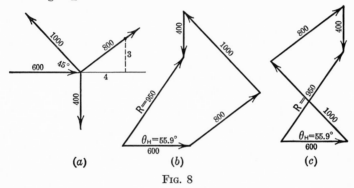

$$(a) \qquad\qquad (b) \qquad\qquad (c)$$

Fig. 8

Solution: The forces are laid out in order to some convenient scale as shown in Fig. 8 (b). The resultant R is the closing side of the polygon and scales 950 lb. The angle θ_H scales 55.9°.

Fig. 8 (c) shows the same forces laid out in a different order without changing the final results.

b. Trigonometric Method. When the resultant of only two forces is required, the parallelogram or triangle may be sketched free-hand and the resultant obtained by means of the laws of trigonometry.

Example 2

Determine the resultant of the 50-lb. and 80-lb. forces shown in Fig. 9.
Solution: By the law of cosines,

$$R^2 = (50)^2 + (80)^2 + 2(50)(80) \cos 120°;$$
$$R = 70 \text{ lb.}$$
$$\theta = \tan^{-1} \frac{50 \sin 120°}{80 + 50 \cos 120°} = 38.3°$$

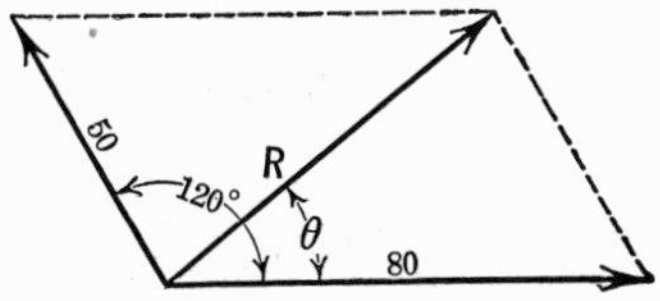

Fig. 9

When there are more than two forces to be combined, the above procedure becomes tedious and cumbersome. The algebraic method which follows is preferable in such problems.

c. Algebraic Method. It was shown in Art. 4, Ex. 3 and 4, that a force may easily be resolved trigonometrically into horizontal and vertical components. If every force in a given system is subjected to this process, the original system is thus replaced by an equivalent system containing two groups of forces, one consisting of forces having a common line of action in the horizontal direction, and the other consisting of forces having a common line of action in the vertical direction. The resultant of the horizontal group is their algebraic sum, represented by the symbol ΣF_H. The resultant of the vertical group is their algebraic sum, represented by the symbol ΣF_V. The resultant of the original system of forces is therefore:

$$R = \sqrt{(\Sigma F_H)^2 + (\Sigma F_V)^2}$$

and its angle with the horizontal is

$$\theta_H = \tan^{-1}\frac{\Sigma F_V}{\Sigma F_H}$$

Example 3

Solve Ex. 1 of Art. 5, using the algebraic method.

Solution: For convenience, the forces are shown again in Fig. 10 (*a*). Direction to the right is taken as positive, to the left as negative, upward as positive,

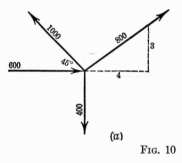
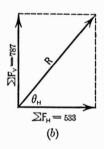

(*a*)   (*b*)

Fig. 10

and downward as negative, and the summations of horizontal and vertical components are made.

$$\Sigma F_H = 800 \times \tfrac{4}{5} + 600 - 1000 \cos 45° = +533 \text{ lb.}$$

$$\Sigma F_V = 800 \times \tfrac{3}{5} + 1000 \sin 45° - 400 = +787 \text{ lb.}$$

These results are shown in Fig. 10 (*b*), from which

$$R = \sqrt{(787)^2 + (533)^2} = 950 \text{ lb.}$$

$$\theta_H = \tan^{-1}\frac{787}{533} = 55.9°$$

Problems

(Graphic, trigonometric, or algebraic methods may be used in the following problems. Select the method which seems most convenient for the problem under consideration.)

1. Determine the amount of the resultant of the two forces shown in Fig. 11, and its angle with the horizontal.   *Ans.* $R = 2750$ lb.; $\theta_H = 49.1°$.

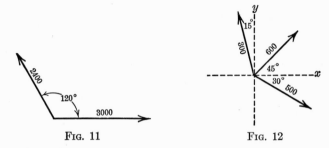

Fig. 11   Fig. 12

2. Determine the amount and direction of the resultant of the three forces shown in Fig. 12.   *Ans.* $R = 907$ lb.; $\theta_x = 30.7°$.

3. Determine the value of angle θ and the force F necessary to balance the two forces shown in Fig. 13.   *Ans.* $F = 2500$ lb.; $\theta = 36.8°$.

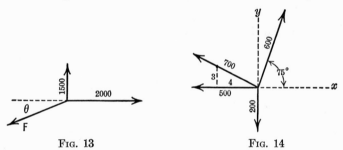

Fig. 13   Fig. 14

4. Determine the amount and direction of the resultant of the four forces shown in Fig. 14.   *Ans.* $R = 1210$ lb.; $\theta_x = 138.5°$.

5. Determine the amount and direction of the resultant of the five forces shown in Fig. 15.   *Ans.* $R = 765$ lb.; $\theta_x = 231.2°$.

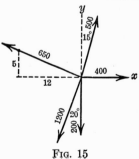

Fig. 15

6. In Fig. 16 the resultant of the four forces shown is to be 500 lb., acting horizontally toward the right. Determine the required values of F and θ.

Ans. $F = 1330$ lb.; $\theta = 70.6°$.

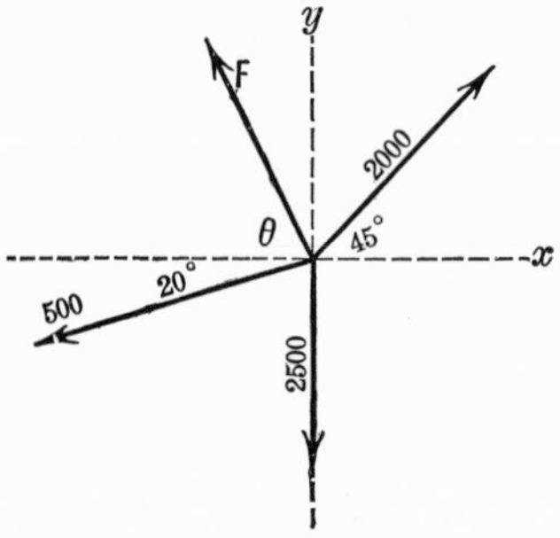

7. Solve for the resultant force F and angle θ of the three forces shown in Fig. 16.

Ans. -1570 lb.; $53.0°$.

Art. 6. Composition and Resolution of Coplanar, Parallel Forces; Force Couples.

The resultant of any number of parallel forces must occupy a line of action parallel to those of its components, and its magnitude must be the algebraic sum of the forces composing the system, the direction being indicated by the sign of their algebraic sum. The position of the resultant with respect to its components may now be determined either algebraically or graphically.

FIG. 16

a. Algebraic Method. The location of the resultant is obtained by applying the principle that the moment of the resultant with respect to any given axis must equal the algebraic sum of the moments of the components with respect to the same axis. The entire process may be expressed algebraically as follows:

$$R = \Sigma F$$

$$R \cdot r = \Sigma M = F_1 r_1 + F_2 r_2 + F_3 r_3 \cdots$$

where r represents the distance of R from the axis of moments, r_1 the distance of F_1 from the same axis, etc.

Example 1

Determine the amount and location of the resultant of the three parallel forces shown in Fig. 17.

Solution: If upward is taken as positive in direction, the summation of forces gives

$$R = \Sigma F = 20 - 50 - 30 = -60 \text{ lb.}$$

The resultant is therefore directed downwards. To determine its location, let point O be selected as the axis of moments and let clockwise moments be taken as positive. Then

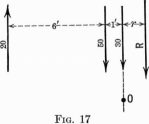

FIG. 17

$$60 \times r = \Sigma M_O = 20 \times 7 - 50 \times 1 - 30 \times 0 = +90$$

$$r = 1.5 \text{ ft.}$$

b. Graphic Method. The principle of moments is also used in devising a graphic method of locating the resultant. In Fig. 18, A and B are two parallel forces in the same direction; a and b are their respective distances from the resultant R. By moments with respect to any point on the line of action of R

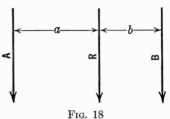

$$R \times 0 = \Sigma M = A \times a - B \times b$$

or

$$\frac{A}{B} = \frac{b}{a}$$

Fig. 18

This result shows that the resultant of two parallel forces in the same direction divides the distance between them in inverse proportion to the forces.

Any straight line m–n, known as a base line, is now drawn so as to intersect the forces A and B, as shown in Fig. 19. A length, representing force A to scale, is laid off on the line of action of force B on one side of the base line. A length, representing force B to scale, is laid off on the line of action of force A but on the opposite side of the base

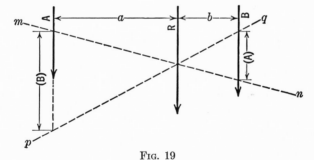

Fig. 19

line. The ends of these lengths are now connected by the diagonal p–q. The intersection of p–q and m–n locates the position of R since, by similar triangles resulting from the construction,

$$\frac{A}{B} = \frac{b}{a}$$

as required. The resultant is seen to lie between the forces, on the side of the larger force.

The same procedure is followed in combining two parallel forces acting in opposite directions except that the distances representing the forces must be laid off on the same side of the base line. The construction for this case, Fig. 20, shows the resultant to lie outside the forces on the side of the larger component.

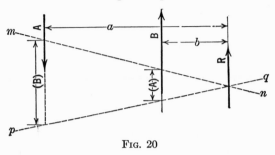

FIG. 20

The graphic method just outlined is called the method of inverse proportion. Only two forces at a time may be combined by this method. If more than two parallel forces are to be combined into their resultant, the inverse proportion method may be used to combine any two of the forces, whose resultant is then combined with a third force, and so on until all the forces have been accounted for.

The resolution of a force into two components parallel to itself may be accomplished algebraically by procedure similar to that in part a above, but the action lines of the components must be specified; otherwise an infinite number of solutions would be possible.

Other graphical methods are available for accomplishing the same result but are considered to lie outside the scope of this book. For further details reference should be made to some textbook designed particularly for graphic methods.*

Example 2

Resolve the force P shown in Fig. 21 into two components parallel to itself and acting at distances of 5 in. and 7 in. from P on the same side.

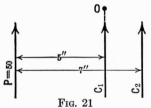

FIG. 21

Solution: Let C_1 and C_2 represent the required components. Then, since $R = \Sigma F$,

$$50 = C_1 + C_2 \qquad (1)$$

With point O as center of moments, the equation $R \cdot r = \Sigma M$ becomes

$$50 \times 5 = C_1 \times 0 - C_2 \times 2 \qquad (2)$$

Solution of equations (1) and (2) gives $C_1 = 175$ lb. and $C_2 = -125$ lb. The negative result shows that C_2 must act in the direction opposite to that shown in the figure.

* Fairman and Cutshall, *Graphic Statics*, McGraw-Hill Book Co., New York, 1932.

The resolution of a force into two components parallel to itself may be accomplished graphically by the inverse proportion method already explained.

Example 3

Solve Ex. 2 graphically by the method of inverse proportion.

Solution: The distances between the force and its components are laid out to scale as shown in Fig. 22. Any convenient base line m–n is drawn, intersecting the forces. The value of P is now laid off on the line of action of either

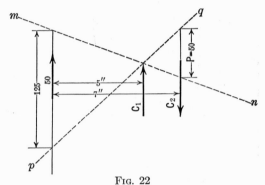

Fig. 22

component, say C_2, starting from the base line. A diagonal p–q is then drawn from the other end of the length representing P and through the intersection of m–n with C_1. The distance along the line of action of P between the lines m–n and p–q now represents the value of C_2 and scales 125 lb. The value of $C_1 = 175$ lb. then follows by algebraic summation.

Two equal but oppositely directed parallel forces constitute a special type of force system known as a *force couple* or, more simply, a *couple*. The vector sum of such a system is zero, but the sum of the moments of the forces is not zero. It follows that, whenever the vector sum of the forces in any system is zero but the sum of their moments is not zero, then the resultant of the given system is a force couple.

In Fig. 23 is shown a force couple consisting of two forces, each of value F, located at any distance d apart. Let O be any point located at distance x from one of the forces. Then

$$\Sigma M_O = F(x + d) - F \cdot x = F \cdot d$$

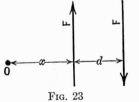

Fig. 23

Hence the moment Fd of the force couple does not involve the distance x and therefore is independent of the position of the axis of rotation. The following propositions regarding force couples may then be deduced.

1. The moment of a force couple is always the product of one of the forces and the distance between them.

2. The moment of a force couple is independent of the position of the axis of moments.

3. A force couple may be moved to any other position in its plane or a parallel plane without changing its effect.

4. A force couple can be balanced only by the addition of another force couple of equal but opposite moment.

Any single force may be replaced by an equal parallel force in the same direction through any designated point and a couple. In Fig. 24, F is any given force and O is any specified point at distance d from the force. If through the point O two opposing forces F_1 and F_2, such that $F_1 = F_2 = F$, are added, the effect of the original system is not changed. Now the two forces F and F_2 constitute a couple of moment Fd, and thus the original force F has been replaced by an equal force F_1 acting through point O, plus the couple of moment Fd. The converse of this proposition, that a system consisting of a force and a couple may always be reduced to a single force, is equally valid.

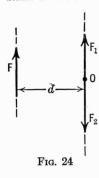

Fig. 24

Since a couple has both magnitude (moment) and direction (of rotation), it is a vector quantity and may be so represented graphically. The vector representing a couple (or moment) is drawn normal to the plane of the couple and with its arrowhead directed according to the well-known right-hand screw rule; that is, the direction of the couple vector is the same as that of the advance of a right-hand screw having the same direction of rotation as the couple. A couple may be resolved vectorially into a system of component couples, and any system of couples may be combined vectorially into a single resultant couple.

Problems

1. Determine the amount and position of the resultant of the forces shown in Fig. 25.   *Ans.* 2.43 ft.

Fig. 25

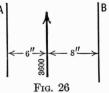

Fig. 26

2. Resolve the force shown in Fig. 26 into parallel components A and B.
Ans. A = 2060 lb. up.

3. Resolve the force shown in Fig. 27 into parallel components A and B.

Ans. A = 1140 lb. down.

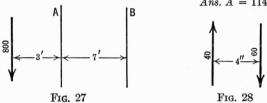

FIG. 27   FIG. 28

4. Determine the amount and position of the resultant of the parallel forces shown in Fig. 28.   *Ans.* 20 lb. down at 12 in. to the right of 40-lb. force.

5. Determine the amount and position of the resultant of the system of parallel forces shown in Fig. 29.

Ans. R = 900 lb. down at 6.56 in. to the right of the 200-lb. force.

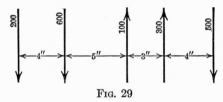

FIG. 29

6. Reverse the 600-lb. force in Prob. 5 and solve.

Ans. R = 300 lb. up at 3.7 in. to the left of 200-lb. force.

7. Determine the resultant of the force system shown in Fig. 30.

Ans. A force couple having a clockwise moment of 2150 ft-lb.

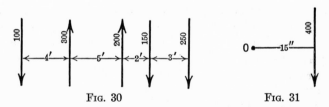

FIG. 30   FIG. 31

8. Resolve the force shown in Fig. 31 into a force at O and a couple.

Ans. 6000 in-lb.

Art. 7. Composition of Coplanar, Non-concurrent, Non-parallel Forces.

To describe the resultant of a general system of forces in a plane completely, its magnitude, its angle with some given line, and its position or distance from a given point must be stated. The magnitude and angle with a given line may be determined by graphic or algebraic methods as previously demonstrated in Art. 5. If successive parallelograms were used in obtaining the resultant graphically, the diagonal of the final parallelogram determines the position of the resultant of the system. Algebraically, the position of the resultant is determined by applying the principle of moments. It is possible for the resultant of this type of force system to be a couple, the requirements for which are given in Art. 6.

Example

Determine completely the resultant of the three forces acting on the pole shown in Fig. 32.

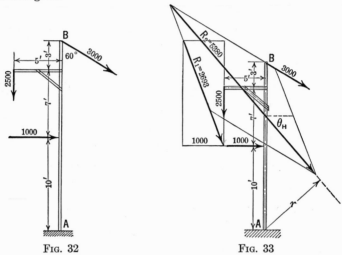

Fig. 32   Fig. 33

Solution: In the graphical solution shown in Fig. 33, the structure is first laid out to scale. Then the 2500-lb. and 1000-lb. forces are combined by the parallelogram method into their resultant R_1, which scales 2693 lb. This resultant is similarly combined with the 3000-lb. force to obtain R_2, the resultant of the entire system, which scales 5380 lb. Its angle with the horizontal, θ_H, scales 48°, and its perpendicular distance r from the foot of the pole scales 9.2 ft. The distance from the foot of the pole to the point where the resultant intersects it scales 13.8 ft.

The algebraic solution of the above example is obtained as follows:

$$\Sigma F_H = 3000 \sin 60° + 1000 = 3600 \text{ lb.}$$

$$\Sigma F_V = -3000 \cos 60° - 2500 = -4000 \text{ lb.}$$

$$R_2 = \sqrt{(3600)^2 + (4000)^2} = 5380 \text{ lb.}$$

$$\theta_H = \tan^{-1} \frac{4000}{3600} = 48°$$

$$r = \frac{\Sigma M_A}{R} = \frac{3000 \sin 60° \times 20 + 1000 \times 10 - 2500 \times 5}{5380} = 9.2 \text{ ft.}$$

The distance from the point where R_2 cuts the pole to the foot is $\dfrac{9.2}{\cos 48°}$
= 13.8 ft.

Problems

1. Determine completely the resultant of the three forces acting on the gear and pulley shown in Fig. 34.   *Ans.* 1860 lb. at 211.3°.

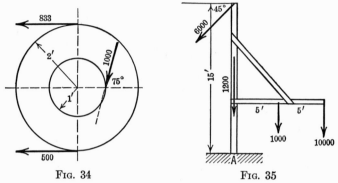

FIG. 34   FIG. 35

2. Determine the position of the resultant of the four forces shown in Fig. 35.
Ans. 2.52 ft. to the right of *A*.

3. Determine where the resultant of the forces shown on the structure in Fig. 36 cuts the ground line *AB*.   *Ans.* 32 ft. to the right of *A*.

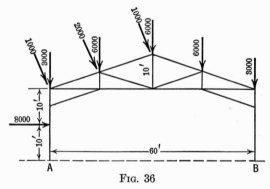

FIG. 36

4. Remove the wind loads on the roof of the structure shown in Fig. 36 and determine where the resultant of all the loads cuts the ground line *AB*.
Ans. 33.3 ft. to the right of *A*.

Art. 8. Resolution and Composition of Non-coplanar, Concurrent Forces. A convenient method used to diagram a force in space is shown in Fig. 37. The components of the force parallel to the coordinate axes in space are easily obtained as follows:

$$F_x = F \cos \alpha$$

$$F_y = F \cos \beta$$

$$F_z = F \cos \gamma$$

Frequently, the angles α, β, and γ are not given directly, but the direction of the force is specified by stating the coordinates of two

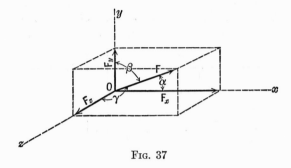

Fig. 37

points in space through which it passes. This is shown in Fig. 38. To obtain values of cos α, cos β, and cos γ, the length of the diagonal OA is computed. The components are then readily obtained.

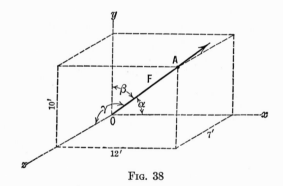

Fig. 38

Example 1

Let the force F in Fig. 38 be 200 lb. Determine its x, y, and z components. *Solution:*

$$OA = \sqrt{(12)^2 + (10)^2 + (7)^2} = 17.1$$

Then

$$F_x = 200 \cos \alpha = 200 \times \frac{12}{17.1} = 140.3 \text{ lb.}$$

$$F_y = 200 \cos \beta = 200 \times \frac{10}{17.1} = 117.0 \text{ lb.}$$

$$F_z = 200 \cos \gamma = 200 \times \frac{7}{17.1} = 81.9 \text{ lb.}$$

The resultant of any number of concurrent forces in space may now be determined by first resolving each force in the system into its x, y, and z components as shown above. The x components are then added algebraically to obtain their sum, ΣF_x. Similarly, ΣF_y and ΣF_z are obtained. Finally, the magnitude of the resultant is

$$R = \sqrt{(\Sigma F_x)^2 + (\Sigma F_y)^2 + (\Sigma F_z)^2}$$

and its direction in space is given by

$$\cos \alpha = \frac{\Sigma F_x}{R} \; ; \cos \beta = \frac{\Sigma F_y}{R} \; ; \cos \gamma = \frac{\Sigma F_z}{R}$$

Example 2

Determine the resultant of the three forces shown in Fig. 39.

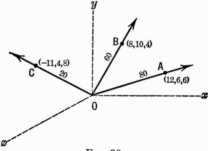

FIG. 39

Solution: The three diagonals are first determined.

$$OA = \sqrt{(12)^2 + (6)^2 + (6)^2} = 14.7$$

$$OB = \sqrt{(8)^2 + (10)^2 + (4)^2} = 13.4$$

$$OC = \sqrt{(11)^2 + (4)^2 + (8)^2} = 14.2$$

Summations of components along each of the three coordinate axes are now made.

$$\Sigma F_x = 80 \times \frac{12}{14.7} + 60 \times \frac{8}{13.4} + 20 \times -\frac{11}{14.2} = 85.6 \text{ lb.}$$

$$\Sigma F_y = 80 \times \frac{6}{14.7} + 60 \times \frac{10}{13.4} + 20 \times \frac{4}{14.2} = 83.1 \text{ lb.}$$

$$\Sigma F_z = 80 \times \frac{6}{14.7} + 60 \times \frac{4}{13.4} + 20 \times \frac{8}{14.2} = 61.8 \text{ lb.}$$

These values are now combined to obtain:

$$R = \sqrt{(85.6)^2 + (83.1)^2 + (61.8)^2} = 134.5 \text{ lb.}$$

$$\alpha = \cos^{-1} \frac{85.6}{134.5} = 50.5°$$

$$\beta = \cos^{-1} \frac{83.1}{134.5} = 51.8°$$

$$\gamma = \cos^{-1} \frac{61.8}{134.5} = 62.7°$$

Problems

1. A force of 300 lb. passes through the origin and a point in space whose co-ordinates are (5,4,3). Compute the x, y, and z components of the force.

Ans. 212; 170; 128.

2. Determine the amount and direction in space of the resultant of the three forces shown in Fig. 40.   *Ans.* $R = 230$ lb.; $\alpha = 54.9°$; $\beta = 81.8°$; $\gamma = 35.9°$.

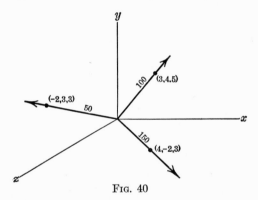

FIG. 40

3. Determine the amount and direction in space of the resultant of the four forces shown in Fig. 41.   *Ans.* $R = 61.6$ lb.; $\alpha = 223.8°$; $\beta = 226.4°$; $\gamma = 266.5°$.

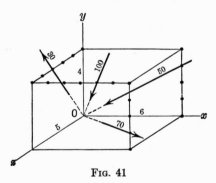

FIG. 41

Art. 9. Composition of Non-coplanar Parallel Forces. The resultant of any number of parallel forces in space is equal in magnitude to the algebraic sum of the forces, it must be parallel to the forces, and its position in space must be such that its moment with respect to any axis in space is equal to the sum of the moments of the forces with respect to the same axis. If the algebraic sum of the forces is zero, but the sum of the moments with respect to any non-parallel axis in space is not zero, then the resultant of the system is a couple. The moment of the resultant couple is usually obtained most conveniently by combining vectorially the component couples taken with respect to any convenient coordinate axes.

Example

Determine the amount and position of the resultant of the three parallel forces shown in Fig. 42.

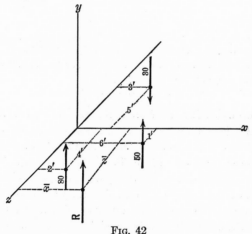

Fig. 42

Solution: Coordinate axes are chosen as shown in Fig. 42. The magnitude and direction of the resultant are first determined by

$$R = \Sigma F = 80 + 50 - 30 = +100 \text{ lb. (upward)}$$

Let the position of R be denoted by the coordinates $\bar{x}$ and $\bar{z}$. Then, since

$$R \cdot \bar{z} = \Sigma M_x \quad \text{and} \quad R \cdot \bar{x} = \Sigma M_z,$$

$$100 \cdot \bar{z} = 80 \times 4 + 50 \times 1 + 30 \times 5$$

$$100 \cdot \bar{x} = 80 \times 2 + 50 \times 6 - 30 \times 3$$

from which

$$\bar{x} \approx 3.7 \text{ ft.} \quad \text{and} \quad \bar{z} = 5.2 \text{ ft.}$$

Problems

1. Determine the magnitude, direction, and location of the resultant of the three parallel forces shown in Fig. 43.

Ans. $R = 400$ lb. down; $\bar{x} = -0.90$ ft.; $\bar{z} = 0.025$ ft.

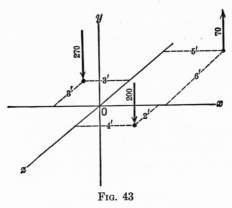

Fig. 43

2. A rectangular platform 10 ft. long and 6 ft. wide carries loads of 600 lb. at its center, 100 lb. midway between the corners at one of the 6-ft. ends, and 150 lb. midway between the corners at one of the 10-ft. sides. Determine the amount and position of the resultant load.

Ans. $R = 850$ lb. acting at 4.41 ft. from the end and 2.47 ft. from the side.

Art. 10. Composition of Non-coplanar, Non-parallel, Non-concurrent Forces.

The resultant of the general system of forces in space may be a single force or a couple. When the resultant is a single force, it is usually convenient to replace this force by an equal and parallel force through some designated point plus a couple. Coordinate axes are taken through the given point, the magnitude of the resultant force and its angles with the coordinate axes are then determined, and finally the resultant couple is obtained by means of its component couples with respect to each of the three axes. When the resultant is a couple, the procedure is the same, except that the resultant force is zero and only the component couples need be specified.

Example

Determine the resultant of the two forces shown in Fig. 44 (a).

Solution: It is first necessary to resolve each force into x, y, and z components by the method of Art. 8. The distances AB and CD are therefore determined:

$$AB = \sqrt{8^2 + 6^2 + 2^2} = 10.2$$

$$CD = \sqrt{5^2 + 6^2 + 4^2} = 8.78$$

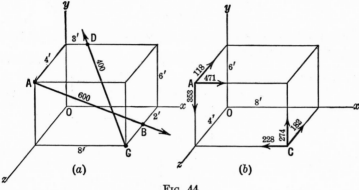

FIG. 44

The components of force AB are thus:

$$AB_x = 600 \times \frac{8}{10.2} = +471 \text{ lb.}$$

$$AB_y = 600 \times \frac{-6}{10.2} = -353 \text{ lb.}$$

$$AB_z = 600 \times \frac{-2}{10.2} = -118 \text{ lb.}$$

and the components of force CD are thus:

$$CD_x = 400 \times \frac{-5}{8.78} = -228 \text{ lb.}$$

$$CD_y = 400 \times \frac{6}{8.78} = +274 \text{ lb.}$$

$$CD_z = 400 \times \frac{-4}{8.78} = -182 \text{ lb.}$$

These components are shown in Fig. 44 (b). From the above results,

$$\Sigma F_x = +243 \text{ lb.}; \quad \Sigma F_y = -79 \text{ lb.}; \quad \Sigma F_z = -300 \text{ lb.}$$

The resultant force through O may now be computed:

$$R = \sqrt{(243)^2 + (79)^2 + (300)^2} = 394 \text{ lb.}$$

The direction of R in space is determined by:

$$\alpha = \cos^{-1}\frac{\Sigma F_x}{R} = \cos^{-1}\frac{243}{394} = 308°$$

$$\beta = \cos^{-1}\frac{\Sigma F_y}{R} = \cos^{-1}\frac{-79}{394} = 101.5°$$

$$\gamma = \cos^{-1}\frac{\Sigma F_z}{R} = \cos^{-1}\frac{-300}{394} = 139.5°$$

The above angles are measured from the positive ends of the respective axes.

It now remains to determine the component moment of the resultant force couple with respect to each coordinate axis. This is most conveniently obtained by summation of the moments with respect to a given axis of the x, y, and z components of the original forces. The components of a given force may be placed at any point along the line of action of the force. In the steps which follow, the components of the 600-lb. force will be taken as acting at point A, and those of the 400-lb. force at point C, as shown in Fig. 44 (b). In obtaining the moments, counterclockwise rotation, as viewed from the positive end of the axis toward the origin, will be taken as positive. Thus:

$$\Sigma M_x = 471 \times 0 + 353 \times 4 - 118 \times 6 + 228 \times 0 - 274 \times 4 + 182 \times 0$$
$$= -392 \text{ ft-lb.}$$

$$\Sigma M_y = 471 \times 4 + 353 \times 0 + 118 \times 0 - 228 \times 4 + 274 \times 0 + 182 \times 8$$
$$= +2428 \text{ ft-lb.}$$

$$\Sigma M_z = -471 \times 6 + 353 \times 0 + 118 \times 0 + 228 \times 0 + 274 \times 8 + 182 \times 0$$
$$= -634 \text{ ft-lb.}$$

These results may be combined vectorially into a resultant force couple, and the direction in space of the axis of rotation of the couple may be determined. However, it is ordinarily sufficient to state the component couples in the form shown.

Problems

1. Combine the three forces shown in Fig. 45 into a single force through O and a couple. *Ans.* $R = 70.7$ lb.; $\alpha = 55.6°$; $\beta = 64.9°$; $\gamma = 45°$; $\Sigma M_x = +150$ ft-lb.; $\Sigma M_y = +160$ ft-lb.; $\Sigma M_z = +150$ ft-lb.

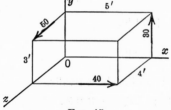

2. Determine the resultant of the two forces shown in Fig. 46. *Ans.* $R = 473$ lb.; $\alpha = 86.1°$; $\beta = 59.1°$; $\gamma = 31.1°$; $\Sigma M_x = 0$; $\Sigma M_y = -648$ ft-lb.; $\Sigma M_z = 390$ ft-lb.

FIG. 45

3. Determine the resultant of the force system shown in Fig. 47. *Ans.* $R = 630$ lb.; $\alpha = 32.5°$; $\beta = 110.2°$; $\gamma = 65.8°$; $\Sigma M_x = 1690$ ft-lb.; $\Sigma M_y = 2440$ ft-lb.; $\Sigma M_z = -1850$ ft-lb.

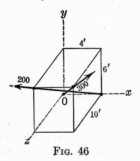

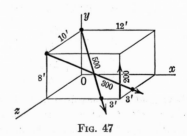

FIG. 46   FIG. 47

CHAPTER II

EQUILIBRIUM OF COPLANAR FORCES

Art. 11. Equilibrium and the Free Body. A body is said to be in *equilibrium* when it is in a state of rest or is moving with constant speed in a straight-line path. Likewise, the system of all forces acting externally on such a body is in equilibrium. Under such conditions the resultant of all the forces in the system must be zero, and the algebraic sum of the moments of all the forces about any axis must be zero.

In the solution of problems in statics involving determination of unknown quantities, it is found convenient to select some object which is acted upon by the forces in question, isolate it from its surroundings, and then consider the equilibrium of the system of forces acting externally upon the object. Such an object, separated from other objects with which it may be in contact, is known as a *free body*. If the free body is in equilibrium, all the forces acting upon it compose a system in equilibrium to which certain methods of solution may then be applied. It should particularly be noted, however, that internal forces, that is, forces acting within the free body itself, have no effect on the motion of the body and therefore are not involved when its equilibrium is considered.

Art. 12. The Conditions of Equilibrium. A system of forces known to be in equilibrium must satisfy the following conditions:

1. The forces when laid out vectorially must form a closed polygon. This follows from Art. 3, in which it is shown that the vector necessary to cause a polygon of forces to close represents the resultant or the equilibrant of the system.

2. The algebraic summation of the components of the forces in any assigned direction of resolution must be zero. This condition is expressed by the equations:

$$\Sigma F_x = 0 \quad \text{and} \quad \Sigma F_y = 0$$

where x and y represent any arbitrarily chosen axes. This follows from Art. 5 (c), where it is shown that $R = \sqrt{(\Sigma F_x)^2 + (\Sigma F_y)^2}$. When $R = 0$, it is necessary that $\Sigma F_x = 0$ and $\Sigma F_y = 0$.

3. The algebraic summation of the moments of the forces with respect to any assigned axis must equal zero, or $\Sigma M = 0$. If this condition were not fulfilled, rotation of the body would occur, and equilibrium could not exist.

4. If three non-parallel forces are in equilibrium, they must be *concurrent*. This follows from the fact that the resultant of any two of the forces must be collinear with the third.

Art. 13.   The Solution of the General Problem of Equilibrium. The analysis and solution of any problem involving equilibrium require the following steps:

1. Selection of the free body.

2. A diagram of the free body showing all dimensions and external forces. The values of all known forces and dimensions should be indicated and some system of notation by letters used to designate those forces or dimensions unknown in value.

3. Application of one or more of the conditions of equilibrium laid down in Art. 12 to determine the various unknowns required.

Art. 14.   Concurrent Forces in Equilibrium. The solution of this type of problem may be carried out graphically by laying out the force polygon vectorially, or algebraically by means of the equations $\Sigma F_x = 0$, $\Sigma F_y = 0$, and $\Sigma M = 0$. When no more than three forces are involved, the force polygon becomes a triangle which may then be solved trigonometrically.

A concurrent, coplanar system of forces must involve no more than two unknowns; otherwise it will be found that there are not sufficient independent conditions of equilibrium to make possible a solution. Such a system, incapable of solution by applying the static conditions of equilibrium, is known as statically indeterminate.

Example 1

Determine the force P, acting at 45° with the horizontal, required to start the wheel shown in Fig. 48 (*a*) over the block.

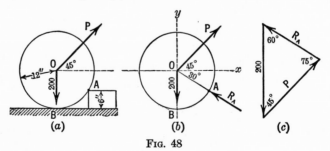

Fig. 48

Solution: a. Graphical Method.   The free body, Fig. 48 (*b*), consists of the wheel itself, acted upon by three external forces, the weight of the wheel acting vertically downward through its center, the force *P*, and the reaction R_A of the block against the wheel.   Since the three forces are not parallel they must be *concurrent*, and so the reaction R_A must pass through *O*, the center of the wheel.   The angle *AOB* is found to be 60°.   The force polygon is then laid out as shown in Fig. 48 (*c*), from which *P* scales 179 lb. and R_A scales 146 lb.

b. Trigonometric Method.   Since the force polygon in this example is a triangle, a trigonometric solution is possible.   By use of the sine law,

$$\frac{P}{\sin 60°} = \frac{200}{\sin 75°} = \frac{R_A}{\sin 45°}$$

from which $P = 179$ lb. and $R_A = 146$ lb.

c. Algebraic Method.   Let *x* and *y* axes be taken in the horizontal and vertical directions as shown in Fig. 48 (*b*).   Then

$$\Sigma F_x = P \cos 45° - R_A \cos 30° = 0 \tag{1}$$

$$\Sigma F_y = P \sin 45° + R_A \sin 30° - 200 = 0 \tag{2}$$

Simultaneous solution of (1) and (2) gives results for *P* and R_A identical with those already stated.

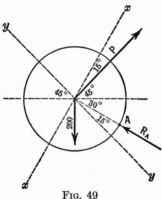

Fig. 49

Simultaneous equations may be avoided by placing the axes so that each is perpendicular to one of the unknowns, as shown in Fig. 49.   The following equations are now obtained:

$$\Sigma F_x = P \cos 15° - 200 \cos 30° = 0 \qquad\qquad P = 179 \text{ lb.}$$

$$\Sigma F_y = R_A \cos 15° - 200 \cos 45° = 0 \qquad\qquad R_A = 146 \text{ lb.}$$

This process is known as shifting the axes.

Example 2

Two cylinders, A and B, rest in a box as shown in Fig. 50 (a). A has a diameter of 10 in. and weighs 200 lb. B has a diameter of 18 in. and weighs 500 lb. The box is 18 in. wide at the bottom. Determine the pressures at all points of contact.

Solution: The dimension AB is seen by inspection to be 14 in. The distance HG is 9 tan 30° = 5.19 in. BC is therefore $18 - 5 - 5.19 = 7.81$ in.,

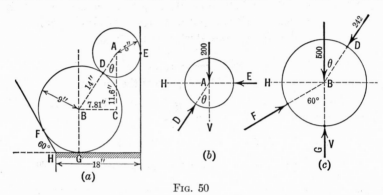

Fig. 50

and AC becomes $\sqrt{(14)^2 - (7.81)^2} = 11.6$ in. Thus the functions of angle θ are sin $\theta = 7.81/14 = 0.558$ and cos $\theta = 11.6/14 = 0.828$.

Cylinder A is selected as the first free body as shown in Fig. 50 (b). By the algebraic method of solution,

$$\Sigma F_V = D \cos \theta - 200 = 0 \qquad\qquad D = 242 \text{ lb.}$$

$$\Sigma F_H = E - 242 \sin \theta = 0 \qquad\qquad E = 135 \text{ lb.}$$

The solution of this free body may also be obtained graphically or trigonometrically.

The cylinder B is now taken as a free body, as shown in Fig. 50 (c). By the algebraic method,

$$\Sigma F_H = F \sin 60° - 242 \sin \theta = 0 \qquad\qquad F = 156 \text{ lb.}$$

$$\Sigma F_V = G + 156 \cos 60° - 500 - 242 \cos \theta = 0 \qquad G = 622 \text{ lb.}$$

The solution of this free body may also be obtained graphically.

Problems

1. An airplane is climbing with no acceleration on a flight path making 10° with the horizontal as shown in Fig. 51. If the weight of the plane is 5000 lb. and the drag force is 500 lb., what are the lift and thrust forces?

Ans. $T = 1370$ lb.

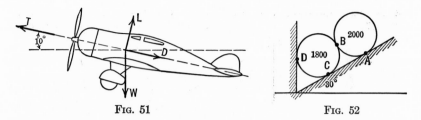

FIG. 51   FIG. 52

2. The cylinders shown in Fig. 52 are equal in diameter and have weights as indicated. Determine the pressures at A, B, C, and D.

Ans. $A = 1730$ lb.; $B = 1000$ lb.; $C = 2660$ lb.; $D = 2200$ lb.

3. A 200-lb. weight is supported by a system of cords as shown in Fig. 53. Determine the tension in each cord.

Ans. $T_1 = 179$ lb.; $T_2 = 53.6$ lb.; $T_3 = 18.5$ lb.; $T_4 = 47$ lb.

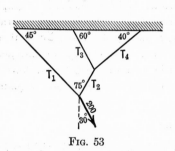

FIG. 53

FIG. 54

4. Determine the forces exerted by the members in the simple structure shown in Fig. 54.   *Ans.* $AB = 6080$ lb. C; $BC = 5280$ lb. T.

5. Solve Prob. 4 if the 3500-lb. force is vertical and downward.

Ans. $AB = 5000$ lb. C; $BC = 6100$ lb. T.

6. The three cylinders in Fig. 55 are equal in diameter and have weights as indicated. Solve for the forces at A, B, C, and D. Assume no force between the 200-lb. and 300-lb. cylinder.

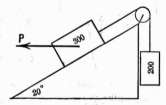

FIG. 55

FIG. 56

Ans. $A = 28.9$ lb.; $B = 250$ lb.; $C = 326$ lb.; $D = 37.7$ lb.

7. What horizontal force P will be required to start the 300-lb. block down the plane as shown in Fig. 56? What is the normal force between the block and the plane?   *Ans.* $P = 104$ lb.; $N = 246$ lb.

8. Determine the forces exerted by members AB and BC of the structure shown in Fig. 57.   *Ans.* $AB = 1110$ lb. C; $BC = 833$ lb. T.

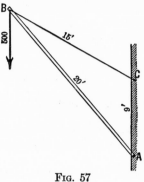

FIG. 57

Art. 15. Parallel Forces in Equilibrium.

Either algebraic or graphic methods may be applied in the solution of problems involving parallel forces in equilibrium. The conditions of equilibrium, $\Sigma F = 0$ and $\Sigma M = 0$, are used in the algebraic method. Since only two independent equations are possible, there must be no more than two unknowns. In the graphic method the principle of inverse proportion explained in Art. 6 may be applied.

Example

A beam 30 ft. long weighing 50 lb. per ft. is supported at the right end and at 5 ft. from the left end. It carries a uniformly distributed load of 200 lb. per ft. over a length of 10 ft. from the right end and a concentrated load of 750 lb. at 10 ft. from the left end. Compute the reactions at the supports.

Solution: a. Algebraic Method. The beam is shown as a free body in Fig. 58. If moments are taken about point B, the reaction R_2 is eliminated and the

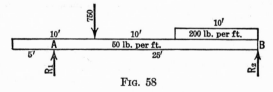

FIG. 58

resulting equation contains only one unknown. Since a uniformly distributed load is a set of parallel forces located at equal distances apart, the resultant of such a load acts at the center of distribution, and the moment may be obtained as the product of the total load and the distance of the center of distribution from the moment center. Thus:

$$\Sigma M_B = 25R_1 - 750 \times 20 - (50 \times 30) \times 15 - (200 \times 10) \times 5 = 0$$

$$R_1 = 1900 \text{ lb.}$$

In similar manner moments are taken about A.

$$\Sigma M_A = 25R_2 - 750 \times 5 - (50 \times 30) \times 10 - (200 \times 10) \times 20 = 0$$

$$R_2 = 2350 \text{ lb.}$$

The equation, $\Sigma F_V = 0$, may be used as a check:

$$\Sigma F_V = 1900 + 2350 - 750 - (50 \times 30) - (200 \times 10) = 0$$

$$4250 - 4250 = 0$$

b. Graphic Method. Figure 59 shows the beam laid out with all distances measured to scale. The resultant of the 750- and 1500-lb. loads is 2250 lb.,

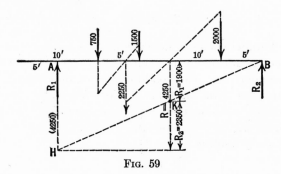

Fig. 59

whose location is obtained by the inverse proportion method. The beam itself is used as the base line; the 750-lb. force is laid off to scale above the base line on the action line of the 1500-lb. force. The 1500 lb. is laid off to scale below the base line on the action line of the 750-lb. force. The connecting diagonal is drawn, its intersection with the base line locating the 2250-lb. resultant. The resultant of the 2250 lb. and the remaining 2000-lb. load is 4250 lb., whose location is likewise determined by the inverse proportion method as shown in the diagram.

The resultant of all the loads which has just been determined is now resolved by the inverse proportion principle into two components acting at A and B. To do this, the value 4250 is laid off to scale from A to H on the line of action of the reaction R_1. The line HB then divides the resultant load at K into two components which scale 1900 lb. and 2350 lb. and act at A and B, respectively. The reactions R_1 and R_2 must be equal and opposite to the corresponding load components.

An alternative graphic method is available involving the use of the funicular polygon. A discussion of the procedure involved may be found in Art. 21 and in textbooks dealing more fully with graphic methods.

Problems

1. Determine the reactions R_1 and R_2 of the beam shown in Fig. 60.

$Ans.\ R_1 = 2750$ lb.

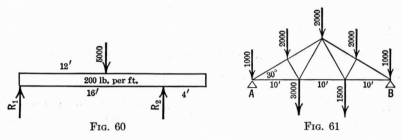

FIG. 60   FIG. 61

2. Determine the reactions at the supports A and B of the roof truss shown in Fig. 61. $Ans.\ R_A = 6500$ lb.; $R_B = 6000$ lb.

3. Solve for the reactions at A and B of the beam shown in Fig. 62.

$Ans.\ R_A = 12,800$ lb.; $R_B = 7600$ lb.

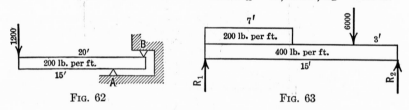

FIG. 62   FIG. 63

4. Compute the reactions R_1 and R_2 of the beam shown in Fig. 63.

$Ans.\ R_1 = 5270$ lb.; $R_2 = 8130$ lb.

5. Solve for the reactions of the beam shown in Fig. 64. $Ans.\ R_1 = 3350$ lb.

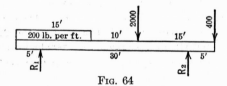

FIG. 64

6. Solve for the position of the 750-lb. load on the beam shown in Fig. 65 to produce a 1200-lb. reaction at R_1. $Ans.\ x = 2.56$ ft.

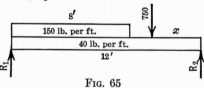

FIG. 65

Art. 16. Non-concurrent, Non-parallel Forces in Equilibrium.
Both algebraic and graphic methods will be considered in the solution of this type of problem. In the algebraic method the conditions of

equilibrium, $\Sigma F_x = 0$, $\Sigma F_y = 0$, and $\Sigma M = 0$, are used. By a proper selection of moment centers and directions of resolution all but one of the unknowns may usually be eliminated from a given equation, and thus simultaneous equations are avoided. Since it is possible to set up three independent equations, such a system of forces may involve as many as three unknowns and remain statically determinate.

The graphic method of solution usually consists of combining all known forces into their resultant so as to reduce the system to three forces, if possible. These three, if not parallel, must be concurrent, and the solution is completed by the methods of Art. 14. When the system cannot be reduced to three forces, other schemes are available. It is left to the ingenuity of the student particularly interested in graphic methods to develop the necessary means.

Example 1

The arm ABC in Fig. 66 (a) is pinned to the wall at A and supported at C by the cable CD. Compute the tension in the cable and the pin reaction at A when the arm carries a 400-lb. load at B.

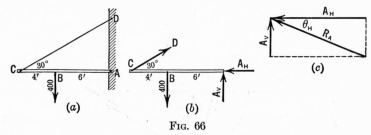

FIG. 66

Solution: The arm ABC is selected as a free body as shown in Fig. 66 (b). The reaction at A is unknown in both magnitude and direction. Although the direction of this reaction could be determined by using the principle of concurrence of three forces, it is often convenient to replace such an unknown by its rectangular components. So, in this example, R_A has been replaced by vertical and horizontal components, A_V and A_H. By taking moments about A, both of these unknowns are eliminated, thus:

$$\Sigma M_A = 400 \times 6 - CD \times (10 \sin 30°) = 0$$

from which $CD = 480$ lb.-tension. Then

$$\Sigma F_V = A_V + 480 \sin 30° - 400 = 0$$

$$A_V = 160 \text{ lb.}$$

and

$$\Sigma F_H = A_H - 480 \cos 30° = 0$$

$$A_H = 416 \text{ lb.}$$

The total reaction at A, shown in Fig. 66 (c), may be completely determined from its components:

$$R_A = \sqrt{(160)^2 + (416)^2} = 446 \text{ lb.}$$

$$\theta_H = \tan^{-1}\frac{160}{416} = 21°$$

Example 1 may be solved by alternative methods. For instance, the intersection of the 400-lb. force and the cable tension determines the line of action of the pin reaction R_A. This intersection may be located and the solution completed graphically, or the intersection may be located by trigonometric methods, the angle θ_H determined, and the solution completed by either trigonometric or algebraic methods. It is left to the student to follow out these suggested alternatives.

Example 2

The tensions in the two sides of a belt driving the windlass in Fig. 67 are 350 lb. and 150 lb. Solve for the resistance W that can be overcome and for the magnitude and direction of the bearing pressure at A.

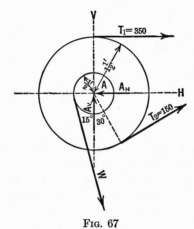

Fig. 67

Solution: a. Algebraic Method. The unknown bearing reaction at A is represented by its components A_V and A_H as shown in Fig. 67. These two unknowns may be eliminated by moments about A.

$$\Sigma M_A = W \times \tfrac{1}{2} + 150 \times 1\tfrac{1}{2} - 350 \times 1\tfrac{1}{2} = 0 \qquad\qquad W = 600 \text{ lb.}$$

Then

$$\Sigma F_V = A_V - 600 \cos 15° + 150 \sin 30° = 0 \qquad A_V = 505 \text{ lb.}$$

$$\Sigma F_H = A_H - 600 \sin 15° - 150 \cos 30° - 350 = 0 \qquad A_H = 635 \text{ lb.}$$

The resultant bearing pressure may now be found from its components.

$$R_A = \sqrt{(635)^2 + (505)^2} = 810 \text{ lb.}$$

$$\theta_H = \tan^{-1}\frac{505}{635} = 38.5°$$

b. Graphic Method. The windlass itself must first be laid out to scale as shown in Fig. 68. The number of forces is reduced to three by combining

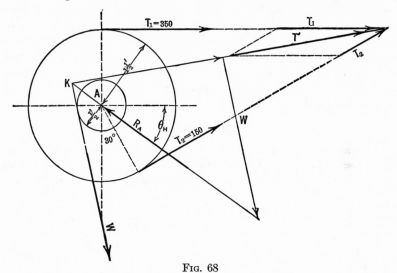

FIG. 68

the two known belt pulls into their resultant, $T' = 485$ lb., by the parallelogram law. The free body is now acted upon by a system of three forces, T', W, and the bearing reaction R_A. Since these forces are not parallel, they must be concurrent, as explained in Art. 12. The forces T' and W are therefore extended to their intersection K. The bearing reaction R_A must also pass through this point, thus determining its line of action and the angle θ_H, which scales 38.5°. From the known value of T' the force triangle consisting of T', W, and R_A is constructed as shown, from which W scales 600 lb. and R_A scales 810 lb.

Problems

1. Solve for the tension BD and the V and H components of the pin reaction at A in Fig. 69.

Ans. BD = 12,000 lb. T; A_H = 10,400 lb.; A_V = 2000 lb.

2. Solve Prob. 1 if the 4000-lb. load acts downward and to the left at an angle of 30° with vertical.   *Ans. BD* = 10,400 lb. T; A_H = 11,000 lb.; A_V = 1730 lb.

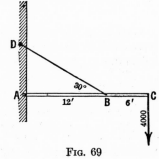

FIG. 69

3. Determine the tension in AD and the H and V components of the pin reaction at B in the crane shown in Fig. 70.

Ans. $AD = 1220$ lb. T; $B_H = 1870$ lb.; $B_V = 2600$ lb.

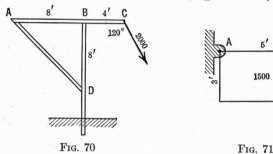

FIG. 70   FIG. 71

4. The block in Fig. 71 is held in place by the force P and the hinge A. The block weighs 1500 lb. Solve for force P and the hinge reaction.

Ans. $P = 643$ lb. C; $A_H = 322$ lb.; $A_V = 944$ lb.

5. A steam hoist is shown in Fig. 72. When the crank pin B is in the position shown, determine the tension in the connecting rod BC and the H and V components of the bearing reaction at A. Assuming that the cross head C moves between smooth guides, determine the reaction of the guide upon the cross head and the steam force P.

Ans. $BC = 3420$ lb.; $P = 3280$ lb.

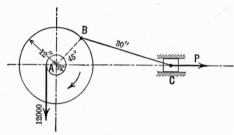

FIG. 72

6. A ladder 20 ft. long and weighing 30 lb. rests against a smooth wall at A and a smooth floor at B, as shown in Fig. 73. A block fastened to the floor at B prevents slipping. Solve for reactions at A and B when the ladder carries an additional load of 120 lb. at 5 ft. from B.

Ans. $A = 33.8$ lb.; $B_V = 150$ lb.

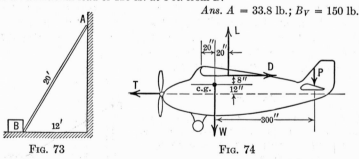

FIG. 73   FIG. 74

7. A monoplane weighing 3000 lb., shown in Fig. 74, is in steady horizontal flight. The center of gravity is 20 in. back from the leading edge of the wing, 12 in. above the thrust line, and 8 in. below the line of action of the total drag. If the drag is 300 lb., compute the tail force, lift, and thrust.   Ans. $P = 193$ lb.

Supplementary Problems

1. Solve for the force P applied to the bell crank in Fig. 75 to overcome the 350-lb. and 400-lb. resistance. Determine the amount and direction of the bearing reaction at B. *Ans. $P = 604$ lb.; $R_B = 777$ lb.; $\theta_H = 88°$.*

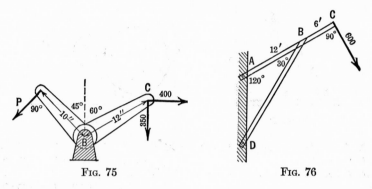

FIG. 75   FIG. 76

2. Determine the force in the brace BD and the H and V components of the reaction at A in the crane shown in Fig. 76.

Ans. $BD = 1800$ lb. C; $A_H = 1200$ lb.; $A_V = 1040$ lb.

3. Solve Prob. 2 when the 600-lb. load is vertical and directed downward.

Ans. $BD = 1560$ lb. C; $A_H = 780$ lb.; $A_V = 750$ lb.

4. Solve Prob. 2 when the 600-lb. load is horizontal and directed to the left.

Ans. $BD = 900$ lb. T; $A_H = 1050$ lb.; $A_V = 780$ lb.

5. Assuming $T_2 = 2T_1$, solve for the belt pulls required to overcome resistance $P = 1200$ lb. when the water pump of Fig. 77 is in the position shown. Neglect friction. *Ans. $T_2 = 1600$ lb.*

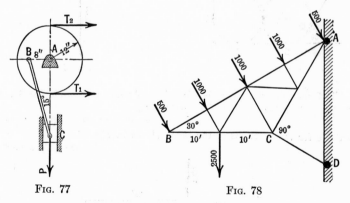

FIG. 77   FIG. 78

6. The cantilever truss in Fig. 78 is supported by a hinge at A and a brace CD. Solve for the compression in the brace and the components of the reaction at A.

Ans. $CD = 5970$ lb.; $A_H = 3170$ lb.; $A_V = 2980$ lb.

7. Solve Prob. 6 when the five loads on top of the truss act vertically downward.

Ans. $CD = 5500$ lb.

8. A 30-ft. ladder weighing 60 lb. rests on a smooth floor at A and a smooth wall at B as shown in Fig. 79. A tie rod CD keeps the ladder from slipping. Solve for tension CD and the reactions at A and B.   *Ans.* $CD = 33.8$ lb. $= B_H$.

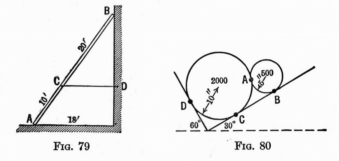

FIG. 79   FIG. 80

9. Two cylinders are placed as shown in Fig. 80. Compute the reactions at A, B, C, and D.   *Ans.* $A = 265$ lb.; $D = 1250$ lb.

10. Interchange the two cylinders in Fig. 80 and solve.
          Ans. $A = 1060$ lb.; $D = 1250$ lb.

11. Solve for the reactions at A, B, C, and D for the cylinders shown in Fig. 81.
          Ans. $A = 5.77$ lb.; $D = 6.66$ lb.

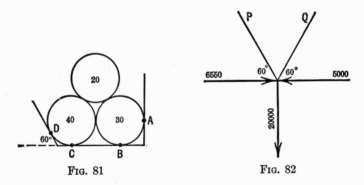

FIG. 81   FIG. 82

12. The forces acting on a certain joint of a roof truss are shown in Fig. 82. Solve for the forces P and Q necessary for equilibrium.
          Ans. $P = 13,100$ lb.; $Q = 10,000$ lb.

13. Solve for the reactions of the beam shown in Fig. 83.
          Ans. $R_1 = 6500$ lb.

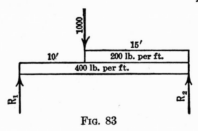

FIG. 83

14. Compute the least force P to start the wheel of Fig. 84 over the block.

$Ans.$ $P = 260$ lb.

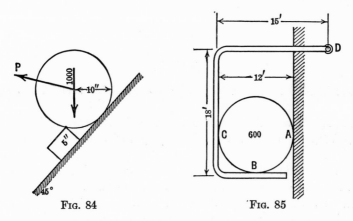

FIG. 84   FIG. 85

15. A 600-lb. cylinder is supported by the frame BCD as shown in Fig. 85. The frame is hinged at D. Determine the reactions at A, B, C, and D.

$Ans.$ $A = 450$ lb.; $D = 750$ lb., $\theta_H = 53.2°$.

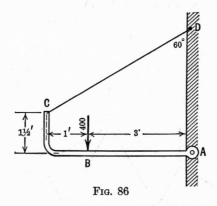

FIG. 86

16. A 400-lb. load rests at point B on the bracket in Fig. 86 which is hinged at A and held in position by cable CD. Determine the tension in CD and the reaction at A. $Ans.$ $CD = 364$ lb.; $A = 384$ lb.

CHAPTER III

STRESSES AND REACTIONS IN SIMPLE STRUCTURES

Art. 17. Two-force Members. When forces are applied at only *two points* on a member, the system may be reduced to two resultant forces, and the member is known as a *two-force* member. For equilibrium the resultant of the forces at one of these points must be equal, opposite, and collinear with the resultant of the forces at the other point. Thus the force or stress in the member must be directed along the axis connecting the two points, and it is known as an axial stress. Such a stress action will be either tension or compression. In frames or structures containing two-force members it is possible to cut through such members in selecting a free body because the internal forces thus exposed are known to be axial in direction with respect to the members through which a section has been made.

A truss is a structure composed of members joined together to form triangles as shown in Fig. 87. If it is assumed that the weights

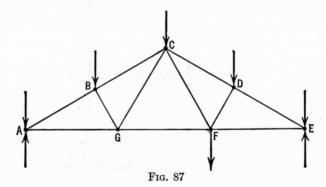

Fig. 87

of the members are negligible in comparison with the loads carried, that the loads are applied only at the joints, and that the members are connected by pins with no member extending beyond the joints at its ends, it becomes evident that each member will be a two-force member as described above.

In most trusses the members are riveted together at the joints, and some members may extend continuously through several joints.

40

There will be some bending action on the member resulting from such construction, thus making the stress more complex.   However, in analyzing such trusses it is customary to treat them as if pin-connected. In the following articles all trusses are to be considered as pin-connected at the joints.

Art. 18.   Internal Stresses in Trusses; Method of Joints.   The stresses in the various members of a truss may be determined by taking successive joints as free bodies.   If all members in the truss are two-force members, then each joint when taken as a free body is acted upon by a system of concurrent forces in equilibrium as shown in Fig. 88.   Two unknown forces may be determined for each joint

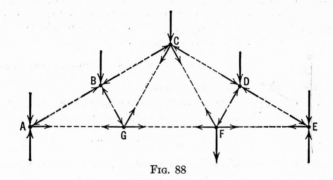

FIG. 88

by application of the conditions of equilibrium, $\Sigma F_x = 0$ and $\Sigma F_y = 0$. In the design and construction of a truss it is necessary to make a compression member considerably heavier than a tension member carrying the same load because of the buckling or column effect taking place in compression members of appreciable length.   Hence, in stating the stress in a given member, the nature of the stress, whether tension or compression, should be given, as well as the magnitude.   The stress may be indicated by the letters at the joints which it connects.   Thus, the stress in the member connecting joints A and B is known as AB.

Example

Solve for the stress in each member in the left half of the roof truss shown in Fig. 89.

Solution: The reaction R_1 is first obtained, the entire truss being the free body.

$$\Sigma M_G = 30R_1 - 8000 \times 15 - 3000 \times 10 = 0 \qquad R_1 = 5000 \text{ lb.}$$

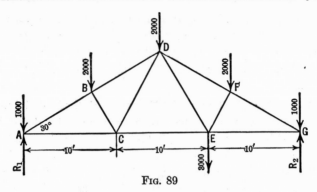

FIG. 89

The joint A is now taken as a free body and is shown in Fig. 90. It is acted upon by four concurrent forces of which two are known and two, AB and AC, are unknown in magnitude only. The directions of AB and AC are easily determined by inspection.

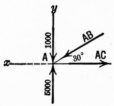

$$\Sigma F_y = AB \sin 30° + 1000 - 5000 = 0$$

gives $AB = 8000$ lb. C.

The direction of AB in Fig. 90 shows that it is pressing against the joint and is therefore compression.

$$\Sigma F_x = AC - 8000 \cos 30° = 0$$

FIG. 90

gives $AC = 6930$ lb. T. The direction of AC in Fig. 90 shows that it is tension.

The joint B is taken as the next free body, shown in Fig. 91. The stress AB, determined from the preceding free body, becomes a known force on joint B. Being a compressive stress, it must press against B as shown.

$$\Sigma F_x = BD + 2000 \sin 30° - 8000 = 0$$

$$BD = 7000 \text{ lb. } C$$

$$\Sigma F_y = BC - 2000 \cos 30° = 0$$

$$BC = 1732 \text{ lb. } C$$

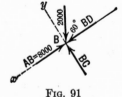

FIG. 91

The joint C is now taken as a free body as shown in Fig. 92.

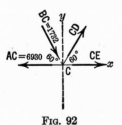

$$\Sigma F_y = CD \sin 60° - 1732 \sin 60° = 0$$

$$CD = 1732 \text{ lb. } T$$

$$\Sigma F_x = CE + 1732 \cos 60° + 1732 \cos 60° - 6930 = 0$$

$$CE = 5198 \text{ lb. } T$$

FIG. 92

The stresses in the remaining members of the truss may be obtained in a similar manner. If, in the analysis of a joint, the direction of an unknown stress is not evident by inspection, the stress may be assumed as either tension or compression. In the subsequent solution for this stress a positive result will indicate the assumed direction to be correct; a negative result will indicate the assumed direction to be wrong.

Problems

1. Solve for the stress in each member of the truss shown in Fig. 93.

Ans. AB = 2000 lb. *C; CD* = 2240 lb. *T.*

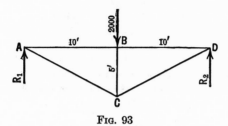

FIG. 93

2. Determine the stress in each member of the truss shown in Fig. 94.

Ans. AB = 24,800 lb. *C; BD* = 19,000 lb. *C.*

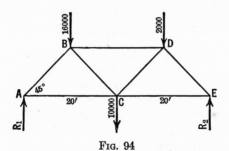

FIG. 94

3. The truss shown in Fig. 95 is supported vertically at *A* and both horizontally and vertically at *G*. Determine the reactions and internal stresses.

Ans. R₂ = 1080 lb.; *CD* = 2730 lb. *T; EG* = 865 lb. *T.*

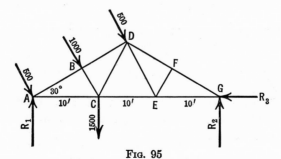

FIG. 95

4. Solve for the reactions and internal stresses of the truss shown in Fig. 96.

   Ans. BC = 7500 lb. *C; CE* = 10,000 lb. *T.*

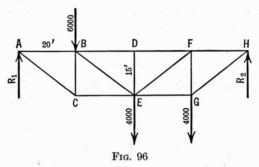

FIG. 96

5. Solve for the reactions and stresses in the cantilever truss shown in Fig. 97.

   Ans. AB = 4330 lb. *T; EF* = 1500 lb. *C.*

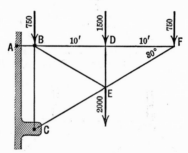

FIG. 97

6. Solve for the reactions and stresses in the cantilever truss shown in Fig. 98.

   Ans. BC = 866 lb. *T; EF* = 2430 lb. *C.*

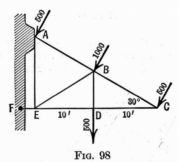

FIG. 98

Art. 19.   Internal Stresses in Trusses; Method of Sections.   The stress in any designated member of a truss may sometimes be determined more advantageously by passing a section through the truss cutting the member in question and then considering as a free body the entire part of the truss lying on either side of the section. If the stresses in only a few members of a truss are required, this method is shorter than the method of joints.

Example 1

Solve for the stresses in members DF and DE of the truss shown in Fig. 99.

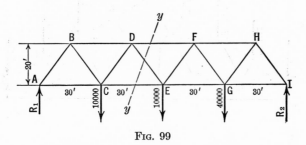

FIG. 99

Solution: The reactions may be found by moments, using the entire truss as the free body.

$$\Sigma M_I = 120R_1 - 10,000 \times 90 - 10,000 \times 60 - 40,000 \times 30 = 0$$

$$R_1 = 22,500 \text{ lb.}$$

The section y–y is now passed through the truss, and the portion of the truss on the left of this section is selected as the free body, as shown in Fig. 100. Three unknown forces appear, but since the system is non-concurrent, a solution can be obtained. The unknown stress DF may be obtained by applying $\Sigma M_E = 0$.

$$DF \times 20 + 10,000 \times 30 - 22,500 \times 60 = 0$$

$$DF = 52,500 \text{ lb. } C$$

The unknown stress DE may be found by applying $\Sigma F_V = 0$.

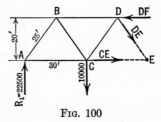

FIG. 100

$$DE \times \tfrac{20}{25} + 10,000 - 22,500 = 0$$

$$DE = 15,600 \text{ lb. } T$$

In order to obtain these same stresses by the method of joints it would be necessary to solve successively the joints at A, B, C, and D.

The method of sections is also useful if the method of joints is inadequate to complete the solution; an example follows.

Example 2

Solve for the internal stresses in the truss shown in Fig. 101.

Solution: By symmetry the reactions R_1 and R_2 are seen to be 16,000 lb. each. The internal stresses in members intersecting at joints A, B, and C

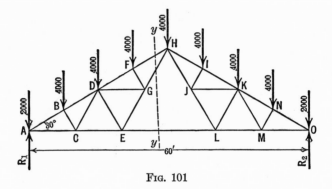

FIG. 101

may be found by the method of joints. However, each of the adjacent joints D and E involves three unknowns and, since the system of forces for each joint is concurrent, a solution cannot be made; hence it becomes impossible to proceed further by this method. A section y–y is now passed through the truss, and the part of the truss lying on the left of the section is selected as the free body as shown in Fig. 102. There are three unknown forces but,

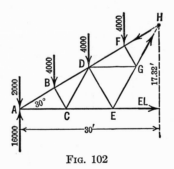

FIG. 102

since the system is non-concurrent, the unknowns may be determined. The condition of equilibrium $\Sigma M_H = 0$ is applied.

$$EL \times 17.32 + 16,000 \times 15 - 16,000 \times 30 = 0$$

$$EL = 13,900 \text{ lb. } T$$

Since the stress EL is known, the joint E involves only two unknowns and may be solved; the remainder of the internal stresses may now be obtained by the method of joints or by the method of sections.

Problems

1. Solve for the stresses in members BG, CG, and GF of the truss shown in Fig. 103.   *Ans. $BG = 1730$ lb. C; $GF = 5200$ lb. T.*

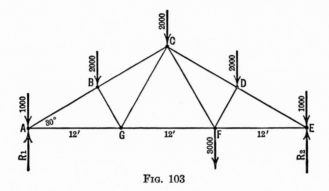

FIG. 103

2. Solve for the stresses in the structure shown in Fig. 104.
Ans. $CD = 6250$ lb. T; $DE = 5000$ lb. C.

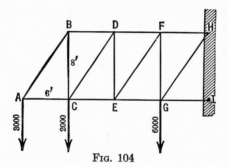

FIG. 104

3. Solve for the stresses in the structure shown in Fig. 105.
Ans. $CD = 6350$ lb. T; $EF = 11,500$ lb. C.

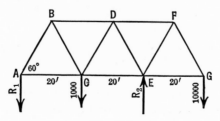

FIG. 105

4. Solve for the stresses in the cantilever truss shown in Fig. 106.

Ans. $AB = 5460$ lb. $T;$ $CE = 8430$ lb. C.

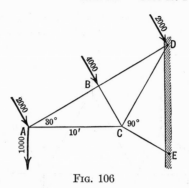

Fig. 106

5. Each of the loads acting on the truss shown in Fig. 107 is 4000 lb. Determine the stresses in members a, b, c, d, and e.

Ans. $a = 22,500$ lb. $C;$ $e = 14,000$ lb. T.

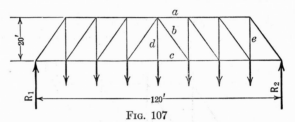

Fig. 107

6. Solve for the stresses in members a, b, and c of the truss shown in Fig. 108.

Ans. $c = 8660$ lb. T.

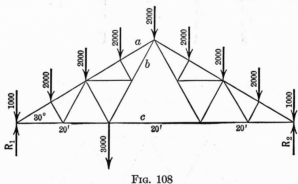

Fig. 108

Art. 20. Bow's Notation. In the graphic method of determining internal stresses in a truss a lettering scheme known as Bow's notation is of considerable advantage. In this method of notation spaces are lettered rather than joints, and a force or stress is then denoted by the letters of the spaces which it separates. In Fig. 109 is shown a truss lettered according to this scheme. In lettering, the spaces are

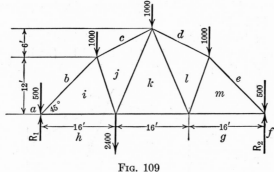

FIG. 109

taken in order in the clockwise direction. In designating the forces acting upon a given joint, the letters are also taken in a clockwise direction. Thus, the joint at the left end of the truss is acted upon by four forces: the reaction R_1, separating spaces h and a, is known as HA; the 500-lb. load becomes AB; the remaining unknown stresses are BI and IH.

Art. 21. The Funicular Polygon. Bow's notation is applicable to the funicular or string polygon method of determining positions of resultants of force systems or in solving for unknown reactions of beams or trusses by graphical methods.

The two forces ab and bc in Fig. 110 (a) can be combined into their resultant in the following manner. The forces are laid down to scale as shown in Fig. 110 (b); then any point O, known as the pole point, is selected. From this pole point the rays OA, OB, and OC are drawn. Through any point on force ab, Fig. 110 (a), string oa is drawn parallel to ray OA. In a similar manner strings ob and oc are drawn parallel to rays OB and OC. The resultant force R or ac acts through the point of intersection of strings oa and oc.

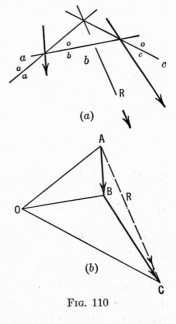

FIG. 110

This method is really one of combining components of forces into resultants. Thus OA and OB are components of force ab, and OB and OC are components of force bc. In the combination, components OB cancel each other, and the final resultant is found from OA and OC. The position of this resultant is obtained in Fig. 110 (a) and the magnitude from Fig. 110 (b).

Reactions on beams and trusses can be obtained by use of the funicular polygon. The forces need not be parallel. Let it be required to solve for the reactions R_1 and R_2 of the beam shown in Fig. 111 (a).

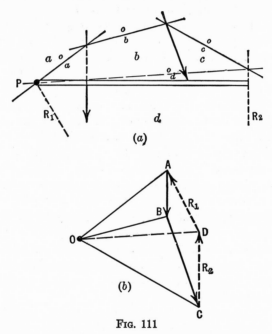

Fig. 111

Reaction R_2 is to be vertical, and reaction R_1 is to act at point P and be inclined at some unknown angle. Loads AB and BC are laid down to scale in Fig. 111 (b). Any pole point O is selected, and rays are drawn as before. Strings oa, ob, and oc are drawn in Fig. 111 (a) as described above, except that string oa must be drawn through point P, the only known point on the line of action of R_1. The last string od, drawn from the point of intersection of R_1 and oa to the point of intersection of R_2 and oc and transferred to Fig. 111 (b), divides the resultant force AC into a vertical reaction CD or R_2 and the diagonal reaction DA or R_1.

Art. 22.   Internal Stresses in Trusses; Graphic Method. The physical dimensions of many trusses are such that algebraic methods of solving for internal stresses are very cumbersome and laborious; the graphic method of analysis may be shorter and easier. The use of Bow's notation facilitates the graphic solution. The steps involved are as follows:

1. The truss is drawn completely to some convenient scale. This is known as the space diagram.

2. All loads are combined graphically into a single resultant. The constructions required may be superimposed on the space diagram.

3. Since the resultant load and the reactions are in equilibrium, a graphic construction may be made to obtain the reactions. This construction likewise is made on the space diagram.

4. As a separate figure, the equilibrium polygon, consisting of external loads and reactions on the entire truss as a free body, is laid out to scale. This will be known as the external load line.

5. The method of joints is now applied to the joint at one end of the truss, the equilibrium polygon of the forces acting on this joint being constructed. Since certain forces involved in this polygon form part of the load line, the polygon is attached directly to the load line.

6. In a similar manner polygons for the remaining joints are constructed in succession. The completed figure consisting of load line and the connected force polygons for the joints is called the force diagram.

7. Magnitudes of the unknown stresses are scaled off directly from the force diagram.

8. The nature of each stress, whether tension or compression, is determined by the direction of the stress in the force diagram, the order of letters being taken in clockwise direction around the joint on which the stress is considered to act.

Example 1

By the graphic method solve for the reactions and stresses in the truss shown in Fig. 109.

Solution: The truss is laid out to scale and lettered according to Bow's notation, as shown in Fig. 112 (a).

The loads on the truss are combined graphically by the method of inverse proportion into their resultant, 6400 lb., which is then resolved by the same principle into components equal and opposite to R_1 and R_2, which scale 3600 lb. and 2800 lb., respectively.

The external load line is now constructed, starting with force AB and closing with force HA, as shown in Fig. 112 (b). The polygon $A-B-I-H-A$ of the forces acting on the joint at the left end of the truss is constructed, from which the magnitudes of the unknown stresses BI and IH are found to scale 4380 lb. and 3100 lb., respectively. Since spaces around a joint are taken in clockwise order, the stress in the member separating spaces b and i is known as BI. In the force diagram the direction B to I shows the way in which the stress is acting on the joint under consideration. The direction is

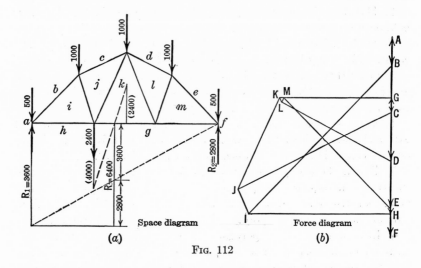

Fig. 112

downward to the left, showing that member bi is pushing on the joint, and thus the stress BI is compression. Similarly IH acts to the right on the joint and is therefore tension.

The force polygons for the remaining joints are then laid out to form the complete force diagram. Thus $IJ = 580$ lb. $T;$ $JK = 2100$ lb. $T;$ $MG = 2300$ lb. $T;$ etc.

If all constructions are accurately made, the final force polygon will close. A failure of the last polygon to close indicates some error in construction. The process thus becomes self-checking.

Example 2

By the graphic method solve for the reactions and stresses in the airplane engine nacelle of Fig. 113 (a).

Solution: The truss is laid out to scale (dimensions not shown) and lettered according to Bow's notation, as shown in Fig. 113 (a).

The loads are combined and the reactions FG and GA determined by the funicular polygon method, as explained in Art. 21. The force polygon is shown in Fig. 113 (b). Reaction FG scales 640 lb., and GA scales 2560 lb. Upon the load line already in place the polygons for the internal stresses are constructed, starting with joint a–b–h and ending with joint e–f–n, as explained in Ex. 1. The stresses can now be scaled off and tabulated, among them $BH = 700$ lb. T and $JK = 1600$ lb. C.

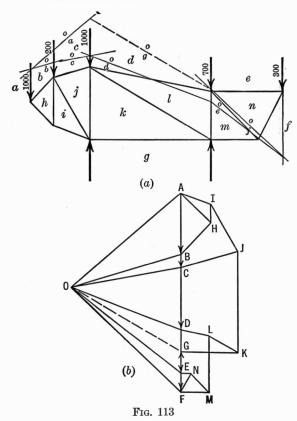

Fig. 113

Art. 23. Internal Stresses in Trusses; Method of Substitution.

In the solution of trusses the method of joints which was used in the previous examples has its limitations and cannot be used in the complete solution of the truss shown in Fig. 114 (a). The method of joints is used on joints 1, 2, and 3, and by it points L, M, and N are located on the force diagram, Fig. 114 (b), as explained in Ex. 1, Art. 22. However, joint 4 has three unknowns, as has joint 5; thus the solution by the method of joints cannot be carried further until one of the unknowns is otherwise determined.

An inspection of the free body to the left of section y–y, Fig. 114 (a), shows that the stress in member eq is independent of the framework of the structure. By the method of substitution, members op and pq are removed, and a false member p'q, shown dotted, is substituted. Joint 4 thus becomes solvable by the method of joints, and from its solution point P' is located in the force diagram. Joint 6 is solvable next, and from its solution point Q is located on the force diagram.

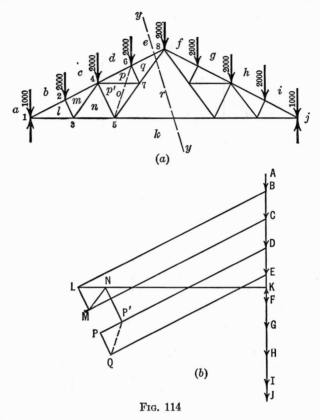

(a)

(b)

Fig. 114

Force *EQ* thus determined is a correct stress, and the false member is now removed and the original members put back. Joint 6 is used again, and from it point *P* is located in the force diagram. Joints 4, 5, and 6 may then be used, and the remaining points *O* and *R* determined. These points are not shown in the figure. Thus all the stresses in the left half of the structure can be scaled off and tabulated.

Problems

(Solve the following problems by graphical methods.)

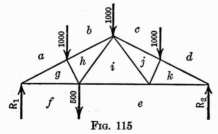

Fig. 115

1. Solve for the stresses in the truss shown in Fig. 115. The truss is 60 ft. long and 15 ft. high.

2. Solve for the stresses in the members of the airplane engine nacelle shown in Fig. 116.

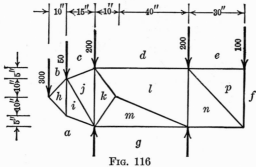

FIG. 116

3. Solve for the stresses in the nacelle shown in Fig. 117.

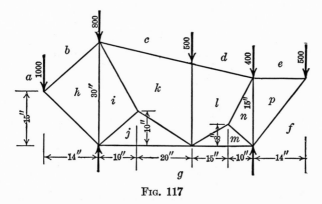

FIG. 117

4. Determine the stresses in the cambered roof truss shown in Fig. 118.

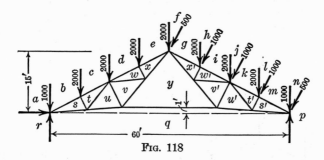

FIG. 118

Art. 24. Three-force Members. When forces are applied at more than two points on a member, the system cannot be reduced to two forces, as was done with the two-force member in Art. 17, and the member is known as a *three-force member*. It is not necessary now that the resultant stress action be directed along the axis of the member.   In general, the stress action is more complex, involving bending and shear.   No attempt will be made here to investigate further the stresses in such members, but the reactions exerted where they are joined to other members may be determined.   Since the direction and nature of the stress action in a three-force member are unknown, a section should not be taken through a member of this type in selecting a free body; hence the free body must contain the entire member. In analyzing structures or frames containing three-force members, it will usually be necessary to use the entire frame as the first free body for the purpose of determining unknown external reactions.   Individual members are then taken out as successive free bodies in order to determine the pin reactions at joints.

Example 1

The A-frame shown in Fig. 119 rests on a smooth floor at A and F.   Solve for the external reactions at these points and for the pin reactions at B, C, and D.

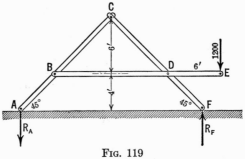

Fig. 119

Solution: Each of the three members of the frame is acted upon by forces at more than two points and is therefore a three-force member.   Since the frame rests on a smooth surface, the reactions at A and F are normal to the surface. With the entire frame as the first free body, Fig. 119, these reactions are determined.

$$\Sigma M_F = 20R_A - 1200 \times 2 = 0 \qquad R_A = 120 \text{ lb.}$$

Either

$$\Sigma F_V = 0 \quad \text{or} \quad \Sigma M_A = 0 \quad \text{gives} \quad R_F = 1320 \text{ lb.}$$

The cross bar BDE is the next free body as shown in Fig. 120 (a).   The reactions at B and D, unknown in both magnitude and direction, are represented by means of their vertical and horizontal components.   There are thus four unknowns, so that a complete solution cannot be made.   The following results, however, may be obtained:

$$\Sigma M_D = 12B_V - 1200 \times 6 = 0 \qquad B_V = 600 \text{ lb.}$$

$$\Sigma F_V = 0 \quad \text{or} \quad \Sigma M_B = 0 \quad \text{then gives} \quad D_V = 1800 \text{ lb.}$$

$$\Sigma F_H = B_H - D_H = 0 \qquad B_H = D_H$$

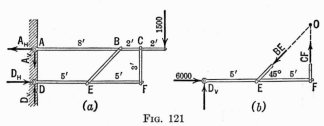

(a)

(b)

FIG. 120

Either of the diagonal members may now be taken as a free body. The member ABC is shown in Fig. 120 (b); since R_A and B_V have already been determined, only three unknowns remain, and the solution may be completed.

$$\Sigma M_C = 6B_H + 120 \times 10 - 600 \times 6 = 0 \qquad B_H = 400 \text{ lb.} = D_H$$

$$\Sigma F_V = C_V - 600 + 120 = 0 \qquad C_V = 480 \text{ lb.}$$

$$\Sigma F_H = C_H - 400 = 0 \qquad C_H = 400 \text{ lb.}$$

The magnitude and direction of the total pin reactions may be determined, if desired, by combining the H and V components.

Example 2

Solve for the components of the pin reactions at A and D and the stresses in members BE and CF of the frame shown in Fig. 121 (a).

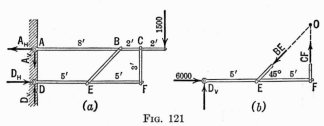

(a)   (b)

FIG. 121

Solution: In this frame the members ABC and DEF are three-force members; members BE and CF are two-force members in which the stress is axial.

The entire frame is the first free body, shown in Fig. 121 (a). Since the directions of the pin reactions at A and D are unknown, they are represented by their V and H components. Since there are four unknowns, only a partial solution is possible. The conditions of equilibrium are applied as follows:

$$\Sigma M_D = 3A_H - 1500 \times 12 = 0 \qquad A_H = 6000 \text{ lb.}$$

$$\Sigma F_H = 0 \quad \text{or} \quad \Sigma M_A = 0 \qquad \text{then gives} \quad D_H = 6000 \text{ lb.}$$

$$\Sigma F_V = D_V - A_V - 1500 = 0 \qquad A_V = D_V - 1500$$

Either of the two three-force members may be selected as the next free body. Let member DEF be chosen, as shown in Fig. 121 (b). There are but three unknowns, and the solution may be completed by the following equations.

$$\Sigma M_O = 10D_V - 6000 \times 5 = 0 \qquad D_V = 3000 \text{ lb.}$$

$$\Sigma F_H = BE \cos 45° - 6000 = 0 \qquad BE = 8484 \text{ lb. } C$$

$$\Sigma M_E = 5CF - 3000 \times 5 = 0 \qquad CF = 3000 \text{ lb. } T$$

Since

$$A_V = D_V - 1500 \qquad A_V = 1500 \text{ lb.}$$

Problems

1. Assume that the reactions at A and E of the A-frame in Fig. 122 are vertical. Solve for the horizontal and vertical components of the pin reactions at B, C, and D.
$Ans. A_V = 367$ lb.; $B_H = 113$ lb.; $B_V = 400$ lb.

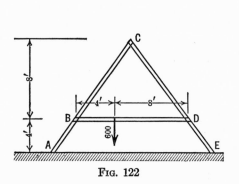

FIG. 122   FIG. 123

2. The crane shown in Fig. 123 is supported at A and D; the reaction at D is horizontal. Solve for the components of the reactions at A and C, and the stress in member BE. $Ans. A_H = 3000$ lb.; $BE = 7500$ lb. C.

3. Solve for the components of the reactions at A, B, C, D, and E of the crane in Fig. 123 if each member weighs 60 lb. per ft.
$Ans. E_H = 6900$ lb.; $E_V = 4875$ lb.

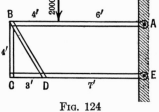

FIG. 124

4. Determine the reactions at A and E and the stresses in members BD and BC of the structure shown in Fig. 124.
$Ans. A_H = 3000$ lb.; $BD = 5000$ lb. C.

5. Place the load on the structure in Fig. 124 on the joint at B and solve.
$Ans. AB = 5000$ lb. T; $BD = 8330$ lb. C.

Art. 25. Redundant Members. When a structure consists of more members than are necessary for stability, it is said to be redundant, and the members not required for stability are called redundant members. The truss shown in Fig. 125 furnishes an example of a redundant system. If a section m–n is taken through the truss, the resulting free body is acted upon by four unknown stresses, and the system is statically indeterminate. If the members a and b can carry either tension or compression, both are not needed to maintain stability of the truss, and either may be designated as a redundant member. However, if

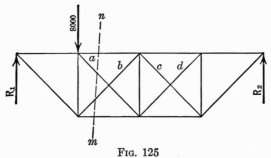

FIG. 125

these members are of such nature that they are capable of carrying tension only, such as cables or slender rods, only one of the two will be acting under a given condition of loading, and the system is reduced to three unknowns, becoming statically determinate. If member b in Fig. 125 is removed, member a will be in compression. When member a is removed, b will be in tension. Therefore if these members are capable of carrying tension only, member b acts while a remains idle. Similarly, in the next panel, member c is not acting.

Problems

1. Assume that members BF and CE of the truss in Fig. 126 can carry tension only. Determine the stress in the one which is acting. *Ans.* $CE = 5000$ lb. *T.*

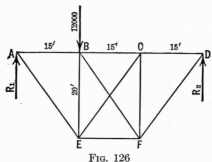

FIG. 126

2. Assume that the diagonal members of the truss in Fig. 127 can carry tension only. Determine the stresses in those which are acting.

Ans. $AD = CF = EH = 11{,}500$ lb. T; $GJ = 9240$ lb. T; $IK = 2310$ lb. T.

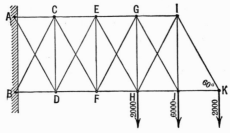

Fig. 127

Art. 26. Parabolic Cables. When a flexible cable or cord is suspended between two points of support and is subjected to a distributed loading, the cable will assume the form of a curve the exact shape of which is dependent on the nature of the distribution of the load. A load distributed uniformly horizontally will be considered first. The suspension bridge illustrated in Fig. 128 furnishes an example of this type of loading, provided that the floor of the bridge is loaded uniformly and that the vertical cables are spaced equal distances

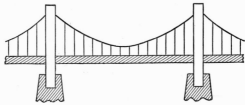

Fig. 128

apart and relatively close together. It will now be shown that under such loading conditions the cable will take the shape of a parabola.

In Fig. 129 (*a*) is shown a cord suspended from points *A* and *B* and loaded with a load, *w* pounds per foot, distributed uniformly along the horizontal. The horizontal distance *l* between supports is known as the span, and the distance *d* from the level of the supports to the lowest point *O* of the cord is known as the sag. The portion of the cord included between *O* and any other point *P* is taken as a free body, shown in Fig. 129 (*b*). With *O* as the origin of coordinate axes the coordinates of point *P* are *x*, *y*. The resultant load on this portion of the cord is *wx*, acting midway between *O* and *P*, since the load is distributed uniformly horizontally. Since *O* is the lowest point in the cord, the tangent here is horizontal, and the tension H at this point is horizontal. The tension T in the cord at P must be concurrent with H and the load wx as shown. By moments about P,

$$Hy - wx\frac{x}{2} = 0$$

or

$$y = \frac{w}{2H}x^2$$

This equation is of the form $y = ax^2 + bx + c$ and therefore represents a parabola with vertical axis.

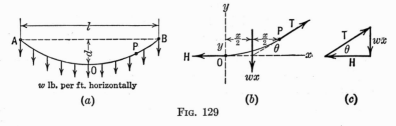

w lb. per ft. horizontally

(a)   (b)   (c)

FIG. 129

The triangle of forces shown in Fig. 129 (c) shows that the tension T is greater than H and increases when x increases, so that the maximum tension T occurs at the points of support. At either A or B, x and y become $l/2$ and d, respectively, and the equation of moments becomes

$$Hd - \frac{wl}{2}\cdot\frac{l}{4} = 0$$

or

$$H = \frac{wl^2}{8d}$$

From the triangle of forces,

$$T = \sqrt{H^2 + \left(\frac{wl}{2}\right)^2}$$

$$\theta = \tan^{-1}\frac{wl}{2H} = \tan^{-1}\frac{4d}{l}$$

The length s of the cord will next be determined. From calculus the length of any curve is given by

$$s = \int\left[1 + \left(\frac{dy}{dx}\right)^2\right]^{\frac{1}{2}}dx$$

By differentiation of $y = \dfrac{wx^2}{2H}$, the result $\dfrac{dy}{dx} = \dfrac{wx}{H}$ is obtained. If this result is substituted above,

$$s = 2 \int_0^{\frac{l}{2}} \left[1 + \left(\frac{wx}{H}\right)^2 \right]^{\frac{1}{2}} dx = 2 \int_0^{\frac{l}{2}} \left[1 + \frac{64d^2x^2}{l^4} \right]^{\frac{1}{2}} dx$$

the exact expression for s from this integral is a logarithmic function and is cumbersome to use. A simple expression for s may be obtained by expanding the term in brackets into a converging series and integrating term by term:

$$s = l + \frac{8d^2}{3l} - \frac{32d^4}{5l^3} + \cdots$$

The fourth and succeeding terms of the above series are so small that they may be neglected without appreciable error.

A load distributed uniformly along the length of the cord will next be considered. An example is a cord loaded only by its own weight. The loads on successive unit lengths of the cord are not spaced at equal horizontal distances, and the cord assumes the shape of a curve called a catenary. The equation of the catenary involves exponential functions and is much more complex than the equation of the parabola. In fact, many problems involving the catenary can be solved only by trial. If, however, the sag is small in relation to the span, the loading approaches uniform distribution horizontally, and the catenary curve approximates very closely a parabola. When the sag is not more than one-tenth of the span, the error involved in solving as if the load were distributed uniformly horizontally is negligible for most engineering purposes. In the problems of this article the foregoing conditions may be assumed.

Example 1

The floor of a suspension bridge is 400 ft. long and 20 ft. wide and is supported by a cable on each side having a sag of 25 ft. The bridge carries a load of 100 lb. per sq. ft. of floor area. Solve for the tension at the middle, the tension at the ends, and the length of the cables.

Solution: The total load on one cable is

$$\frac{400 \times 20 \times 100}{2} = 400{,}000 \text{ lb. or } 1000 \text{ lb. per ft.}$$

One half of the cable is taken as a free body as shown in Fig. 130. By moments about the point of support A,

$$H \times 25 = 200,000 \times 100 \qquad\qquad H = 800,000 \text{ lb.}$$

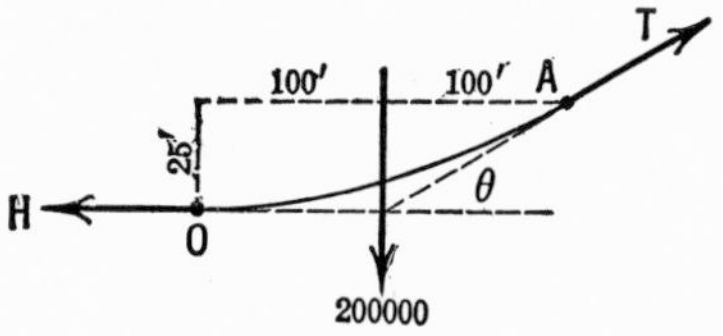

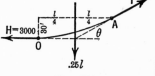

FIG. 130

From the triangle of forces,

$$T = \sqrt{(800,000)^2 + (200,000)^2} = 825,000 \text{ lb.}$$

$$\theta = \tan^{-1}\frac{200,000}{800,000} = 14°$$

The length of the cable is

$$s = 400 + \frac{8(25)^2}{3(400)} - \frac{32(25)^4}{5(400)^3} = 404.13 \text{ ft.}$$

Example 2

A cable can safely carry 3000 lb. tension. Its weight is 0.5 lb. per linear foot. If the allowable sag is 30 ft., what is the maximum spacing for the supports?

Solution: If it is assumed that the unknown span l is more than 10 times the sag, the condition of load distributed uniformly horizontally is approximated, and furthermore H is approximately equal to $T = 3000$. Half of the cable is shown as a free body in Fig. 131. By moments

$$3000 \times 30 - \frac{0.5l}{2}\cdot\frac{l}{4} = 0$$

$$l^2 = 1,440,000 \quad \text{and} \quad l = 1200 \text{ ft.}$$

FIG. 131

The ratio of sag to span is now $30/1200 = 1/40$, and the initial assumption is justified.

Problems

1. A cable having a span of 400 ft. and a sag of 50 ft. carries a uniformly distributed load of 1000 lb. per horizontal foot. Solve for the maximum tension and the length of the cable.   *Ans.* $T = 448,000$ lb. at 26.5° with H; $s = 416$ ft.

2. Determine the maximum spacing of poles to carry a wire weighing 0.05 lb. per ft. if the allowable tension in the wire is 300 lb. and the allowable sag is 2 ft.
Ans. $l = 310$ ft.

3. If a wire weighing 0.1 lb. per ft. is stretched between points 100 ft. apart until the tension reaches 600 lb., what will be the resulting sag?   *Ans. d* = 0.208 ft.

4. A cable of a suspension bridge has a span of 800 ft. and a sag of 100 ft. If the allowable tension for the cable is 500,000 lb., what is the maximum allowable load in pounds per foot distributed uniformly horizontally?   *Ans. w* = 560 lb. per ft.

Art. 27. The Catenary.

It was stated in Art. 26 that a cable loaded uniformly along its length assumes the shape of a catenary curve and that, when the ratio of span to sag is small, the methods developed for the parabolic cable may be used to a close degree of approximation. Consideration will now be given to the problem in which the ratio of span to sag is too large to permit the use of the approximate method.

Let AQB in Fig. 132 (*a*) represent a cable loaded with w pounds per foot distributed uniformly along its length and suspended from

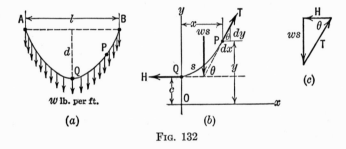

(a)   (b)

Fig. 132

points A and B on the same horizontal level and at distance l apart. Let Q represent the lowest point on the cable, P any other point, and s the distance along the cable from Q to P. This portion of the cable is shown as a free body in Fig. 132 (*b*), where H represents the horizontal tension at Q, T the tension at P, and ws the resultant of the vertical loads. The equilibrium triangle of forces for the free body is shown in Fig. 132 (*c*), from which

$$\tan \theta = \frac{ws}{H} = \frac{s}{c}$$

where $c = \dfrac{H}{w}$ is a constant. Let O, at distance c below Q, be taken as the origin of coordinates, as indicated in Fig. 132 (*b*).

$$\frac{dy}{dx} = \tan \theta = \frac{s}{c} \tag{1}$$

$$ds^2 = dx^2 + dy^2 \quad \text{or} \quad dy = \sqrt{(ds)^2 - (dx)^2} \tag{2}$$

By eliminating dy from equations (1) and (2),

$$dx = \frac{c\,ds}{\sqrt{c^2 + s^2}}$$

or

$$\int_0^x dx = c \int_0^s \frac{ds}{\sqrt{c^2 + s^2}}$$

By integration

$$x = c \log_e \frac{s + \sqrt{c^2 + s^2}}{c} \tag{3}$$

Reducing to exponential form,

$$e^{\frac{x}{c}} = \frac{s + \sqrt{c^2 + s^2}}{c} \tag{4}$$

Solving for s,

$$s = \frac{c}{2}(e^{\frac{x}{c}} - e^{-\frac{x}{c}}) \tag{5}$$

By substitution of (5) in (1)

$$dy = \frac{1}{2}(e^{\frac{x}{c}} - e^{-\frac{x}{c}})\,dx \tag{6}$$

Let (6) be integrated over the portion of the curve from Q to P,

$$\int_c^y dy = \frac{1}{2}\int_0^x (e^{\frac{x}{c}} - e^{-\frac{x}{c}})\,dx$$

$$y - c = \frac{c}{2}(e^{\frac{x}{c}} + e^{-\frac{x}{c}}) - c$$

$$y = \frac{c}{2}(e^{\frac{x}{c}} + e^{-\frac{x}{c}}) \tag{7}$$

Equation (7) is the equation of the catenary curve in cartesian coordinates. By squaring (5) and (7) and subtracting,

$$y^2 = s^2 + c^2 \tag{8}$$

Substituting (8) in (3),

$$x = c \log_e \frac{s + y}{c} \tag{9}$$

From Fig. 132 (b)

$$T^2 = w^2s^2 + H^2 = w^2s^2 + w^2c^2 = w^2(s^2 + c^2)$$

$$T = w\sqrt{s^2 + c^2} = wy \tag{10}$$

Equations (5) and (7) may also be written in terms of hyperbolic functions as follows:

$$s = \frac{c}{2}(e^{\frac{x}{c}} - e^{-\frac{x}{c}}) = c \sinh \frac{x}{c} \tag{11}$$

$$y = \frac{c}{2}(e^{\frac{x}{c}} + e^{-\frac{x}{c}}) = c \cosh \frac{x}{c} \tag{12}$$

In problems involving the catenary the span l becomes $2x$ in equations (1) to (12), the length of the cable becomes $2s$, and the sag d becomes $y - c$. Because of the form of the equations many problems can be solved only by trial. A table of hyperbolic functions may facilitate solution when equations (11) and (12) are used. *For any given tension there are two values of the sag that will produce that tension.*

Example

A cable weighing 4 lb. per ft. is suspended between two supports on the same level and 1000 ft. apart. The sag is 200 ft. Compute the maximum tension and the length of the cable.

Solution:

$$y = c + 200$$

From (8),

$$y^2 = s^2 + c^2 = c^2 + 400c + 40{,}000$$

$$s = \sqrt{400c + 40{,}000}$$

From (9),

$$x = 500 = c \log_e \frac{\sqrt{400c + 40{,}000} + (c + 200)}{c}$$

By trial it is found that the value $c = 660$ will very nearly satisfy this equation. Hence,

$$y = c + 200 = 860 \text{ ft.}$$

$$T = wy = 4 \times 860 = 3440 \text{ lb. at the supports}$$

$$s = \sqrt{y^2 - c^2} = \sqrt{(860)^2 - (660)^2} = 550 \text{ ft.}$$

$$2s = 1100 \text{ ft. (the length of cable)}$$

Problems

1. Compute the span and sag of a cable 600 ft. long weighing 1 lb. per ft. and supported at points on the same level with a maximum tension of 800 lb.

Ans. 583 ft.; 59 ft.

2. A cable weighing 6 lb. per ft. is suspended between points 800 ft. apart on the same level. The sag is 200 ft. Compute the maximum tension and the length of the cable.

Ans. 3780 lb.; 918 ft.

3. A cable weighing 2 lb. per ft. is to be suspended between two supports on the same level and 600 ft. apart. If the maximum allowable tension in the cable is 1200 lb., determine the minimum sag to which the cable may be drawn up, and the length of the cable. *Ans.* 92 ft.; 636 ft.

Supplementary Problems

1. The truss shown in Fig. 133 is supported by a horizontal and vertical reaction at E and by only a vertical reaction at D. Determine the stresses in this structure.
Ans. $BC = 1120$ lb. T; $BE = 1680$ lb. T.

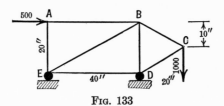

FIG. 133

2. Solve Prob. 1 when the 1000-lb. load is horizontal and points to the right and the 500-lb. load is reduced to zero. *Ans. $BC = 558$ lb. T.*

3. Assume that the wing in the high-wing monoplane shown in Fig. 134 is hinged at C, and solve for the stress in the strut AB and the reaction at C.
Ans. $AB = 4720$ lb. T.

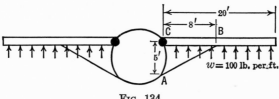

FIG. 134

4. Solve for the reactions at A, D, and F and the stress in member BC of the crane in Fig. 135. *Ans. $BC = 4240$ lb. C.*

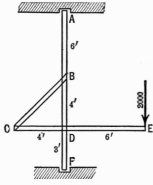

FIG. 135

5. The rear portion of a side truss of an airplane fuselage is shown in Fig. 136. Find the force in member AB when the tail load is 1200 lb. *Ans.* 5900 lb. *T.*

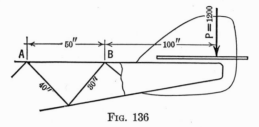

FIG. 136

6. Solve for the forces in the members of the cantilever truss shown in Fig. 137. *Ans.* $CG = 8400$ lb. *T*; $DG = 10,100$ lb. *C.*

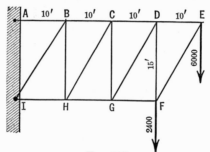

FIG. 137

7. Assume the reactions at A and E, Fig. 138, to be vertical, and solve for the reaction at C and the stress in member BD. *Ans.* $BD = 700$ lb. *T.*

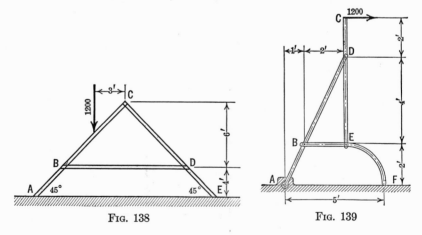

FIG. 138   FIG. 139

8. The reaction at F of the frame shown in Fig. 139 is vertical. Determine the reaction at F and the horizontal and vertical components of the reactions at B, D, and E. *Ans.* $F_V = 1920$ lb.; $D_H = 1800$ lb.

9. A cable carrying 100 lb. per horizontal ft. is suspended as shown in Fig. 140. Solve for the tensions at *A* and *B*.   *Ans.* *A* = 19,000 lb.

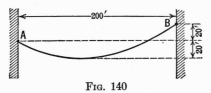

FIG. 140

10. Assume that the diagonal braces below *BC* in the tower in Fig. 141 can carry tension only. Solve for all internal stresses.

Ans. BC = 750 lb. *C; CD* = 2500 lb. *T.*

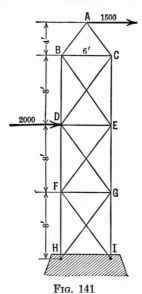

FIG. 141

11. Solve for all the internal stresses in the truss of Fig. 142.

Ans. FM = 66,700 lb. *T.*

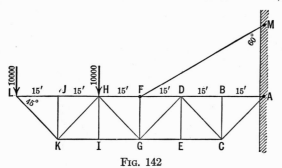

FIG. 142

12. Solve for the stresses in the members of the truss shown in Fig. 143.

Ans. KM = 10,000 lb. *C; LN* = 8000 lb. *T.*

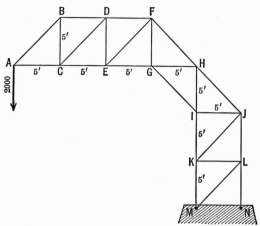

Fig. 143

13. The frame of Fig. 144 is hinged at *A* and rests on a smooth surface at *F*. Compute the reactions at *A* and *F* and the stress in member *BE*.

Ans. A_V = 1000 lb.; *BE* = 1390 lb. *T.*

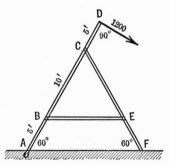

Fig. 144

14. Place the load in Fig. 144 vertically downward and solve for all reactions and stresses.   *Ans. C_H* = 693 lb.; *C_V* = 800 lb.

15. Solve for all reactions and stresses in the frame shown in Fig. 145.

Ans. B_H = 2600 lb.; *CD* = 4330 lb. *C.*

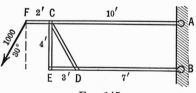

Fig. 145

16. By the graphical method solve for all reactions and stresses in the truss shown in Fig. 146. *Ans. LE* = 270,000 lb. *C; AK* = 352,000 lb. *T.*

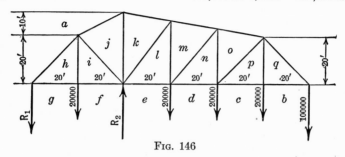

FIG. 146

17. The cable of a transmission line is suspended between towers 800 ft. apart. The cable weighs 1.5 lb. per ft., and the sag is 80 ft. Compute the maximum tension, using the catenary equations. *Ans.* 1643 lb.

18. Solve for an approximate value of the maximum tension in the cable described in Prob. 17, using the parabolic method. What is the percentage of error?
Ans. 1616 lb.; 1.64 per cent.

19. Solve for the reactions at *B* and *E* and the stresses in members *CD* and *CF* of the frame shown in Fig. 147.

Ans. CD = 15,300 lb. *T; B_H* = 13,000 lb.; *B_V* = 9970 lb.

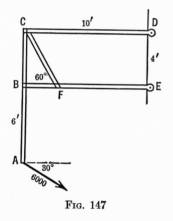

FIG. 147

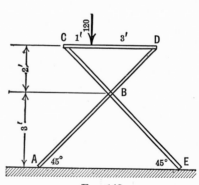

FIG. 148

20. Assume that the reactions at *A* and *E* of the frame shown in Fig. 148 are vertical. Solve for the reactions at *B*, *C*, and *D*. *Ans. B_H* = 150 lb.; *B_V* = 50 lb.

CHAPTER IV

EQUILIBRIUM OF FORCES IN SPACE

Art. 28. Conditions of Equilibrium. The conditions of equilibrium for a system of non-coplanar forces are:

1. The algebraic sum of the moments of the forces about any axis in space must equal zero.

2. The algebraic sum of the components of the forces parallel to any given direction in space must equal zero.

3. The polygon of the forces in space must close. It follows also that the projection of this polygon into any plane must close, and hence the projection of the forces in space upon any plane in space must form a coplanar system of forces in equilibrium.

Art. 29. Concurrent Forces in Space. Any of the conditions of equilibrium stated above may be applied in the solution of a problem involving concurrent, non-coplanar forces. The following example illustrates the various possibilities.

Example

The frame shown in Fig. 149 (*a*) consists of three members *AD*, *CD*, and *DE* attached to a vertical wall *ACFG* and joined at *D* to support the 3000-lb. load. Determine the stress in each member of the frame.

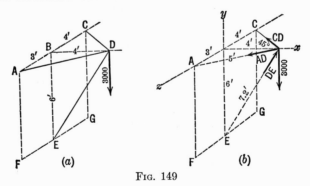

FIG. 149

Solution: First Method. The forces acting at *D*, as shown in Fig. 149 (*b*), constitute a system of concurrent, non-coplanar forces in equilibrium. The additional dimensions shown in this figure can be determined from those originally given. Coordinate axes are taken as shown, and the three force summations in the directions of these axes follow:

$$\Sigma F_x = AD \times \frac{4}{5} + CD \cos 45° - DE \times \frac{4}{7.2} = 0 \tag{1}$$

$$\Sigma F_y = DE \times \frac{6}{7.2} - 3000 = 0 \tag{2}$$

$$\Sigma F_z = AD \times \frac{3}{5} - CD \cos 45° = 0 \tag{3}$$

Simultaneous solution of these equations gives:

$$AD = 1430 \text{ lb. } T$$
$$CD = 1210 \text{ lb. } T$$
$$DE = 3600 \text{ lb. } C$$

Second Method. Instead of using force summations, three moment equations may be written, the lines AC, AF, and CG being used as axes.

$$\Sigma M_{AC} = 3000 \times 4 - DE \times \frac{6}{7.2} \times 4 = 0 \qquad DE = 3600 \text{ lb. } C$$

$$\Sigma M_{AF} = CD \cos 45° \times 7 - 3600 \times \frac{4}{7.2} \times 3 = 0 \quad CD = 1210 \text{ lb. } T$$

$$\Sigma M_{CG} = AD \times \frac{4}{5} \times 7 - 3600 \times \frac{4}{7.2} \times 4 = 0 \qquad AD = 1430 \text{ lb. } T$$

Third Method. If the forces of the Fig. 149 (*b*) are projected into the xy plane, a coplanar system results, consisting of the 3000-lb. load and force DE, which appear in their real values since they lie in this plane, and a third force Q, which represents the combined projections of forces AD and CD. This projected system is shown in Fig. 150 (*a*).

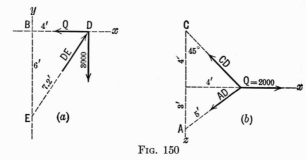

Fig. 150

This coplanar system can be solved in any of the usual ways. For instance

$$\Sigma F_y = DE \times \frac{6}{7.2} - 3000 = 0 \qquad DE = 3600 \text{ lb. } C$$

$$\Sigma M_E = Q \times 6 - 3000 \times 4 = 0 \qquad Q = 2000 \text{ lb.}$$

The forces are now projected into the x–z plane as shown in Fig. 150 (b). Here the projection of DE will be the force Q reversed in direction. This coplanar system is then solved by any of the usual methods. For instance,

$$\Sigma M_A = 2000 \times 3 - CD \sin 45° \times 7 = 0 \qquad CD = 1210 \text{ lb. } T$$

$$\Sigma M_C = 2000 \times 4 - AD \times \tfrac{4}{5} \times 7 = 0 \qquad AD = 1430 \text{ lb. } T$$

The graphic method may also be applied to the above example, in which case the projections shown in Fig. 150 must be used.

Problems

1. Solve for the stress in each member of the frame shown in Fig. 151.

              Ans. AB = 3040 lb. *T; AD = AF* = 2500 lb. *C.*

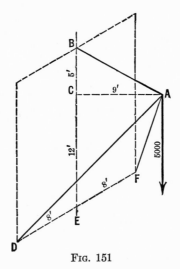

FIG. 151

2. The frame shown in Fig. 152 is known as a shear-legs crane. Solve for the stress in each member of the crane.

              Ans. AB = 31,400 lb. *T; BC = BE* = 17,200 lb. *C.*

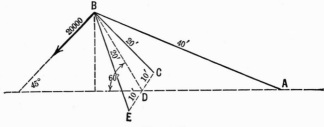

FIG. 152

3. The legs of the tripod shown in Fig. 153 are 6 ft. long and are spaced 120° apart. Solve for the stress in each leg.   *Ans.* 770 lb. *C.*

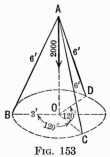

Fig. 153

4. Solve Prob. 3 if *B* is moved toward *C* so that the angle *BOC* is 90°.
                    Ans. AB = 845 lb. *C; AD* = 975 lb. *C.*

5. Solve for the forces in the legs of the tripod shown in Fig. 154.
                    Ans. AB = 124 lb.; *AD* = 615 lb.

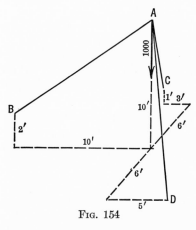

Fig. 154

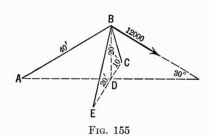

Fig. 155

6. Solve for the stress in each member of the shear-legs crane in Fig. 155.
                    Ans. AB = 12,000 lb. *T; BC* = 8960 lb. *C; BE* = 5640 lb. *C.*

7. Solve Prob. 6 if the point where the line of the load strikes the ground is 15 ft. to the right of line *CE* and 10 ft. in front of line *AD*. (Suggestion: Resolve the 12,000-lb. pull into three rectangular components at *B*.)
                    Ans. AB = 7720 lb. *T; BE* = 10,200 lb. *C.*

Art. 30. Parallel Forces in Space.

A table or platform carrying vertical loads and supported by vertical reactions constitutes a typical example of non-coplanar parallel forces. Three supports not in the same plane are sufficient for stability; any additional supports are redundant and make the system statically indeterminate. The solution may readily be made by means of the force summation and the summations of moments about convenient axes.

Example

The rectangular platform shown in Fig. 156 is supported at A, B, and C and carries a load of 600 lb. at the position indicated. Compute the reactions at the supports.

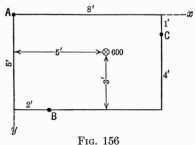

Fig. 156

Solution: The necessary three equations may be chosen as follows:

$$\Sigma M_x = B \times 5 + C \times 1 - 600 \times 2 = 0 \tag{1}$$

$$\Sigma M_y = B \times 2 + C \times 8 - 600 \times 5 = 0 \tag{2}$$

$$\Sigma F = A + B + C - 600 = 0 \tag{3}$$

Simultaneous solution of these equations gives

$$A = 94.4 \text{ lb.}; \quad B = 173.6 \text{ lb.}; \quad C = 332 \text{ lb.}$$

Problems

1. A rectangular platform is supported at A, B, and C, and carries a 600-lb. load as shown in Fig. 157. Solve for the reactions at the supports.

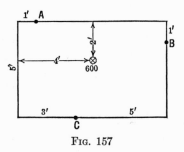

Fig. 157

2. A triangular platform with sides of 10 ft. each is supported at each vertex. The platform weighs 200 lb. and carries an additional concentrated load of 400 lb. at a point situated on one of the medians and 3 ft. from the vertex. Solve for the reactions at the supports. (Note: The weight of the platform may be considered to act at the intersection of the medians.)   *Ans.* 328 lb.; 136 lb.; 136 lb.

3. The circular table top shown in Fig. 158 weighs 60 lb. and carries a load of 400 lb. as shown. Determine the leg reactions. *Ans.* $A = 220$ lb.; $C = 62.5$ lb.

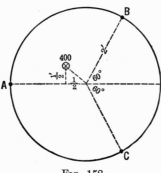

FIG. 158

4. Solve Prob. 3 if the support at B is moved 15° toward A. *Ans.* $B = 182$ lb.

5. If a square platform is supported at one corner and at the midpoint of each of the opposite sides, show that each support carries one-third the weight of the platform.

Art. 31. Non-concurrent, Non-parallel Forces in Space.

This is the most general type of force system. All the possible conditions of equilibrium may be needed to complete the solution of such a system, but projection into convenient planes will generally be found of most advantage.

Example 1

A vertical windlass weighing 150 lb. and supported in frictionless bearings at A and B is shown in Fig. 159 (a). The load W is raised by means of the belt pulls applied to pulley C. The belt pulls are parallel to each other and make an angle of 60° with the x–y plane as indicated. Determine the load W that can be raised and the x, y, and z components of the bearing reactions.

Solution: The various forces acting on the windlass are first projected into the x–z plane and appear as shown in Fig. 159 (b).

$$\Sigma M_C = W \times \tfrac{1}{4} + 200 \times 1 - 400 \times 1 = 0$$

from which

$$W = 800 \text{ lb.}$$

The forces are now projected into the x–y plane as shown in Fig. 159 (c).

$$\Sigma M_A = B_x \times 6 + 300 \times 2 - 800 \times 4 = 0$$

$$B_x = 433 \text{ lb.}$$

$$\Sigma F_x = A_x + 433 + 300 - 800 = 0$$

$$A_x = 67 \text{ lb.}$$

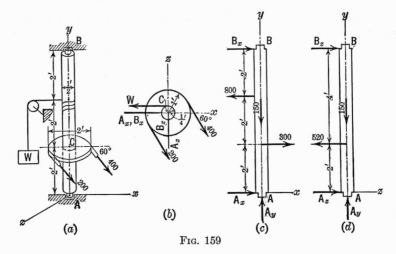

Fig. 159

If it is assumed that there is no way for the bearing at B to exert a vertical effect, the reaction $B_y = 0$. Then

$$\Sigma F_y = A_y - 150 = 0 \quad \text{and} \quad A_y = 150 \text{ lb.}$$

A third projection is then made into the y–z plane as shown in Fig. 159 (d), from which:

$$\Sigma M_A = 6B_z - 520 \times 2 = 0 \quad \text{gives} \quad B_z = 173 \text{ lb.}$$

$$\Sigma F_z = A_z + 173 - 520 = 0 \quad \text{gives} \quad A_z = 347 \text{ lb.}$$

Example 2

The crane shown in Fig. 160 (a) is supported by two backstays DG and DH. Determine the stress in each backstay when the plane of the boom BF bisects the angle GAH between the backstays.

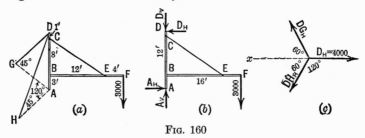

Fig. 160

Solution: The effect of the backstays in maintaining equilibrium of the crane may be represented by the forces D_V and D_H acting at D as shown in Fig. 160 (b).

$$\Sigma M_A = D_H \times 12 - 3000 \times 16 = 0 \quad \text{gives} \quad D_H = 4000 \text{ lb.}$$

The horizontal plane at D now contains the horizontal components of DG and DH, of which D_H is the resultant. If D_H is reversed in direction, it becomes the equilibrant of the system as shown in Fig. 160 (c). It is evident by symmetry that DG_H and DH_H are equal. Their values may be obtained by

$$\Sigma F_X = 2(DG_H \cos 60°) - 4000 = 0$$

from which

$$DG_H = DH_H = 4000 \text{ lb.}$$

Since each backstay is at 45° with the ground, the actual stress in each backstay may be found from the relation

$$DG_H = DG \cos 45°$$

or

$$DG = DH = \frac{4000}{0.707} = 5660 \text{ lb. } T$$

Example 3

Assuming that the boom of the crane in Ex. 2 may be rotated in the horizontal plane about the mast, determine the position of the boom for maximum tension in DG. Solve for this stress and the corresponding stress in DH.

Solution: The position of the boom for maximum tension in DG is found in the following manner. Let the boom, and consequently D_H, be placed at

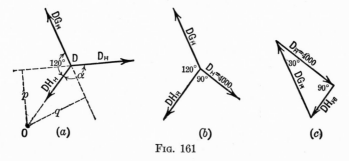

FIG. 161

any angle α with DH_H as shown in Fig. 161 (a). Let O be taken as any point on the line of action of DH_H and let p and q be the perpendicular distances from O to D_H and DG_H. Then

$$\Sigma M_O = DG_H \times q - D_H \times p = 0$$

and

$$DG_H = D_H \times \frac{p}{q}$$

In this expression for DG_H the factors D_H and q remain unchanged as the boom rotates. Therefore DG_H will be maximum when distance p is maximum. The maximum possible value of p, however, is the distance OD, and p has this value only when the angle α is 90° or 270°. Consequently, it follows that DG_H and hence DG itself will be maximum when the vertical plane of the boom is at right angles with the plane of the other backstay DH. When $\alpha = 90°$, the stress in DG will be maximum tension; when $\alpha = 270°$, the stress in DG will be maximum compression.

The solution for the stresses required is shown in Fig. 161 (b) and (c). D_H is placed at 90° with DH_H and the force triangle is drawn, from which

$$DG_H = \frac{4000}{\cos 30°} = 4620 \text{ lb. and } DH_H = 4000 \tan 30° = 2310 \text{ lb.}$$

The actual stresses in the backstays are then determined from their horizontal components.

$$\text{max. } DG = \frac{4620}{\cos 45°} = 6530 \text{ lb. } T$$

$$DH = \frac{2310}{\cos 45°} = 3265 \text{ lb. } T$$

Examples 1, 2, and 3 may be solved graphically, using projections into convenient planes.

Problems

1. The windlass shown in Fig. 162 is driven by belt pulls T_2 and T_1, which are parallel to the z axis. Assuming that $T_2 = 2T_1$, determine the belt tensions and the components of the bearing reactions.

Ans. $T_2 = 150$ lb.; $A_y = 257$ lb.; $A_z = 32$ lb.; $B_y = 343$ lb.; $B_z = 193$ lb.; $A_x = B_x = 0$.

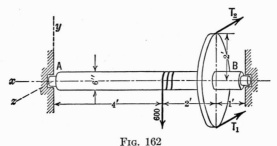

FIG. 162

2. Let the 600-lb. load hang downward and at an angle of 30° to the right in the windlass of Fig. 162 and solve as in Prob. 1. Assume that all the horizontal thrust is carried at B.

Ans. $T_2 = 130$ lb.; $B_x = 300$ lb.; $B_y = 297$ lb.; $B_z = 178$ lb.

3. The load on the windlass of Fig. 163 is held by force P acting perpendicular to the crank handle D. Solve for force P and the y and z components of the bearing reactions at A and B. *Ans.* $P = 133$ lb.; $A_y = 583$ lb.; $A_z = 28.8$ lb.

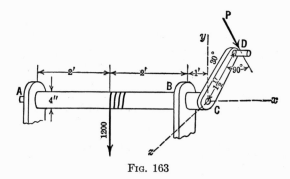

FIG. 163

4. The pole AB in Fig. 164 is braced by backstays BC and BD. The 4000-lb. pull may be rotated around AB at the fixed angle of 60°. Place the load in the position for maximum compression in AB and solve for its value.

Ans. 8930 lb. *C.*

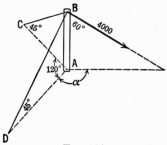

FIG. 164

5. Place the 4000-lb. load in Fig. 164 in the position to produce maximum tension in BC and solve for this tension and the corresponding stresses in BD and AB.

Ans. BC = 5650 lb. *T; AB* = 8000 lb. *C.*

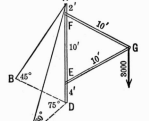

FIG. 165

6. With the boom EG of the derrick shown in Fig. 165 in the position for maximum compression in AB, solve for stresses AB and AC.

Ans. AB = 2380 lb. *C; AC* = 866 lb. *T.*

Supplementary Problems

1. Three cords each 6 ft. long are hung from a horizontal ring 6 ft. in diameter and are joined at their lower ends to support a load of 200 lb. On the ring two cords are 90° apart, and the third bisects the remaining arc. Solve for the tension in each cord.

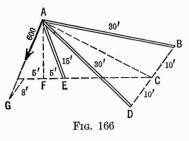

Fig. 166

Ans. 67.6 lb.; 67.6 lb.; 95.6 lb.

2. Solve Prob. 1 if the length of the first two cords is changed to 4.5 ft.

Ans. 102 lb.; 102 lb.; 35 lb.

3. Solve Prob. 1 if the three cords are equally spaced on the horizontal ring.

Ans. 77 lb.

4. Solve for the stresses in members *AB*, *AD*, and *AE* of Fig. 166.

Ans. AB = 691 lb. *T; AE* = 798 lb. *C.*

5. Solve Prob. 4 if the 600-lb. load acts vertically downward.

Ans. AB = 161 lb.; *AE* = 798 lb. *C.*

6. Solve Prob. 4 if the 600-lb. load acts horizontally and to the left.

Ans. AE = 461 lb. *C.*

7. Determine the stresses in the tripod shown in Fig. 167.

Ans. AB = 132 lb.; *AC* = 107 lb.

8. Solve Prob. 7 if the 200-lb. load is directed through point *E*.

Ans. AB = 82.7 lb.; *AC* = 67.1 lb.

9. The derrick shown in Fig. 168 is supported by three guy wires, *OA*, *OB*, and *OC*, which can carry tension only. Place the boom in the position to produce maximum tension in *OC* and solve for this tension. *Ans.* 818 lb.

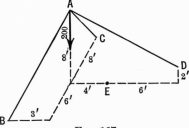

Fig. 167

10. Determine the guy wire which carries the greatest tension in the derrick of Fig. 168 and solve for that tension. *Ans. OA* = 1100 lb.

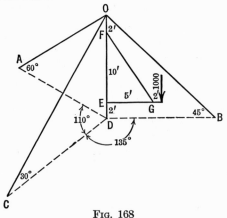

Fig. 168

11. By graphical means solve for the stresses in the legs of the tripod shown in Fig. 169. *Ans. AB* = 440 lb.; *AD* = 265 lb.

12. A horizontal circular platform of radius R is supported at three points A, B, and C on its circumference. A and B are 90° apart, and C is 120° from A. The platform carries a vertical load of 400 lb. at its center and one of 100 lb. at a point D on the circumference diametrically opposite A. Determine the reactions at all supports. *Ans. C* = 254 lb.

13. If the platform of Prob. 12 is not fastened to support A, what is the maximum load that can act on D before tipping occurs? *Ans.* 146 lb.

14. If the 100-lb. load is removed from the platform of Prob. 12, determine the reactions.

Ans. C = 169 lb.

15. A vertical windlass, weighing 200 lb. and supported by frictionless bearings at A and B, is shown in Fig. 170. The load W is raised by means of the belt pulls applied to pulley C. The belt pulls lie in the horizontal plane of the pulley, are parallel to each other,

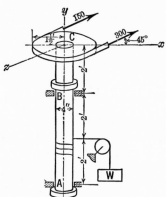

FIG. 170

and make an angle of 45° with the x axis as indicated. Determine the load W that can be raised and the x, y, and z components of the bearing reactions.

Ans. W = 1350 lb.; A_x = 516 lb.;
B_x = 1150 lb.; A_y = 0;
B_y = 200 lb.; A_z = 159 lb.;
B_z = 477 lb.

16. A horizontal countershaft 6 ft. long and weighing 100 lb. is supported by bearings A and B at the ends. At 2 ft. from end A is a pulley of 2-ft. diameter weighing 80 lb. and carrying belt pulls of 600 lb. and 300 lb. acting vertically upward. At 2 ft. from end B is another pulley of $1\frac{1}{2}$-ft. diameter weighing 60 lb. and carrying horizontal belt pulls T_2 and T_1. Assuming that $T_2 = 2T_1$, determine the unknown belt pulls and the vertical and horizontal components of the bearing reactions.

Ans. T_2 = 800 lb.; T_1 = 400 lb.; A_H = 400 lb.; A_V = 477 lb.;
B_H = 800 lb.; B_V = 183 lb.

17. Solve for the stresses in members AB and BC of the stiff-leg derrick shown in Fig. 171. If the boom AB is capable of rotation in the horizontal plane through A, state the value of α for (*a*) maximum tension in *CD*; (*b*) maximum compression in *CD*; (*c*) maximum compression in *AC*. Solve for the stresses in *AC*, *CD*, and *CE* for each position.

Ans. (*a*) *CD* = 22,200 lb.;
(*c*) *AC* = 31,400 lb.

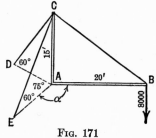

FIG. 171

CHAPTER V

FRICTION

Art. 32. Fundamental Relations. Friction is the force exerted tangentially by one surface upon another with which it is in contact, tending to prevent motion of either surface relative to the other. As long as motion does not occur, the resistance to motion is known as *static friction*. When motion of one surface relative to the other does occur, the resistance is known as *kinetic friction*.

In Fig. 172 (*a*) the force P tends to cause motion of the block relative to the surface below, and the friction F tends to resist this motion.

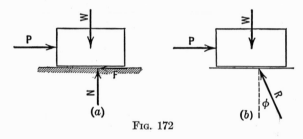

(*a*)   (*b*)

Fɪɢ. 172

As long as motion does not occur, the static friction F is just sufficient in amount to maintain static equilibrium. It is therefore an *adjustable* force, varying from zero to a maximum value which is reached when motion impends. This maximum value is known as the *limiting* static friction. The *coefficient* of static friction f is defined as the ratio of the limiting static friction F to the normal pressure N between the surfaces, or

$$f = \frac{F}{N}$$

The forces F and N in Fig. 172 (*a*) may be represented by their resultant R as shown in Fig. 172 (*b*). The angle ϕ between R and the normal to the surface is called the *angle of friction*. As the static friction increases, the angle ϕ increases and becomes a maximum when the condition of impending motion is reached. The maximum value of ϕ is called the limiting angle of friction. From Fig. 172

$$\text{max. } \phi = \tan^{-1}\frac{F}{N} = \tan^{-1}f$$

84

If the force P in Fig. 172 is increased to a value sufficient to overcome the maximum static friction, motion begins; the friction decreases and becomes *kinetic friction*. The ratio of the kinetic friction F to the normal pressure N is called the coefficient of kinetic friction and is also represented by f,

$$f = \frac{F}{N}$$

The coefficient of friction is determined by experiment, and the values thus obtained vary considerably, as the following table shows.

Materials	Static f
Wood on wood	0.30 to 0.70
Metal on metal	0.15 to 0.30
Wood on metal	0.20 to 0.60
Leather on wood	0.25 to 0.50
Leather on metal	0.30 to 0.60

The coefficient of kinetic friction is somewhat less than that for static friction.

Art. 33.   Angle of Repose and Cone of Friction. If the surface on which a body rests is gradually tilted, a position such that the body is on the verge of slipping is eventually reached. In Fig. 173 (*a*) the

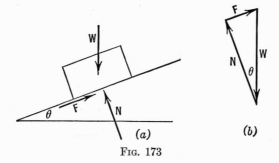

(a)

(b)

Fig. 173

angle θ represents the inclination of the surface when slipping impends and is called the *angle of repose*. From Fig. 173 (*b*)

$$\theta = \tan^{-1} \frac{F}{N}$$

It has previously been shown, however, that the limiting angle of static friction is

$$\phi = \tan^{-1} \frac{F}{N}$$

It thus follows that the angle of repose is equal to the limiting angle of static friction. Since the angle of repose represents the angle of inclination for impending slipping, a body placed on a surface inclined at any greater angle will slide down unless held, whereas a body placed on a surface inclined at a smaller angle will remain at rest unless acted upon by forces other than gravity.

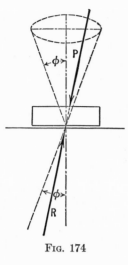

The *cone of friction* is the cone generated by revolving, about the normal to the surface, a line inclined to the normal at an angle equal to the limiting angle of static friction, as shown in Fig. 174. If the resultant P of all external forces acting on the body, except the reaction R of the surface, lies within the cone of friction, no motion can occur, since the equal and opposing surface reaction R must be acting at an angle with the normal less than the limiting angle of static friction. Similarly, if P lies in the surface of the cone, motion is impending; and if P lies outside the cone, motion actually occurs.

Fig. 174

Art. 34. Laws of Friction. The results of experiments by Coulomb, confirmed later by Morin, have led to the following laws of friction for dry surfaces:

1. Limiting static friction and kinetic friction are proportional to the normal pressure. In other words, the coefficient of friction is independent of the normal pressure.

2. The coefficient of friction is independent of the area of contact.

3. The coefficient of kinetic friction is less than that for static friction and for low speeds is independent of the relative velocity of the surfaces.

4. Friction is only slightly affected by ordinary temperature changes.

The laws of friction for lubricated surfaces differ greatly from those for dry surfaces. For instance, the friction is practically independent of the nature of the surfaces and of the normal pressure as long as a film of lubricant lies between the surfaces. The temperature greatly affects the friction of lubricated surfaces.

Art. 35. Equilibrium Involving Friction. The conditions of static equilibrium as previously stated also apply, of course, to a system of forces in which friction is involved. The reaction of the surface upon the free body with which it is in contact may be represented by its normal and tangential components, N and F, or by the resultant reaction R inclined at angle ϕ to the normal. If slipping impends or actually occurs, $F = fN$ and $\phi = \tan^{-1} f$. If slipping is neither occurring nor impending, the friction force F and the angle ϕ are merely sufficient to maintain equilibrium. The direction of the frictional reaction is always such as to *oppose the motion* of the free body; or it may be stated as being in the direction that the rubbing surface tends to move *relative* to the free body.

Problems of equilibrium involving friction may be solved by graphic, trigonometric, or algebraic methods. In graphic or trigonometric solutions the resultant reaction R at the rubbing surface must be used. The proper position of R is easily laid out graphically. For instance, if the coefficient of friction is 0.3, ten units to any convenient scale are laid out in a direction perpendicular to the surface; then three units to the same scale are laid out in a direction parallel to the surface. Thus the tangent of the angle of the resulting diagonal with the normal is 0.3 and conforms to the requirements.

Example 1

Determine the force P in Fig. 175 (*a*) to produce impending motion of the block up the plane if the coefficient of friction is 0.3.

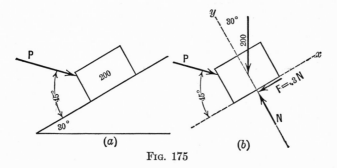

Fig. 175

Solution: First Method. The free-body diagram of the block is shown in Fig. 175 (*b*) with the reaction at the surface represented by its components F and N. Since slipping impends, $F = fN = 0.3N$. The friction F is directed down the plane because it must oppose the motion of the free body; this is also the direction of impending motion of the plane relative to the free body. Force summations are now made in the x and y directions as indicated.

$$\Sigma F_y = N - 200 \cos 30° - P \sin 45° = 0$$

$$\Sigma F_x = P \cos 45° - 200 \sin 30° - 0.3N = 0$$

Simultaneous solution of these equations gives $P = 307$ lb.

Second Method. The free-body diagram of the block is shown again in Fig. 176 (*a*), but with the components F and N of the surface reaction replaced by their resultant R, which acts at an angle ϕ with the normal to the surface.

$$\phi = \tan^{-1} f = \tan^{-1} 0.3 = 16.7°$$

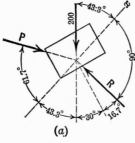
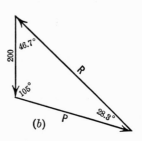

(*a*)   (*b*)

Fig. 176

Since the number of forces acting on the free body is now reduced to three, a solution may be made trigonometrically from the force triangle shown in Fig. 176 (*b*).

$$\frac{P}{\sin 46.7°} = \frac{200}{\sin 28.3°} \qquad\qquad P = 307 \text{ lb.}$$

The same result is obtained by summation of forces in the x direction, Fig. 176 (*a*), at 90° with R.

$$\Sigma F_x = P \cos 61.7° - 200 \cos 43.3° = 0 \qquad P = 307 \text{ lb.}$$

The solution may also be made graphically.

Example 2

The coefficient of friction is 0.2 between the ladder and wall, Fig. 177 (*a*), and 0.5 between ladder and floor. Determine the force P, applied horizontally at the bottom, to produce impending motion to the left.

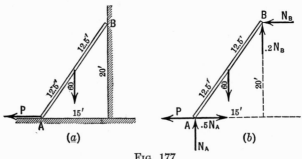

Fig. 177

Solution: The free-body diagram of the ladder is shown in Fig. 177 (*b*), the reaction at each rubbing surface being represented by its *F* and *N* components. The conditions of equilibrium are applied as follows:

$$\Sigma M_A = N_B \times 20 + 0.2 N_B \times 15 - 60 \times 7.5 = 0 \qquad N_B = 19.6 \text{ lb.}$$

$$\Sigma F_V = N_A - 60 + 0.2(19.6) = 0 \qquad N_A = 56.1 \text{ lb.}$$

$$\Sigma F_H = P - 0.5(56.1) + 19.6 = 0 \qquad P = 8.45 \text{ lb.}$$

Problems

1. Solve for the horizontal force *P* required to produce impending motion of a 60-lb. block up a 20° plane if $f = 0.2$. *Ans.* 36.5 lb.

2. Solve Prob. 1 for the least force to start the block up the plane.
Ans. 31.2 lb.

3. Solve Prob. 1 for impending motion down the plane. *Ans.* 9.18 lb.

4. If $f = 0.25$ for both blocks in Fig. 178, compute the value of weight *W* for impending motion.
Ans. 99.7 lb.

5. If the weight *W* in Fig. 178 is 200 lb., determine the tension in the cord and the friction under the weight *W*.
Ans. $T = 27.6$ lb.; $F = 26.6$ lb.

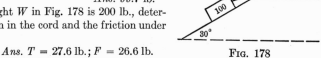

FIG. 178

6. Solve for the least force applied to the 100-lb. block of Fig. 178 to produce impending motion down the plane if $W = 200$ lb.
Ans. 27.8 lb.

7. A ladder weighing 45 lb. is placed against a wall. The ladder is 20 ft. long and rests against the wall at a point 16 ft. above the floor. The coefficient of friction at the wall is 0.2 and at the floor is 0.5. What vertical load can be placed at the upper end of the ladder before it starts to slip? *Ans.* 29.3 lb.

8. The hanger *ABC* shown in Fig. 179 slides up and down the vertical post. If $f = 0.3$, determine the minimum distance *x* at which a load *W* may be placed

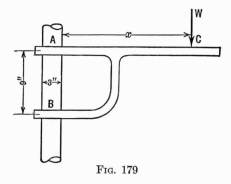

FIG. 179

without causing the hanger to slide down. Neglect the weight of the hanger. (Solve algebraically and graphically.) *Ans.* $x = 13.5$ in.

Art. 36. Wedge and Block. Wedges are used as lifting devices and keys for shafting. In the solution of problems involving the wedge, it is usually more convenient to make use of the resultant reaction at the rubbing surfaces. Graphic, trigonometric, or algebraic procedures may be used.

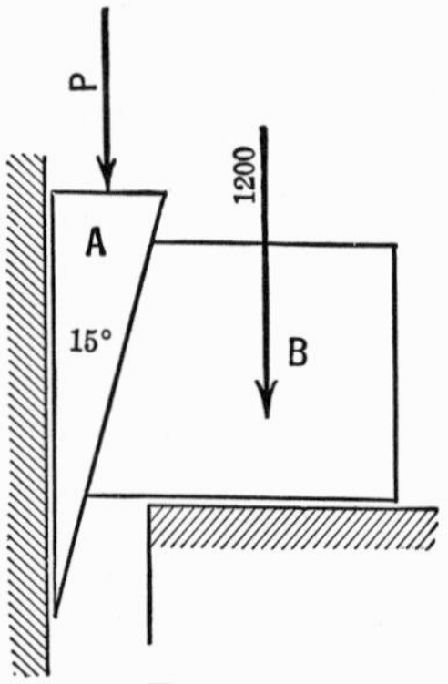

Fig. 180

Example

The coefficient of friction is 0.25 at all rubbing surfaces for the wedge and block shown in Fig. 180. Determine the force P to start the wedge downward.

Solution: The block B is selected as the first free body as shown in Fig. 181 (a). The friction angle is 14°, since $\phi = \tan^{-1} f = \tan^{-1} 0.25$. Since slipping is impending, the resulting reactions R_1 and R_2 act at this angle with the normal to each of the sliding surfaces and are inclined in the directions in which the sliding surfaces tend to move relative to the free body.

The system of forces may now be solved graphically by drawing to scale the force triangle shown in Fig. 181 (b), from which R_2 scales 397 lb.

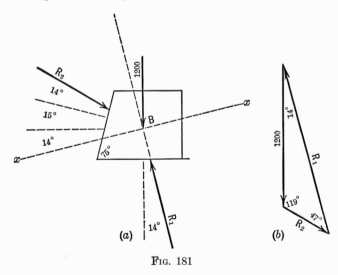

(a)   (b)

Fig. 181

The solution may be obtained trigonometrically by applying the law of sines to the force triangle,

$$\frac{R_2}{\sin 14°} = \frac{1200}{\sin 47°} \qquad R_2 = 397 \text{ lb.}$$

The solution may be made algebraically from Fig. 181 (a) by placing the x axis at 90° with R_1 and applying $\Sigma F_x = 0$,

$$\Sigma F_x = R_2 \cos 43° - 1200 \sin 14° = 0 \qquad R_2 = 397 \text{ lb.}$$

The wedge A is now taken as a free body as shown in Fig. 182 (a). The proper positions for the reactions are determined in the same manner as for

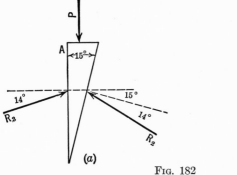

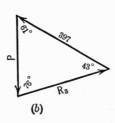

(a)   (b)

FIG. 182

the preceding free body. The force triangle is shown in Fig. 182 (b), and the trigonometric solution gives

$$\frac{P}{\sin 43°} = \frac{397}{\sin 76°} \qquad P = 279 \text{ lb.}$$

Problems

1. The coefficient of friction for the wedge and block of Fig. 183 is 0.268. Determine the force P to cause impending motion of the wedge to the right. (The block rubs on one vertical side only.)   *Ans.* 1430 lb.

2. Solve Prob. 1 when impending motion is to the left.   *Ans.* −212 lb.

3. Solve Prob. 2 if the angle of friction is 30°.   *Ans.* −820 lb.

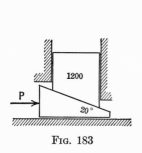

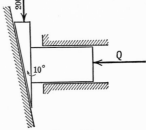

FIG. 183   FIG. 184

4. If $f = 0.25$ for all surfaces, what resistance Q in Fig. 184 can be overcome by the 200-lb. force on the wedge?   *Ans.* 270 lb.

5. If the block in Fig. 184 weighs 150 lb., solve for the resistance Q as in Prob. 4.   *Ans.* 232 lb.

Art. 37. The Jackscrew. The jackscrew is a mechanical device used to raise or lower heavy loads. The threads of the screw may be either square or triangular, but only the square thread will be discussed here. The thread may be considered as an inclined plane wound around a cylinder. The operation of raising or lowering a load consists essentially of pushing the load up or down an inclined plane by means of a horizontal force applied to the end of a lever. In Fig. 185 (a), P is the horizontal force acting at the end of the lever of length l;

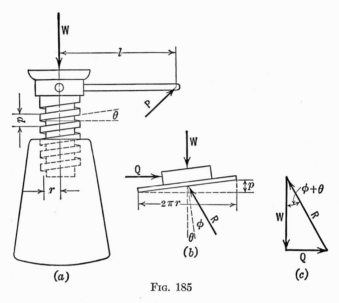

Fig. 185

p is the pitch of the thread; θ is the pitch angle; and r is the mean radius of the thread. The effect of force P acting on the lever is to produce an equivalent horizontal pressure Q, which acts at the mean radius from the axis of the screw and which is given by

$$Q = \frac{Pl}{r}$$

The pitch angle θ is given by

$$\theta = \tan^{-1} \frac{p}{2\pi r}$$

Although the load is actually distributed over the circumference of several threads, for convenience it will be considered as acting over a small section as shown in Fig. 185 (b). Here one turn of the thread has been unwound and is shown as an inclined plane. The load W

is being pushed up the plane by the horizontal force Q. The reaction R at the rubbing surface acts at the angle of friction ϕ with the normal to the surface, where $\phi = \tan^{-1} f$. From the triangle of forces shown in Fig. 185 (c)

$$Q = W \tan (\phi + \theta)$$

and

$$P = \frac{Qr}{l} = \frac{Wr}{l} \tan (\phi + \theta) \text{ to raise the load}$$

When the load is being lowered, the resultant R lies on the other side of the normal to the surface and, by following the same procedure as above, P is given by

$$P = \frac{Qr}{l} = \frac{Wr}{l} \tan (\phi - \theta) \text{ to lower the load}$$

It is evident from this equation that, when $\phi = \theta$, the load will be on the verge of slipping down without application of any force. If, then, θ is greater than ϕ, the load will not remain at rest unless held by a resisting force P. For the jackscrew to be self-locking, that is, for the load to be held by friction alone, ϕ must be greater than θ. Since $\phi = \tan^{-1} f$ and $\theta = \tan^{-1} \dfrac{p}{2\pi r}$, it follows that the pitch p must be less than $2\pi rf$.

Problems

1. The mean radius of the threads of a jackscrew is 2 in. and the pitch is $\frac{3}{8}$ in. If $f = 0.07$, determine the force P applied at the end of a lever 20 in. long to raise a load of 6000 lb.   *Ans. P* = 60 lb.

2. Determine the force P in Prob. 1 to lower the weight.   *Ans. P* = 24 lb.

3. A hand press has four square-threaded screws to the inch with a mean diameter of $1\frac{1}{2}$ in. If $f = 0.1$, what pressure W can be exerted by the press if a force of 50 lb. is applied at the end of a 24-in. lever? Is the screw self-locking?
    Ans. W = 10,400 lb.; yes.

Art. 38. Axle Friction and the Friction Circle. Because of a slight but necessary difference between the diameters of an axle or journal and the bearing in which it rotates, contact takes place between the two along a small arc instead of around the complete circumference. In a frictionless bearing the resultant reaction between journal and bearing would pass through their center and through the point of contact. If there is friction, however, the journal will roll along the surface of the bearing until the resultant reaction acts at the angle of friction ϕ with the normal line or radius at the point of contact, when slipping of the journal on the bearing will occur. As the journal continues to rotate, it will remain in this position, which is shown in

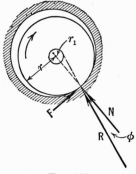

Fig. 186. Here the journal is rotating clockwise in a stationary bearing and rolls up the side of the bearing until slipping begins. The resultant reaction R does not pass through the center but is tangent to a small circle, concentric with the journal, whose radius is $r_1 = r \sin \phi$. This circle is called the *friction circle*. If the coefficient of friction is small, $\sin \phi$ may be replaced by $\tan \phi$. Thus $r_1 = r \tan \phi = fr$.

When the radius r of the bearing and the coefficient f are known, the friction circle is determined and may be used to locate the position of the bearing reaction. The reaction is always tangent to the friction circle on the side toward which the journal rolls. The use of the friction circle is of particular advantage in graphic determination of reactions and stresses in mechanisms.

Fig. 186

Example

A freight car weighing 250,000 lb. has wheels of 33-in. diameter and axles of 6-in. diameter. If the coefficient of axle friction is 0.02, determine the draw-bar pull on the car necessary to overcome axle friction.

Solution: For purposes of solution the entire weight may be considered as acting on one wheel, which is shown as a free body in Fig. 187. The wheel is acted upon by three forces, the weight $W = 250,000$ lb. acting vertically downward, P representing the horizontal pressure of the car against the axle, and the reaction R of the track on the wheel. The reaction R must pass through the point of contact between wheel and track and also be tangent to the friction circle. Contact between axle and bearing occurs along the top. As the axle turns clockwise, it tends to roll to the left on the bearing; hence R is tangent on the left side. Forces P and W must intersect somewhere on

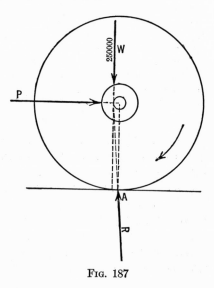

Fig. 187

the line of action of R. In Fig. 187 P is shown as acting through the center; W will then be approximately tangent to the friction circle and may be taken as actually tangent without appreciable error.

The radius of the friction circle is $r' = fr = 0.02 \times 3 = 0.06$ in.

The equation $\Sigma M_A = 0$ then gives $P \times 16.5 - 250,000 \times 0.06 = 0$, from which $P = 910$ lb.

From Fig. 187 it is seen that P is equal to the component of R representing the resistance offered by the track to the forward motion of the car. Since the drawbar pull acting on the car must be just sufficient to overcome the resistance at the track, it follows that P is the value of the required drawbar pull.

Problems

1. A 200,000-lb. car has 33-in.-diameter wheels and 6-in.-diameter axles. If $f = 0.06$ at the bearings, determine the drawbar pull P required to move the car up a 1 per cent grade.   *Ans. $P = 4180$ lb.*

2. Determine the steepest grade on which the car of Prob. 1 would not start down.   *Ans. 1.09 per cent.*

3. The 1000-lb. weight in Fig. 188 is to be raised by force P. The coefficient of journal friction is 0.08. Solve for the force P to raise the weight. *Ans. 767 lb.*

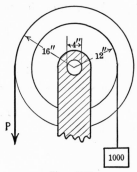

Fig. 188

4. Solve for the force P necessary to lower the 1000-lb. weight of Prob. 3.
                    Ans. 733 lb.

5. Solve Prob. 3 if the wheel weighs 200 lb.   *Ans. 769 lb.*

Art. 39. Rolling Resistance.
If a wheel or roller and the track or roadway on which it rests were absolutely rigid, no resistance would be encountered at the track to the rolling of the wheel. Because of the elasticity of the materials, however, deformations occur, the track being somewhat depressed and the surface of the wheel slightly flattened out. A resistance is thus set up to the rolling of the wheel, the effect being equivalent to a small obstruction constantly in front of the wheel. This resistance is called *rolling resistance* or, less accurately, rolling friction.

In Fig. 189 is shown a wheel carrying a vertical load W and pulled forward by a horizontal force P applied at the axle. The resultant reaction R of the track acts through a point B at distance a in front

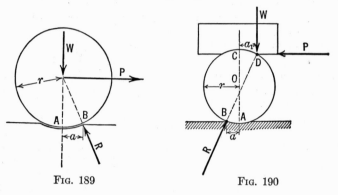

FIG. 189   FIG. 190

of the vertical radius. If motion is uniform and the depression of the surface is small, $\Sigma M_B = 0$ gives

$$Pr = Wa \quad \text{(approximately)}$$

$$P = \frac{Wa}{r}$$

If the load rests on the surface of the roller and the force P is applied to the load as is shown in Fig. 190, a similar relation may be obtained.

$$\Sigma M_B = 2Pr - W(a + a_1) = 0 \quad \text{(approximately)}$$

$$P = \frac{W(a + a_1)}{2r}$$

The arrangement in Fig. 190 is commonly used for moving very heavy objects.

Although the results of many investigations of rolling resistance are not in entire agreement, it appears that the distance a is practically constant for a given material, being independent, within reasonable limits, of the load and the radius of the wheel. It is called the *coefficient* of rolling resistance. The values of the coefficient, obtained from experiments of several investigators, are given for a few materials in the following table.

MATERIALS	a (inches)
Elm on oak	0.0327
Steel on steel	0.007 to 0.020
Steel on wood	0.06 to 0.10
Steel on soft earth	3.0 to 5.0

The fact that the coefficient of rolling resistance is very low for hardened steel is put to practical use in ball and roller bearings.

Example

Determine the pull required to keep in uniform motion on a level track a 100,000-lb. car having 33-in.-diameter wheels and 6-in.-diameter axles, if the coefficient of axle friction is 0.05 and the coefficient of rolling resistance is 0.01 in.

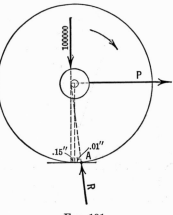

FIG. 191

Solution: The load may be taken as acting on a single wheel as shown in Fig. 191. The radius of the friction circle is $fr = 3 \times 0.05 = 0.15$ in. The reaction R of the track must pass through the point A at 0.01 in. in front of the vertical radius and must also be tangent to the friction circle. With load P acting through the center of the wheel and axle, the load W, passing through the intersection of P and R, will be very nearly tangent to the friction circle and its distance from A will thus be 0.01 in. + 0.15 in. = 0.16 in. The equation $\Sigma M_A = 0$ then gives

$$P \times 16.5 = 100,000 \times 0.16$$

$$P = 970 \text{ lb.}$$

Problems

1. Solve for the pull required to move the car in the above example up a 1 per cent grade with uniform speed.   *Ans. P* = 1970 lb.

2. If the pull required to overcome the rolling resistance of a freight car is 2 lb. per ton of weight, what is the value of the coefficient? Use 33-in.-diameter wheels.   *Ans. a* = 0.0165 in.

3. A 2-ton weight is to be moved by use of 2-in.-diameter rollers. If the coefficient of rolling resistance for the rollers and floor is 0.07 and that for rollers and weight is 0.02, determine the pull required.   *Ans.* 180 lb.

Art. 40. Belt or Band Friction. The transmission of power by belt or rope drive is dependent on friction between the pulley surface and the belt or rope. The holding of large loads by means of band brakes or ropes wound around posts is similarly dependent on friction. Fig. 192 (*a*) shows a pulley of any radius r driven by a belt whose angle of contact with the pulley surface is β. The tension T_2 on the driving side of the belt is greater than the tension T_1 on the slack side. A portion of the belt of differential length ds with an angle of contact $d\theta$ is shown as a free body in Fig. 192 (b). The normal pressure on this piece of the belt is represented by dN and the friction by dF. If T

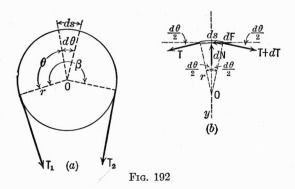

Fig. 192

is the belt tension on the slack side, then the tension on the driving side is $T + dT$. The free body is in equilibrium under the action of the four forces and ΣM_0 gives

$$(T + dT)\cdot r - T \cdot r - dF \cdot r = 0$$

from which

$$dT = dF \tag{1}$$

The equation $\Sigma F_y = 0$ gives

$$dN - T \sin \frac{d\theta}{2} - (T + dT) \sin \frac{d\theta}{2} = 0$$

$$dN = 2T \sin \frac{d\theta}{2} + dT \sin \frac{d\theta}{2}$$

The term $dT \sin \dfrac{d\theta}{2}$ is negligible, since it is an infinitesimal of higher order. Since $\dfrac{d\theta}{2}$ is an infinitesimal angle, $\sin \dfrac{d\theta}{2}$ may be replaced by $\dfrac{d\theta}{2}$. The preceding equation then becomes

$$dN = T\, d\theta \tag{2}$$

When slipping of belt on pulley surface impends or occurs,

$$dF = f\, dN \tag{3}$$

Equations (1), (2), and (3) may now be combined,

$$dT = dF = f\, dN = fT\, d\theta$$

or

$$\frac{dT}{T} = f\, d\theta$$

This equation may be integrated to obtain the relation between T_2 and T_1 as follows:

$$\int_{T_1}^{T_2} \frac{dT}{T} = f \int_0^\beta d\theta$$

$$\log_e \frac{T_2}{T_1} = f\beta \qquad\qquad (4)$$

or

$$\frac{T_2}{T_1} = e^{f\beta} \qquad\qquad (5)$$

or

$$\log_{10} \frac{T_2}{T_1} = f\beta \log_{10} e = 0.4343 f\beta \qquad\qquad (6)$$

In equations (4) to (6) the angle β is in radians and T_2 must be the larger of the two tensions. The same relations apply to a band brake or to a rope wrapped around a post. It should be particularly noted that the equations hold only for the condition of *slipping impending or actually occurring.*

Problems

1. A weight of 1000 lb. is to be lowered uniformly by means of a cable making 2.5 turns around a snubbing post. If $f = 0.3$, what force is required at the slack end of the cable?   *Ans.* 9.08 lb.

2. How many turns of rope around a snubbing post are required for a force of 10 lb. on the slack end to hold a load of 25,000 lb. at the other end if $f = 0.4$?   *Ans.* 3.12 turns.

3. A belt runs between two pulleys of equal diameter for which $f = 0.3$. If the tension in the slack side of the belt is 300 lb., what tension can be developed in the taut side of the belt before the belt will start to slip?   *Ans.* 770 lb.

4. Determine the frictional moment produced on the rotating drum of Fig. 193 if the band-brake coefficient is 0.3.   *Ans.* 365 in-lb.

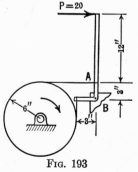

FIG. 193

Supplementary Problems

1. If the coefficient of friction for the blocks of Fig. 194 is 0.2, will the system move? Solve for the friction under each body.

Ans. $F_A = 62.2$ lb.; $F_B = 37.9$ lb.

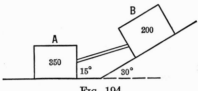

FIG. 194

2. What force applied to block B and parallel to the plane is required to produce impending motion to the left? See Fig. 194.   *Ans.* 12.5 lb.

3. Determine the value of weight W necessary to produce impending motion of the system shown in Fig. 195. The flexible cord slides over the stationary post at A. The coefficient of friction for all surfaces is 0.25.   *Ans.* 213 lb.

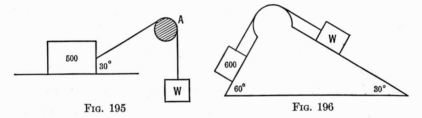

FIG. 195   FIG. 196

4. Solve for the value of weight W in Fig. 196 to cause impending motion of W down the plane if $f = 0.3$.   *Ans.* 4060 lb.

5. Solve Prob. 4 for impending motion up the plane.   *Ans.* 354 lb.

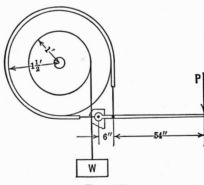

FIG. 197

6. A band brake as shown in Fig. 197 is used to control the motion of the load W. If $f = 0.4$ and $P = 15$ lb., what weight W will descend with a uniform speed?

Ans. 1260 lb.

7. If weight W in Fig. 198 is 300 lb. and $\phi = 14°$, find the value of resistance Q that can be overcome when the wedge is in impending motion down.

Ans. 392 lb.

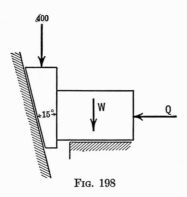

Fig. 198

8. Solve Prob. 7 if weight W is zero. *Ans.* 464 lb.

9. A railroad car weighing 100,000 lb. is on a 2 per cent grade. It has 33-in.-diameter wheels and 6-in.-diameter journals. The coefficient of rolling resistance is 0.012 in. and the coefficient of journal friction is 0.07. Compute the drawbar pull necessary to cause uniform motion up the grade. *Ans.* 3340 lb.

10. Solve Prob. 9 for uniform motion down the grade. *Ans.* 657 lb.

11. Solve by graphic means for force P to raise the weight as shown in Fig. 199. The axle is 2 in. in diameter and $f = 0.15$. *Ans.* 83 lb.

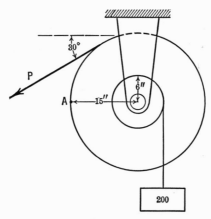

Fig. 199

12. In Fig. 199 let force P act downward and vertically at point A. For this position solve for force P to raise the weight. *Ans.* 82.8 lb.

13. Solve Prob. 12 for the force to lower the weight. *Ans.* 77.2 lb.

14. Solve Prob. 12 if the wheel weighs 400 lb. *Ans.* 86.9 lb.

15. If $f = 0.3$ for both band brake and the incline in Fig. 200, determine the force P that will permit weight $W = 2000$ lb. to be lowered at a uniform speed.

Ans. 52.8 lb.

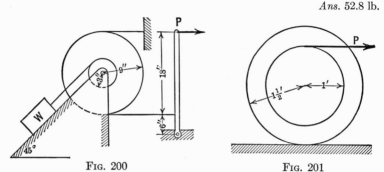

FIG. 200   FIG. 201

16. The spool of Fig. 201 weighs 600 lb. and requires a force P of 5 lb. to cause uniform motion. Compute the value of the coefficient of rolling resistance.

Ans. 0.0208 ft.

17. A pull of 30 lb. on the slack end of a rope wrapped around a spar 2.5 times holds a load of 10,000 lb. Compute the coefficient of friction. *Ans.* 0.37.

18. The weight shown in Fig. 202 is in impending motion down the plane. If for all surfaces $f = 0.25$, compute the number of times the cable must be wrapped around the post A when the tension T is 130 lb. *Ans.* 2.58 turns.

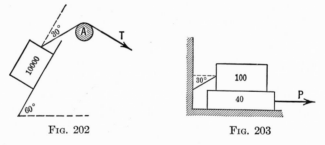

FIG. 202   FIG. 203

19. Compute force P to cause impending motion to the right for the block shown in Fig. 203 if $f = 0.374$. *Ans.* 110 lb.

20. Determine the value of force P to cause impending motion downward of the wedge in the system of blocks shown in Fig. 204 if $\phi = 15°$. *Ans.* 227 lb.

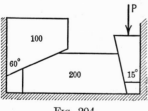

FIG. 204

21. A uniform ladder is placed against a vertical wall with its lower end on a horizontal floor. If $f = 0.35$ for both wall and floor, at what maximum angle with the wall may the ladder be inclined before slipping impends? *Ans.* 38.6°.

22. If the ladder of Prob. 21 is 15 ft. long, weighs 60 lb., and is inclined at 30° with the wall, how far up the ladder may a weight of 100 lb. be placed before slipping impends? *Ans.* 11.1 ft.

CHAPTER VI

CENTROIDS AND CENTER OF GRAVITY

Art. 41. Center of Gravity of a Material Body. The resultant of the attractions of gravity exerted upon all the particles composing a material body is known as the weight of the body. In a rigid body it can be shown that, regardless of the position into which the body is turned, this resultant force always acts through a certain point fixed in the body. This fixed point, at which the entire weight of the body may be considered to be concentrated, is called the *center of gravity* of the body.

To locate the resultant of a system of parallel forces, the principle of moments is used as shown in Art. 6. Let W denote the weight of the body, and w_1, w_2, w_3, etc., the weights of individual particles or parts; let x_1, x_2, x_3, etc., be the distances of these particles or parts from the y–z plane; and let $\bar{x}$ (called *bar x* or *gravity x*) be the distance of the center of gravity of the entire body from the y–z plane. The following moment equation may then be written:

$$W\bar{x} = w_1 x_1 + w_2 x_2 + w_3 x_3 + \text{etc.}$$

until all parts have been included. Similarly, by moments with respect to the x–z plane,

$$W\bar{y} = w_1 y_1 + w_2 y_2 + w_3 y_3 + \text{etc.}$$

and, by moments with respect to the x–y plane,

$$W\bar{z} = w_1 z_1 + w_2 z_2 + w_3 z_3 + \text{etc.}$$

Art. 42. Centroids of Volumes, Areas, and Lines. If the material composing a homogeneous, rigid body is removed from the volume or space which it occupies, the point within that volume formerly known as the center of gravity of the body is now called the *centroid* of the volume. By the principle of moments applied to the volume and its parts, the following equations result:

$$V\bar{x} = v_1 x_1 + v_2 x_2 + v_3 x_3 + \text{etc.}$$

$$V\bar{y} = v_1 y_1 + v_2 y_2 + v_3 y_3 + \text{etc.}$$

$$V\bar{z} = v_1 z_1 + v_2 z_2 + v_3 z_3 + \text{etc.}$$

103

It should be noted that this set of equations may be obtained from those of Art. 41 by dividing each term by a density factor.

If the body consists of a homogeneous thin shell, the limiting position of the center of gravity of the shell as the thickness approaches zero becomes the *centroid* of the resulting surface area. The moment equations necessary to locate the centroid of an area are:

$$A\bar{x} = A_1x_1 + A_2x_2 + A_3x_3 + \text{etc.}$$

$$A\bar{y} = A_1y_1 + A_2y_2 + A_3y_3 + \text{etc.}$$

$$A\bar{z} = A_1z_1 + A_2z_2 + A_3z_3 + \text{etc.}$$

In similar manner, if a body consists of a homogeneous slender rod, the limiting position of the center of gravity of the rod, as the cross section approaches zero, becomes the *centroid* of the resulting line. The following equations locate the position:

$$l\bar{x} = l_1x_1 + l_2x_2 + l_3x_3 + \text{etc.}$$

$$l\bar{y} = l_1y_1 + l^2y^2 + l_3y_3 + \text{etc.}$$

$$l\bar{z} = l_1z_1 + l_2z_2 + l_3z_3 + \text{etc.}$$

The terms center of gravity and centroid are often used interchangeably.

Art. 43. Center of Gravity and Centroids by Symmetry. The centroid of any figure which possesses a line of symmetry must obviously lie on that line. If there are two or more such lines of symmetry, the centroid will lie at their intersection. If there exists a plane of symmetry, the centroid must be in this plane. When there are two planes of symmetry, the centroid must lie on their line of intersection. The same statements apply to the location of the center of gravity of any material body which is homogeneous throughout.

In this way may be determined partly or completely the location of the centroids of many objects, for example:

The centroid of any straight line is at its midpoint.

The centroid of a circular arc is on the bisecting radius.

The centroid of the area of a rectangle is at its geometric center.

The centroid of a sector of a circle is on the bisecting radius.

The centroid of a right circular cone or cylinder is on its geometric axis.

Art. 44. Centroids by Integration. When an object cannot be divided into a few simple parts for the purpose of obtaining the necessary moment equations for locating the centroid, the same principle may still be used by dividing the object into an infinite number of differential parts. The right-hand member of a given moment equation then becomes a summation of an infinite number of differential terms, resulting in an integral. Thus, for an area, the equations would be

$$A\bar{x} = x_1 \, dA_1 + x_2 \, dA_2 + x_3 \, dA_3 + \text{etc.} = \int x \, dA$$

Similarly, for lines and volumes,

$$l\bar{x} = \int x \, dl$$

$$V\bar{x} = \int x \, dV$$

By assigning proper limits to the integral and evaluating, the coordinates of the centroid may be determined.

Example 1

Determine the location of the centroid of a circular arc.

Solution: Let r be the radius of the arc and α the angle subtended at its center. Let coordinate axes be taken with the origin at the center and the

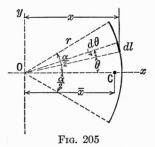

FIG. 205

x axis bisecting the arc as shown in Fig. 205. Then $\bar{y} = 0$ by symmetry. By moments with respect to the y axis

$$l\bar{x} = \int x \, dl$$

In Fig. 205, $l = r\alpha$, $dl = r \, d\theta$, and $x = r \cos \theta$. Thus

$$r\alpha\bar{x} = \int_{-\frac{\alpha}{2}}^{+\frac{\alpha}{2}} r \cos \theta \cdot r \, d\theta$$

and

$$\bar{x} = \frac{2r}{\alpha} \sin \frac{\alpha}{2}$$

For a semicircular arc $\alpha = \pi$, and $\bar{x} = 2r/\pi$. The same expression, $\bar{x} = 2r/\pi$, also applies to an arc of 90°, giving the distance of the centroid from the bounding radii.

Example 2

Show that the centroid of the area of a triangle is located at a distance of one-third the altitude from the base.

Solution: Let b and h represent the base and altitude, respectively, of any triangle. Place the triangle with its base on the x axis as shown in Fig. 206. By moments with respect to the x axis

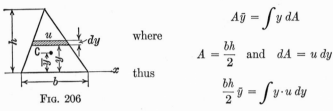

$$A\bar{y} = \int y\, dA$$

where

$$A = \frac{bh}{2} \quad \text{and} \quad dA = u\, dy$$

thus

$$\frac{bh}{2}\bar{y} = \int y \cdot u\, dy$$

FIG. 206

Since, by similar triangles,

$$\frac{u}{b} = \frac{h-y}{h},$$

$$\frac{bh}{2}\bar{y} = \int_0^h y \cdot \frac{b}{h}(h-y)\, dy$$

$$\bar{y} = \frac{h}{3}$$

Example 3

Locate the centroid of the area of a sector of a circle.

Solution: Let the sector of radius r and angle α be placed with its center at the origin and with the x axis bisecting the angle as shown in Fig. 207. Then $\bar{y} = 0$, by symmetry. The differential area shown is actually a differential sector which may be treated as a triangle.

$$A\bar{x} = \int x\, dA$$

where

$$dA = \frac{1}{2} r^2\, d\theta$$

$$A = \int dA = \int_{-\frac{\alpha}{2}}^{+\frac{\alpha}{2}} \frac{1}{2} r^2\, d\theta = \frac{r^2\alpha}{2}$$

$$x = \frac{2}{3} r \cos\theta$$

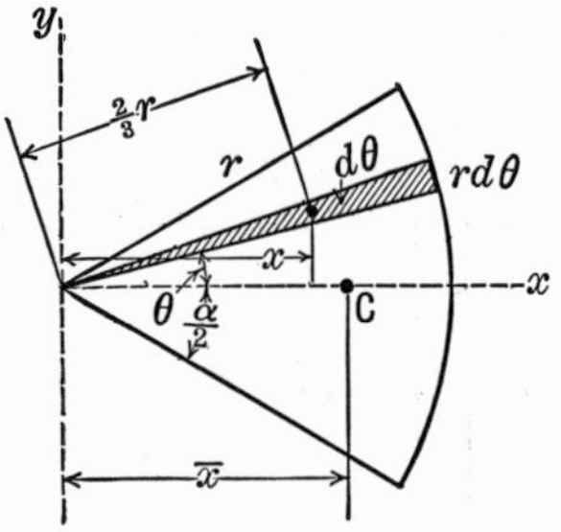

thus

$$\frac{r^2\alpha}{2}\bar{x} = \int_{-\frac{\alpha}{2}}^{+\frac{\alpha}{2}} \frac{2}{3} r \cos\theta \cdot \frac{1}{2} r^2\, d\theta$$

and

$$\bar{x} = \frac{4r}{3\alpha} \sin\frac{\alpha}{2}$$

FIG. 207

For a semicircle $\alpha = \pi$ and $\bar{x} = 4r/3\pi$. The same expression also gives the centroidal distance for a quadrant with respect to the bounding radii.

Example 4

Show that the centroid of the volume of a cone or pyramid is at three-fourths the altitude from the vertex.

Solution: The altitude of the cone is represented by h, and the base, which may be any shape, has area A. The vertex of the cone is placed at the origin with the base parallel to the x axis as shown in Fig. 208. The differential volume is a thin slice parallel to the base. Let A' represent the area of the slice. From the geometry of Fig. 208, $A'/A = y^2/h^2$. By moments with respect to the x axis

$$V\bar{y} = \int y \, dV$$

where

$$V = \frac{1}{3} Ah \quad \text{and} \quad dV = A' \, dy = \frac{A}{h^2} y^2 \, dy$$

thus

$$\frac{1}{3} Ah \, \bar{y} = \int_0^h y \cdot \frac{A}{h^2} y^2 \, dy$$

and

$$\bar{y} = \frac{3}{4} h$$

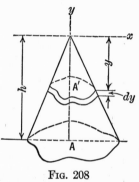

FIG. 208

Example 5

Locate the centroid of the volume of the solid of revolution obtained by rotating about the x axis the area bounded by the parabola $y^2 = 2x$, the x axis, and the line $x = 8$.

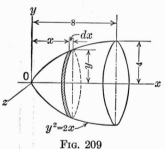

FIG. 209

Solution: The solid of revolution described is shown in Fig. 209. By symmetry, $\bar{y} = 0$ and $\bar{z} = 0$. The differential volume is taken as a thin disk as shown.

$$dV = \pi y^2 \, dx = 2\pi x \, dx$$

$$V = \int dV = \int_0^8 2\pi x \, dx = 64\pi$$

By moments with respect to the yz plane

$$V\bar{x} = \int x \, dV \quad \text{or} \quad 64\pi\bar{x} = \int_0^8 x \cdot 2\pi x \, dx$$

whence

$$\bar{x} = 5.33$$

Problems

1. Solve Ex. 3 by using $dA = \rho\alpha\, d\rho$ as shown in Fig. 210.

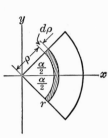

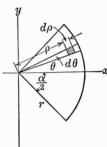

FIG. 210   FIG. 211

2. Solve Ex. 3 by using $dA = \rho\, d\rho\, d\theta$ as shown in Fig. 211.

3. Determine by integration the distance of the centroid of the curved surface of a right circular cone from the vertex.   *Ans.* $\frac{2}{3}h$.

4. Determine by integration the distance of the centroid of the curved surface of a hemisphere from the bounding plane.

Ans. $\frac{1}{2}r$.

5. By integration locate the centroid of the volume of a hemisphere with respect to the bounding plane.   *Ans.* $\frac{3}{8}r$.

6. Locate the centroid of the shaded area shown in Fig. 212.

$$Ans.\ \bar{x} = \tfrac{3}{10}a;\ \bar{y} = \tfrac{3}{4}b.$$

7. Locate the centroid of the area bounded by the parabola of Fig. 212, the x axis, and the line $x = a$.   *Ans.* $\bar{x} = \frac{3}{5}a;\ \bar{y} = \frac{3}{8}b$.

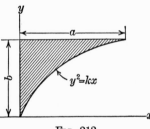

FIG. 212

Art. 45. Centroids of Composite Bodies.

A composite body is one which can be divided into two or more simple parts, each of which has a centroid whose position is already known. Such a body may be a solid having weight, or a volume, surface, or line. The centroid of the body may then be located by the proper moment equations from Arts. 41 and 42.

Example 1

Locate the centroid of the shaded area shown in Fig. 213.

Solution: The shaded area may be subdivided into a rectangle A_1, a triangle A_2, and a semicircle A_3. For convenience the coordinate axes are placed as shown. The data for the various parts are as follows:

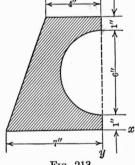

FIG. 213

$$A_1 = 4 \times 8 = 32 \qquad\qquad x_1 = -2 \qquad\qquad y_1 = 4$$

$$A_2 = 3 \times \frac{8}{2} = 12 \qquad\qquad x_2 = -5 \qquad\qquad y_2 = \frac{8}{3}$$

$$A_3 = -\pi \frac{(3)^2}{2} = -14.1 \qquad\qquad x_3 = -4 \times \frac{3}{3\pi} \qquad\qquad y_3 = 4$$

$$A = A_1 + A_2 + A_3 = 29.9$$

The moment equations may now be written:

$$\bar{x} = \frac{A_1 x_1 + A_2 x_2 + A_3 x_3}{A}$$

$$= \frac{(32)(-2) + (12)(-5) + (-9\pi/2)(-4 \times 3/3\pi)}{29.9}$$

$$= -3.54 \text{ in.}$$

$$\bar{y} = \frac{A_1 y_1 + A_2 y_2 + A_3 y_3}{A}$$

$$= \frac{(32)(4) + (12)(8/3) + (-9\pi/2)(4)}{29.9}$$

$$= +3.46 \text{ in.}$$

Example 2

Locate the centroid of the hollow conical frustum shown in Fig. 214 (a). *Solution:* The frustum is extended to show the original cone of which it was a part as shown in Fig. 214 (b). It is now seen that the hollow frustum

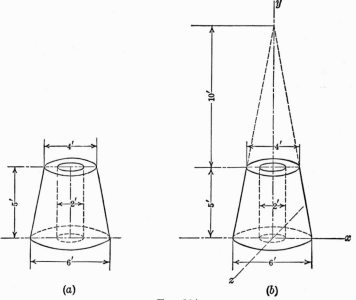

(a)   (b)

Fig. 214

may be considered as a cone V_1 of 15-ft. altitude and 6-ft. base diameter, from which have been taken a smaller cone V_2 of 10-ft. altitude and 4-ft. base diameter, and a cylinder V_3 of 5-ft. altitude and 2-ft. diameter. Coordinate axes are chosen as shown, so that $\bar{x} = \bar{z} = 0$. By moments with respect to the x axis

$$\bar{y} = \frac{V_1 y_1 + V_2 y_2 + V_3 y_3}{V}$$

$$= \frac{[\frac{1}{3}\pi(3)^2(15)][15/4] + [-\frac{1}{3}\pi(2)^2(10)][10/4 + 5] + [-\pi(1)^2(5)][5/2]}{[\frac{1}{3}\pi(3)^2(15)] - [\frac{1}{3}\pi(2)^2(10)] - [\pi(1)^2(5)]}$$

$$= 2.11 \text{ ft. above the bottom}$$

Problems

1. Locate the centroid of the T-section shown in Fig. 215.   *Ans.* $\bar{y} = 3$ in.

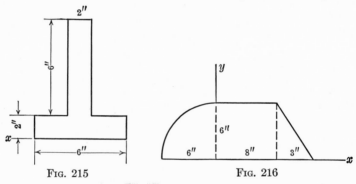

FIG. 215   FIG. 216

2. Locate the centroid of the area shown in Fig. 216.

Ans. $\bar{x} = 2.36$ in.; $\bar{y} = 2.74$ in.

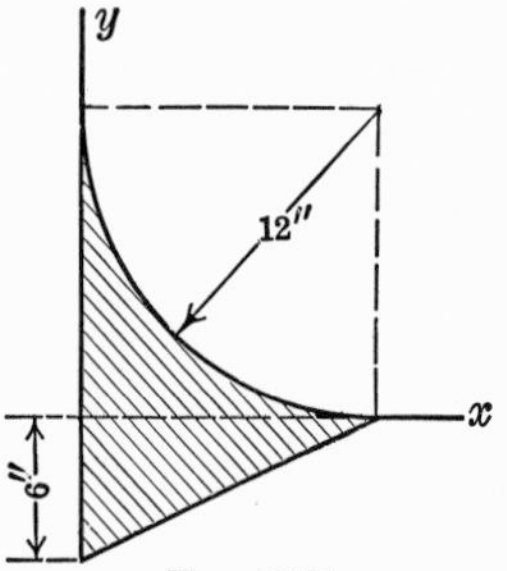

3. Bend the quarter-circular area and the triangle of Fig. 216 forward 90° into planes parallel to the y–z plane, and solve for the position of the center of gravity.   *Ans.* $\bar{x} = 3.1$ in.; $\bar{z} = 0.95$ in.

4. Determine the location of the centroid of the shaded area of Fig. 217.   *Ans.* $\bar{x} = 3.39$ in.

5. A half-sphere, 1 ft. in diameter, of lead is joined to the end of a cylinder of steel which is 1 ft. in diameter and also in length. Locate the center of gravity of the combined weights measured from the base of the cylinder. The specific weights are 710 and 490 lb. per cu. ft., respectively.   *Ans.* 0.724 ft.

FIG. 217

6. The section shown in Fig. 218 is that of a standard 15-in. 33.9-lb. structural-steel channel. Locate its centroid, neglecting fillets and rounded corners.

Ans. $\bar{y} = 0.79$ in.

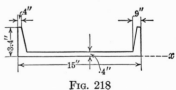

FIG. 218

Art. 46. Surfaces and Solids of Revolution. A surface of revolution is one generated by the rotation of a line about a non-intersecting axis. In Fig. 219, the line AB of length l is rotated about the x axis, thus generating a surface of revolution. Let point C be the centroid of the line and dl any differential portion of the line. By rotation of dl about the x axis a surface is generated whose area is

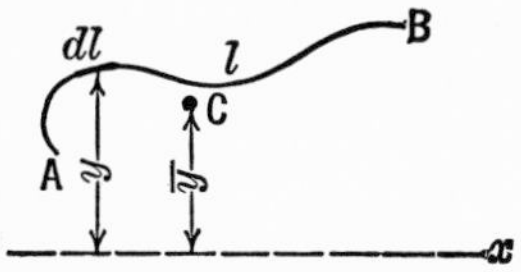

$$dA = 2\pi y\, dl$$

FIG. 219

The area of the entire surface of revolution is then

$$A = \int dA = \int 2\pi y\, dl = 2\pi \int y\, dl = 2\pi \bar{y} l$$

It is thus shown that the area of a surface of revolution is the product of the length of the generating line and the length of the path traced by the centroid of the line.

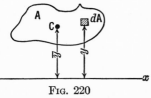

FIG. 220

A solid of revolution is one generated by the rotation of an area about a non-intersecting axis. In Fig. 220, the area A is rotated about the x axis, thus generating a solid of revolution. Let point C be the centroid of the area and dA any differential portion of the area. By rotating dA about the x axis, a differential solid is generated whose volume is

$$dV = 2\pi y\, dA$$

The volume of the entire solid of revolution is

$$V = \int dV = \int 2\pi y\, dA = 2\pi \int y\, dA = 2\pi \bar{y} A$$

Thus it is shown that the volume of a solid of revolution is the product of the generating area and the length of the path traced by the centroid of the area.

The two results thus developed are known as the theorems of Pappus and Guldinus. Their advantage in determining the surface areas or volumes of solids of revolution lies in the fact that by their use integration may be avoided.

Example

The cross section of the rim of a flywheel of 20-in. radius is shown by the shaded area in Fig. 221. Determine the weight of the rim if the material is cast iron, weighing 450 lb. per cu. ft.

Solution: The cross section of the rim will be considered as a rectangle from which a semicircle is cut out.

The volume generated by the rotation of the rectangle about the axis of the wheel is

$$V_1 = 2\pi\bar{y}A = 2\pi \times 17 \times 72 = 7695 \text{ cu. in.}$$

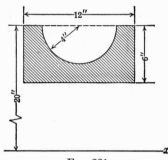

FIG. 221

The volume generated by rotation of the semicircle about the axis of the wheel is

$$V_2 = 2\pi\bar{y}A = 2\pi \times \left(20 - \frac{4 \times 4}{3\pi}\right) \times \frac{\pi(4)^2}{2} = 2890 \text{ cu. in.}$$

The volume of the rim is thus

$$V = 7695 - 2890 = 4805 \text{ cu. in.} = 2.78 \text{ cu. ft.}$$

Its weight is

$$W = 2.78 \times 450 = 1250 \text{ lb.}$$

Problems

1. By the theorems of Art. 46, determine the curved surface area and volume of a cone of radius r, altitude h, and slant height s.

Ans. $A = \pi r s; \ V = \frac{1}{3}\pi r^2 h.$

2. Show by means of the first theorem that the surface area of a sphere is $4\pi r^2$.

3. Given the volume of a sphere $= \frac{4}{3}\pi r^3$, show by means of the second theorem that the centroidal distance of the area of a semicircle is $4r/3\pi$.

4. Determine the surface area and volume of the torus shown in Fig. 222.

Ans. $A = 197$ sq. in.; $V = 98.7$ cu. in.

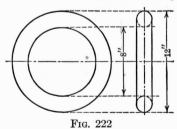

FIG. 222

Supplementary Problems

1. Locate the centroid of the structural-steel angle section shown in Fig. 223. Neglect fillet and rounded corners.   *Ans.* $\bar{y} = 3.04$ in.

2. A wire is bent into the form of a semicircular arc and its chord. Locate the center of gravity.
Ans. $0.389r$ from center.

3. Locate the center of gravity of one quadrant of the ellipse, $x^2/a^2 + y^2/b^2 = 1$.
Ans. $\bar{x} = 4a/3\pi$; $\bar{y} = 4b/3\pi$.

4. Using the result of Prob. 3, determine the volume of the solid of revolution obtained by rotating the area of Prob. 3 about the x axis.   *Ans.* $V = \frac{2}{3}\pi ab^2$.

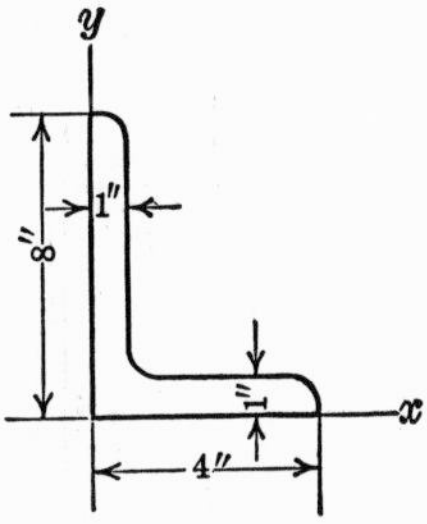

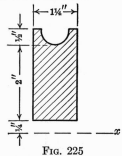

Fig. 223

5. Locate the centroid of the solid of revolution in Prob. 4.   *Ans.* $\bar{x} = \frac{3}{8}a$.

6. Locate the center of gravity of the area shown in Fig. 224.   *Ans.* $\bar{y} = 6.40$ in.

7. Determine the volume as the area of Fig. 224 is turned through a complete revolution about the x axis.   *Ans.* 6170 cu. in.

8. Solve for the surface area of the volume of Prob. 7.   *Ans.* 2210 sq. in.

9. A rope pulley is formed by revolving the area shown in Fig. 225 about the x axis.   *Ans.* 23.2 cu. in.

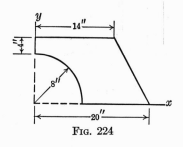

Fig. 224

Determine the volume thus formed.

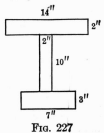

Fig. 225

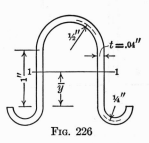

Fig. 226

10. Locate the center of gravity of the stiffener for an airfoil as shown in Fig. 226.
Ans. $\bar{y} = 0.549$ in.

11. Locate the position of the center of gravity of the area shown in Fig. 227.   *Ans.* $\bar{y} = 8.46$ in.

Fig. 227

12. The cross section of a girder consisting of a plate riveted to an I-beam is shown in Fig. 228. The area of the I-beam is 12.49 sq. in. Determine $\bar{y}$ of the section. (Disregard the rivets.)   *Ans.* $\bar{y} = 9.38$ in.

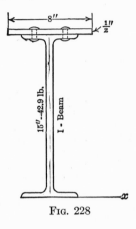

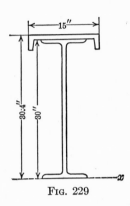

Fig. 228   Fig. 229

13. Fig. 229 shows the cross section of a crane-runway girder consisting of a 15-in. 33.9-lb. channel riveted to a 30-in. 116-lb. Carnegie beam. The area of the

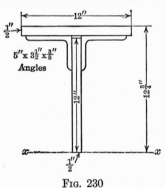

Fig. 230

channel is 9.90 sq. in., and its centroid is 0.79 in. from the outside of the web. The area of the CB section is 34.13 sq. in. Locate the centroid of the girder section.   *Ans.* $\bar{y} = 18.3$ in.

14. The T-section shown in Fig. 230 is composed of two 12-in. by $\frac{1}{2}$-in. plates and two 5-in. by $3\frac{1}{2}$-in. by $\frac{3}{8}$-in. angles. The distance of the centroid of one angle section from the 5-in. leg is 0.86 in., and the area is 3.05 sq. in. Compute $\bar{y}$.   *Ans.* 9.97 in.

15. A cable 200 ft. long hangs over a windlass drum, 50 ft. hanging on one side and 150 ft. on the other. Locate the position of the center of gravity of this cable.   *Ans.* 62.5 ft.

16. A cable 400 ft. long is being wound on a drum. Determine the rise in the center of gravity when 300 ft. has been wound.   *Ans.* 187.5 ft.

17. Locate the center of gravity of the hollow cone shown in Fig. 231.   *Ans.* 4.39 in.

18. Determine the position of the center of gravity of a telephone pole 30 ft. long, 18 in. in diameter at the base, and 6 in. in diameter at the top.   *Ans.* 10.4 ft.

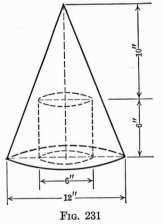

Fig. 231

CHAPTER VII

MOMENT OF INERTIA OF AREA

Art. 47. Moment of Inertia and Radius of Gyration of Area. In the development of certain topics in the mechanics of materials, integral quantities of the form $\int x^2\, dA$, $\int y^2\, dA$, and $\int \rho^2\, dA$ arise and form a part of important and frequently used engineering formulas. In these expressions dA represents a differential element of an area A, as shown in Fig. 232; x and y represent the distances of the element from rectangular axes in the plane of the area; and ρ represents the distance from a polar axis or axis perpendicular to the plane of the area. Since such mathematical expressions occur so frequently, it is desirable to designate them by some name and symbol and to evaluate them for certain commonly occurring areas. The name *moment of inertia of area* has been given to these quantities because they resemble in form the expression $\int r^2\, dM$, which is later defined as the moment of inertia of mass. Since area possesses no inertia, the term moment of inertia of area is somewhat inaccurate, and the term *second moment of area* would be preferable. However, through long usage the term moment of inertia has become conventional and universally accepted.

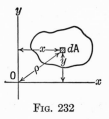

Fig. 232

The moment of inertia of an area about an axis in its plane is called the rectangular moment of inertia and is denoted by I. Thus the moment of inertia of the area A in Fig. 232 with respect to the x axis is given by

$$I_x = \int y^2\, dA$$

Similarly

$$I_y = \int x^2\, dA$$

The moment of inertia of an area with respect to an axis perpendicular to its plane is called the polar moment of inertia and is denoted by J. Thus the polar moment of inertia of the area A in Fig. 232

115

with respect to a z axis passing through O and normal to the x–y plane is given by

$$J = \int \rho^2 \, dA$$

Since the moment of inertia of an area always involves the product of area and square of distance, it is expressed in terms of some unit of length raised to the fourth power and is essentially positive. In most cases the inch is the unit of length used, and the moment of inertia is expressed in inches to the fourth power, written $in.^4$ It is again emphasized that moment of inertia of area is purely a mathematical concept; it has no physical basis and cannot be illustrated by diagram or other graphic representation.

The distance k, which when squared and multiplied by an area equals the moment of inertia of the area, is called the *radius of gyration* of the area. Thus

$$I = k^2 A$$

$$k = \sqrt{\frac{I}{A}}$$

Radius of gyration may also be defined as the distance from the axis of inertia, at which the entire area could be concentrated and still possess the same moment of inertia as in its actually distributed form. Care should be taken not to confuse radius of gyration k with centroidal distance $\bar{y}$, which was discussed in Chap. VI.

Art. 48. Moment of Inertia of Area by Integration. The algebraic expressions for the moments of inertia of some of the more common and basic forms of area will now be determined by means of calculus. In setting up the required integral the element of area dA may be selected in various ways. Either cartesian or polar coordinates may be used and either single or double integration may result, depending on how the element of area is selected. Certain precautions, however, must be observed in selecting the element of area so that it will conform to one of the following rules:

1. All points in the element should be equally distant from the axis of inertia; otherwise the distance x, y, or ρ would be indefinite. Since these distances are squared, the average distance cannot be used.

2. The element is of such form and so located that its moment of inertia with respect to the reference axis is already known. The moment of inertia of the area is then obtained by summing up the moments of inertia of all the elements.

Example 1

By integration determine the moment of inertia and radius of gyration of a rectangle in terms of its base b and altitude d, with respect to an axis through its base.

Solution: The differential element of area dA, selected according to the first rule, is $b \, dy$, as shown in Fig. 233.

$$I_x = \int y^2 \, dA = \int_0^d y^2 \cdot b \, dy = b \int_0^d y^2 \, dy$$

$$I_x = \frac{bd^3}{3}$$

$$k_x = \sqrt{\frac{I_x}{A}} = \sqrt{\frac{bd^3}{3bd}} = \frac{d}{\sqrt{3}}$$

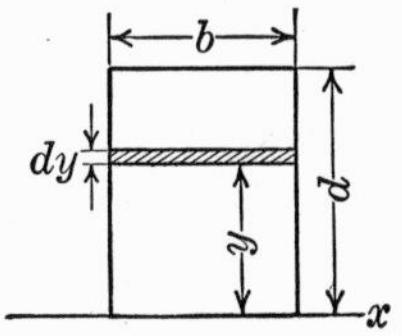

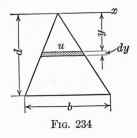

Fig. 233

Example 2

Derive the expression for the moment of inertia and radius of gyration of a triangle of base b and altitude d with respect to an axis through the vertex parallel to the base.

Solution: The element of area, selected in accordance with the first rule, is $u \, dy$, as shown in Fig. 234.

Fig. 234

$$I_x = \int y^2 \, dA = \int y^2 u \, dy$$

By similar triangles

$$\frac{u}{b} = \frac{y}{d} \quad \text{or} \quad u = \frac{b}{d} y$$

$$I_x = \int y^2 \frac{b}{d} y \, dy = \frac{b}{d} \int_o^d y^3 \, dy$$

$$I_x = \frac{bd^3}{4}$$

$$k_x = \sqrt{\frac{I_x}{A}} = \sqrt{\frac{bd^3}{4} \frac{2}{bd}} = \frac{d}{\sqrt{2}}$$

Example 3

Derive the expression for the moment of inertia and radius of gyration of the area of a circle of radius r with respect to a diameter.

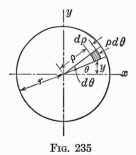

FIG. 235

Solution: If polar coordinates are employed, the differential area, selected according to the first rule, is $\rho \, d\theta \, d\rho$ as shown in Fig. 235.

$$I_x = \int y^2 \, dA$$

From Fig. 235,

$$y = \rho \sin \theta$$

$$I_x = \iint \rho^2 \sin^2 \theta \cdot \rho \, d\theta \, d\rho = \int_0^{2\pi} \int_0^r \rho^3 \, d\rho \cdot \sin^2 \theta \, d\theta$$

$$I_x = \frac{r^4}{4} \int_0^{2\pi} \frac{(1 - \cos 2\theta)}{2} \, d\theta = \frac{r^4}{4} \left[\frac{\theta}{2} - \frac{\sin 2\theta}{4} \right]_0^{2\pi}$$

$$I_x = \frac{\pi r^4}{4}$$

$$k_x = \sqrt{\frac{I_x}{A}} = \sqrt{\frac{\pi r^4}{4\pi r^2}} = \frac{r}{2}$$

Example 4

Determine the polar moment of inertia and radius of gyration of the area of a circle of radius r with respect to an axis through its center.

Solution: The differential area, selected in accordance with the first rule, is $2\pi\rho \, d\rho$ as shown in Fig. 236.

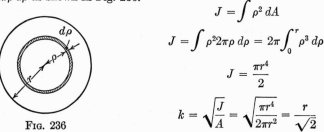

$$J = \int \rho^2 \, dA$$

$$J = \int \rho^2 2\pi\rho \, d\rho = 2\pi \int_0^r \rho^3 \, d\rho$$

$$J = \frac{\pi r^4}{2}$$

FIG. 236

$$k = \sqrt{\frac{J}{A}} = \sqrt{\frac{\pi r^4}{2\pi r^2}} = \frac{r}{\sqrt{2}}$$

Example 5

Determine the moment of inertia, with respect to the x axis, of the area of the parabolic half-segment of base a and altitude b as shown in Fig. 237. The equation of the parabola is $y^2 = mx$.

Solution: Although the element of area could be selected in accordance with the first rule, an opportunity is afforded here to illustrate the use of the second rule. Accordingly, the element is taken as a rectangle whose base is on the x axis. From the result of Ex. 1 of Art. 48 the moment of inertia of the element with respect to the x axis is

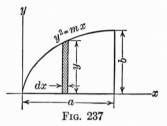

Fig. 237

$$dI_x = \frac{dx \cdot y^3}{3}$$

The moment of inertia of the entire area is now obtained by summing up the moments of inertia of the elements.

$$I_x = \int dI_x = \int \frac{1}{3} y^3 \, dx$$

From the equation of the parabola, $y = m^{\frac{1}{2}} x^{\frac{1}{2}}$. By substitution of the dimensions a and b into the equation of the parabola, $m = b^2/a$, and thus

$$y = \frac{b}{a^{\frac{1}{2}}} x^{\frac{1}{2}}$$

$$I_x = \int_0^a \frac{1}{3} \frac{b^3}{a^{\frac{3}{2}}} x^{\frac{3}{2}} \, dx = \frac{b^3}{3a^{\frac{3}{2}}} \int_0^a x^{\frac{3}{2}} \, dx$$

$$I_x = \frac{2}{15} ab^3$$

Problems

1. Determine the moment of inertia of a rectangle with respect to a centroidal axis parallel to the base.   *Ans.* $bd^3/12$.

2. Derive the expression for the moment of inertia of a triangle with respect to an axis through its base.   *Ans.* $bd^3/12$.

3. Derive the expression for the moment of inertia of a triangle with respect to a centroidal axis parallel to its base.   *Ans.* $bd^3/36$.

4. Determine the polar moment of inertia of a square of side b with respect to an axis through its center.   *Ans.* $b^4/6$.

5. Determine I_x for the ellipse whose equation is $x^2/a^2 + y^2/b^2 = 1$.   *Ans.* $\frac{1}{4}\pi ab^3$.

6. Solve Ex. 3, using cartesian coordinates.

7. Solve Ex. 4, using $dA = \rho \, d\theta \, d\rho$ as in Ex. 3.

8. Determine the moment of inertia with respect to the y axis of the area shown in Fig. 237.   *Ans.* $\frac{2}{7}a^3 b$.

Art. 49. Relation between Polar and Rectangular Moments of Inertia.

In Fig. 238, the x and y axes lie in the plane of the area, and a polar axis passes through O. By definition

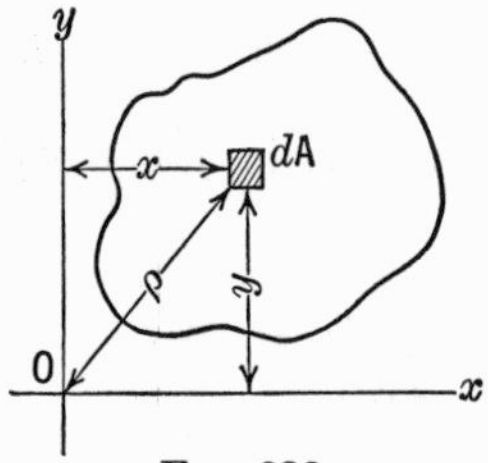

$$J_O = \int \rho^2 \, dA$$

In Fig. 238

$$\rho^2 = x^2 + y^2$$

$$J_O = \int (x^2 + y^2) \, dA = \int x^2 \, dA + \int y^2 \, dA$$

Fig. 238

Since, by definition

$$\int x^2 \, dA = I_y \quad \text{and} \quad \int y^2 \, dA = I_x$$

$$J_O = I_y + I_x$$

The moment of inertia of an area with respect to any polar axis is equal to the sum of its moments of inertia with respect to any two rectangular axes in its plane which intersect on the polar axis.

Problems

1. Verify the above theorem, using the results of Ex. 3 and 4 of Art. 48.

2. Compute the moment of inertia of the rectangle shown in Fig. 239 with respect to a polar axis through its centroid C.

$$Ans. \ J_C = 104 \ \text{in.}^4$$

3. Assuming the result obtained in Prob. 5, Art. 48, determine the moment of inertia of the ellipse with respect to a polar axis through its centroid. $Ans. \ J_C = \dfrac{\pi ab}{4} (a^2 + b^2).$

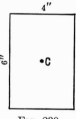

Fig. 239

4. Solve Prob. 4, Art. 48, by means of the theorem of Art. 49.

5. By means of symmetry and the theorem of Art. 49, show that the moment of inertia of a square is the same with respect to any centroidal axis in its plane.

6. Using $J = Ak^2$ and the principle of Art. 49, develop the formula for I_x for a thin, hollow, circular area of mean radius r. Axis x is the centroidal axis.

$$Ans. \ I_x = \pi r^3 t.$$

Art. 50. Relation between Moments of Inertia of Area with Respect to Parallel Axes.

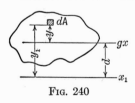

Fig. 240

If the moment of inertia of an area with respect to a centroidal axis in its plane is known, the moment of inertia with respect to any other parallel axis may be obtained without integration. In Fig. 240, gx represents the centroidal or "gravity" axis for the area shown, and x_1 represents any other parallel axis at distance d from the gx axis. By definition

$$I_{x_1} = \int y_1{}^2\, dA = \int (y + d)^2\, dA$$

$$= \int (y^2 + 2yd + d^2)\, dA$$

$$= \int y^2\, dA + d^2 \int dA + 2d \int y\, dA$$

By definition

$$\int y^2\, dA = I_{gx}$$

$$d^2 \int dA = Ad^2$$

$$2d \int y\, dA = 2d \cdot \bar{y} \cdot A$$

Since gx is a centroidal axis, $\bar{y} = 0$ and the last term drops out. The expression for I_{x_1} then becomes

$$I_{x_1} = I_{gx} + Ad^2$$

It is evident from this result that the moment of inertia of an area with respect to any axis in its plane is equal to its moment of inertia about a parallel centroidal axis plus the product of the area and the square of the distance between the two axes. This statement is known as the *transfer formula* or *parallel-axis theorem*.

It should be noted from the above statement that the moment of inertia of an area will always be less about a centroidal axis than about any other parallel axis. *It should also be noted that one of the two axes involved in the equation must be centroidal.* Hence, in transferring the moment of inertia of an area from one to the other of two parallel axes, it is always necessary for one of the axes to be taken through the centroid. If it is desired to transfer the moment of inertia of an area from one axis to another when neither axis is centroidal, the operation may be accomplished in two steps, the moment of inertia about the centroidal axis being an intermediate result.

Example 1

Given $I = bd^3/4$ for a triangle with respect to an axis through the vertex parallel to the base (see Ex. 2, Art. 48), determine without further integration the moment of inertia with respect to an axis through the base.

Solution: The triangle is shown in Fig. 241, in which x_1 is the axis through the vertex and x_2 is the axis through the base. Since neither x_1 nor x_2 is a

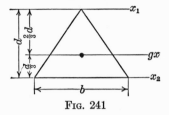

FIG. 241

centroidal axis, the transfer must be made in two steps, that is, from x_1 to the centroidal axis gx, and then from gx to x_2.

$$I_{x_1} = I_{gx} + Ad^2$$

$$\frac{bd^3}{4} = I_{gx} + \left(\frac{bd}{2}\right)\left(\frac{2d}{3}\right)^2$$

$$I_{gx} = \frac{bd^3}{36}$$

Then

$$I_{x_2} = I_{gx} + Ad^2 = \frac{bd^3}{36} + \left(\frac{bd}{2}\right)\left(\frac{d}{3}\right)^2 = \frac{bd^3}{12}$$

Example 2

Compute by means of the transfer formula the moment of inertia of a semi-circle of 10-in. radius with respect to a tangent axis x_2, which is parallel to its bounding diameter as shown in Fig. 242.

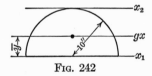

FIG. 242

Solution: From Ex. 3, Art. 48,

$$I_{x_1} = \frac{\pi r^4}{8} = \frac{\pi (10)^4}{8} = 3930 \text{ in.}^4$$

$$\bar{y} = \frac{4r}{3\pi} = \frac{4 \times 10}{3\pi} = 4.24 \text{ in.}$$

$$I_{x_1} = I_{gx} + Ad^2$$

$$3930 = I_{gx} + \frac{\pi (10)^2}{2}(4.24)^2$$

$$I_{gx} = 1110 \text{ in.}^4$$

Then

$$I_{x_2} = I_{gx} + Ad^2 = 1110 + \frac{\pi (10)^2}{2}(10 - 4.24)^2 = 6330 \text{ in.}^4$$

Problems

1. Derive the transfer formula for polar moment of inertia. Hint: In Fig. 243,
$J_O = \int \rho_1^2 \, dA$ and $\rho_1^2 = (a + x)^2 + (y - b)^2$. *Ans.* $J_O = J_C + Ad^2$.

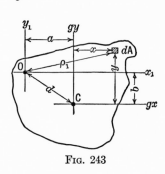

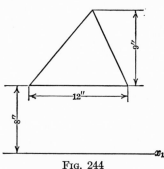

Fig. 243   Fig. 244

2. Compute the moment of inertia of the triangle shown in Fig. 244 with respect to the x_1 axis.   *Ans.* 6780 in.[4]

3. Determine the moment of inertia of the rectangle in Fig. 245 with respect to the y_1 axis.   *Ans.* 2770 in.[4]

4. Determine the moment of inertia of the rectangle in Fig. 245 with respect to a polar axis through O.   *Ans.* 2860 in.[4]

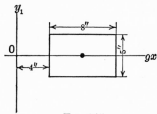

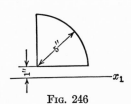

Fig. 245   Fig. 246

5. Compute the moment of inertia of the area of the quadrant shown in Fig. 246 with respect to the x_1 axis.   *Ans.* 225 in.[4]

6. Determine the moment of inertia of the area of a circle of 6-in. diameter with respect to a polar axis through its circumference.   *Ans.* 382 in.[4]

Art. 51. Moment of Inertia of Composite Areas. If an area consists of a combination of two or more simple areas, such as rectangles, triangles, and portions of circles, for which the moments of inertia are known, the moment of inertia of the entire area may be obtained by adding the moments of inertia of the component parts. If a component area represents a portion to be removed, its moment of inertia is, of course, subtracted. *In order to combine moments of inertia of component areas it is necessary that they all be taken with reference to the same axis.* The transfer formula should be used as needed.

Example 1

Locate the centroidal axis 1–1 of the T-section shown in Fig. 247, and compute the moment of inertia of the area with respect to this axis.

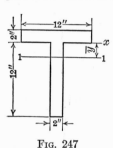

Fig. 247

Solution: First Method. The centroid is located with respect to the x axis by means of the equation

$$A\bar{y} = A_1 y_1 + A_2 y_2$$

$$48\bar{y} = 24 \times 1 + 24(-6)$$

$$\bar{y} = -2.5 \text{ in.}$$

The moment of inertia of the upper rectangle is determined about its own centroidal axis and transferred to the 1–1 axis as follows:

$$I_{1-1} = I_{gx} + Ad^2 = \frac{12(2)^3}{12} + 24(3.5)^2 = 302 \text{ in.}^4$$

For the lower rectangle

$$I_{1-1} = \frac{2(12)^3}{12} + 24(3.5)^2 = 582 \text{ in.}^4$$

The moment of inertia of the entire T-section is

$$I_{1-1} = 302 + 582 = 884 \text{ in.}^4$$

Second Method. A simpler solution is possible when all component areas have a common boundary line. The x axis is a common boundary in this example. The moment of inertia of the entire area about the x axis is first obtained and then transferred to the 1–1 axis.

$$I_x = \frac{12(2)^3}{3} + \frac{2(12)^3}{3} = 1184 \text{ in.}^4$$

$$I_{1-1} = I_x - Ad^2 = 1184 - 48(2.5)^2 = 884 \text{ in.}^4$$

Example 2

Determine the moment of inertia of the I-section shown in Fig. 248 with respect to the centroidal axis 1–1.

Solution: First Method. Since the 1–1 axis is also centroidal for the central rectangle, its moment of inertia is

$$I_{1-1} = \frac{2(6)^3}{12} = 36 \text{ in.}^4$$

The value of I_{1-1} for either upper or lower rectangle is obtained by transfer,

$$I_{1-1} = I_{gx} + Ad^2 = \frac{6(2)^3}{12} + 12(4)^2 = 196 \text{ in.}^4$$

Then

$$\text{total } I_{1-1} = 36 + 2(196) = 428 \text{ in.}^4$$

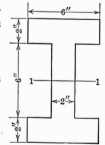

Fig. 248

Second Method. The moment of inertia of this section may also be determined without transfer by considering the section as a 6-in. by 10-in. rectangle from which a 4-in. by 6-in. rectangle is subtracted, the 1–1 axis being centroidal for each.

$$I_{1-1} = \frac{6(10)^3}{12} - \frac{4(6)^3}{12} = 428 \text{ in.}^4$$

It is evident from the preceding examples that the moment of inertia of a given composite area may sometimes be obtained by several methods which may differ considerably in the amount of computation involved. No single rule can be stated which will indicate in all cases the most convenient method to adopt. Each problem must be considered individually.

Problems

1. Compute the moment of inertia and radius of gyration of a hollow circular section of 6-in. outside diameter and 4-in. inside diameter with respect to an axis in its plane through the center.   *Ans.* 51 in.^{4}; 1.8 in.

2. A box column is made up of four 2-in. by 6-in. timbers fastened together as shown in Fig. 249. Determine the moment of inertia and radius of gyration of the section with respect to the centroidal axis 1–1.

Ans. 320 in.^{4}; 2.58 in.

3. Determine the moment of inertia of the American standard 15-in. 33.9-lb. channel section in Fig. 250 with respect to the 1–1 axis.   *Ans.* 313 in.^{4}

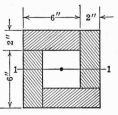

FIG. 249

4. Locate the 2–2 axis of the channel section in Fig. 250, and determine the moment of inertia about this axis.

Ans. $\bar{x} = 0.79$ in.; $I_{2-2} = 8.2$ in.^{4}

5. Determine the moment of inertia of the area shown in Fig. 251 with respect to the gx axis.

Ans. 246 in.^{4}

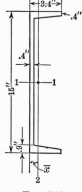

FIG. 250

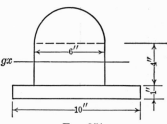

FIG. 251

6. Determine the moment of inertia of the area shown in Fig. 251 with respect to the centroidal polar axis.   *Ans.* 433 in.^{4}

7. Determine the moment of inertia of the area shown in Fig. 252 with respect to the gx axis.   *Ans.* 74.4 in.^{4} ($\bar{y} = 3.22$ in.)

8. Determine the moment of inertia of the area shown in Fig. 252 with respect to the gy axis.   *Ans.* 171 in.^{4}

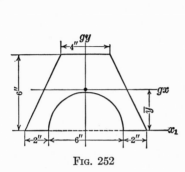

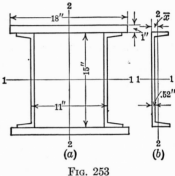

Fig. 252   Fig. 253

9. The cross section of a structural-steel column composed of two 15-in. 40-lb. channels and two 18-in. by 1-in. plates is shown in Fig. 253 (*a*). For one channel, shown in Fig. 253 (*b*), $A = 11.7$ sq. in., $I_{1-1} = 346$, $I_{2-2} = 9.3$, and $\bar{x} = 0.78$ in. Determine the moment of inertia and radius of gyration of the section with respect to each of the axes 1–1 and 2–2.

$$Ans.\ I_{1-1} = 3000\ \text{in.}^4;\ k_{1-1} = 7.10\ \text{in.}$$
$$I_{2-2} = 1770\ \text{in.}^4;\ k_{2-2} = 5.45\ \text{in.}$$

Supplementary Problems

1. Compute the moment of inertia and radius of gyration of the area shown in Fig. 254 with respect to the gx axis.   *Ans.* 5.97 in.^{4}; 1.01 in.

2. Compute the moment of inertia and radius of gyration of the area shown in Fig. 254 with respect to a polar axis through the geometric center.

Ans. 11.9 in.^{4}; 1.43 in.

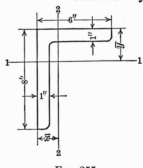

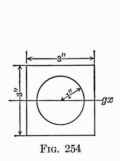

Fig. 254   Fig. 255

3. For the structural-steel angle section shown in Fig. 255, $\bar{x} = 1.65$ in. and $\bar{y} = 2.65$ in. Neglecting fillets and rounded corners, determine the moments of inertia with respect to the centroidal axes 1–1 and 2–2.

Ans. 80.8 in.^{4}; 38.8 in.^{4}

4. The cross section of a 10-in. 49-lb. Carnegie beam is shown in Fig. 256. Determine the moments of inertia of the area with respect to the axes 1–1 and 2–2.

Ans. 273 in.^{4}; 93.0 in.^{4}

5. Determine the moment of inertia of area for a half-circle with respect to the gravity axis parallel to the bounding diameter as shown in Fig. 257.

Ans. 0.11r^4.

6. Determine the moment of inertia of the area shown in Fig. 258 with respect to the gx axis.

Ans. 0.055r^4.

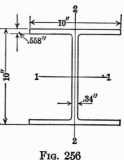

FIG. 256

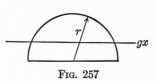

FIG. 257

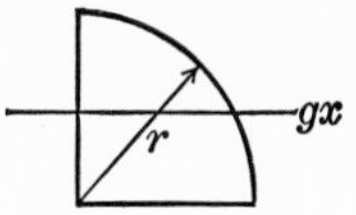

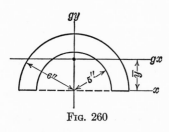

FIG. 258

FIG. 259

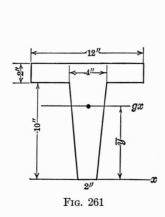

FIG. 260

7. Determine the approximate value of the moment of inertia of the area shown in Fig. 259. *Ans.* $I_{gx} = 0.2978r^3t$.

8. Locate the gx axis of the area shown in Fig. 260 and compute the moments of inertia of the area with respect to the gx and gy axes.

Ans. $\bar{y} = 3.52$ in.; $I_{gx} = 49.6$ in.^{4}

9. Solve Prob. 8 using the approximate formula of Prob. 7.

10. Locate the gx axis of the T-section shown in Fig. 261, and compute the moment of inertia with respect to this axis. *Ans.* $\bar{y} = 7.98$ in.; $I_{gx} = 645$ in.^{4}

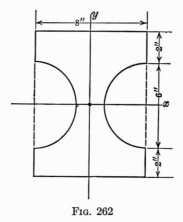

FIG. 261

FIG. 262

11. Compute the moments of inertia of the area shown in Fig. 262 with respect to the x and y axes.

Ans. 603 in.^{4}; 198 in.^{4}

12. The section shown in Fig. 263 (a) consists of four 6-in. by 4-in. by $\frac{1}{2}$-in. angles and one 12-in. by $\frac{1}{2}$-in. web plate. The 4-in. legs of the angles are attached to the

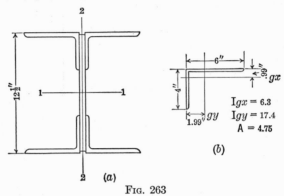

$Igx = 6.3$
$Igy = 17.4$
$A = 4.75$

(b)

(a)

Fig. 263

web plate. The data for one angle are given in Fig. 263 (b). Compute the moments of inertia of the section with respect to axes 1–1 and 2–2.   *Ans.* 623 in.⁴; 165 in.⁴

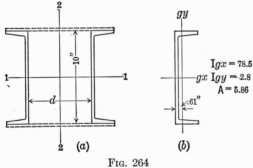

$Igx = 78.5$
$Igy = 2.8$
$A = 5.86$

(a)   (b)

Fig. 264

13. Solve Prob. 12 if two 14-in. by $\frac{1}{2}$-in. flange plates are added, one on the top and one on the bottom.
    Ans. 1220 in.⁴; 394 in.⁴

14. The latticed channel section shown in Fig. 264 (a) consists of two 10-in. 20-lb. channels. The data for one channel are given in Fig. 264 (b). Compute the back-to-back distance d to make $I_{1-1} = I_{2-2}$.
    Ans. 5.96 in.

15. Compute the moment of inertia of area for the stiffener of an airfoil as shown in Fig. 265. For the thin half-circular areas use $A = \pi r t$, $\bar{y} = 0.6366r$ and $I_{gx} = 0.2978 r^3 t$.   *Ans.* $I_{1-1} = 0.0774$ in.⁴

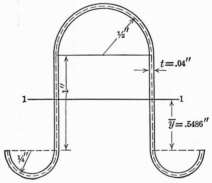

$t = .04''$

$\bar{y} = .5486''$

Fig. 265

CHAPTER VIII

PRODUCT OF INERTIA OF AREA; MAXIMUM AND MINIMUM MOMENTS OF INERTIA

Art. 52. Introduction. Except for special cases the moment of inertia of an area is not the same with respect to all axes in its plane passing through a given point. In certain problems in mechanics of materials it is necessary to locate those axes through a given point for which the moment of inertia has a maximum or minimum value. As will be shown later, the location of these axes and the determination of the corresponding moments of inertia involve a property of the area given by the mathematical expression $\int xy\, dA$ and known as the *product of inertia.* The symbol I_{xy} will be used to represent this quantity.

Art. 53. Product of Inertia by Integration. In the expression $\int xy\, dA$, x and y are the coordinates of an element dA with reference to a pair of rectangular axes in the plane of the area as shown in Fig. 266. The value of the integral, taken between the proper limits so as to cover the entire area, is the product of inertia of the area with respect to the given axes. The product of inertia has the same dimension as the moment of inertia, namely, length to the fourth power. If the inch is used as the unit of length, then the product of inertia is expressed as inches to the fourth power, written $in.^4$

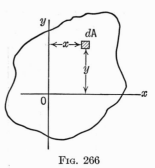

Fig. 266

Unlike moment of inertia of area, which is essentially positive, the product of inertia of an area may be positive, negative, or zero. For instance, if an area lies wholly within the first quadrant formed by the rectangular axes, both x and y distances are positive and the product of inertia is evidently positive. If the area lies wholly within the second quadrant, x distances are negative and y distances are positive; thus the product of inertia becomes negative. Similarly, the result would be positive for an area in the third quadrant and nega-

129

tive for one in the fourth quadrant. If either of the rectangular axes is an axis of symmetry, then, for any element dA lying on one side of this axis for which the product $xy\,dA$ is positive, there will be a corresponding element on the opposite side for which the product $xy\,dA$ will be equal but negative. Thus $\int xy\,dA$, the summation of such products, must be zero when either axis is an axis of symmetry.

Example 1

Determine the product of inertia of a quadrant of a circle with respect to the bounding radii as rectangular axes.

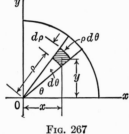

Fig. 267

Solution: If polar coordinates are used, $dA = \rho\,d\rho\,d\theta$, $y = \rho \sin \theta$, and $x = \rho \cos \theta$ as shown in Fig. 267.

$$I_{xy} = \int xy\,dA = \int_0^{\frac{\pi}{2}} \int_0^r (\rho \cos \theta)(\rho \sin \theta)\rho\,d\rho\,d\theta$$

$$= \frac{r^4}{4} \int_0^{\frac{\pi}{2}} \sin \theta \cos \theta\,d\theta = \frac{r^4}{8} [\sin^2 \theta]_0^{\frac{\pi}{2}} = \frac{r^4}{8}$$

Example 2

Determine the product of inertia of the triangle shown in Fig. 268 with respect to the x and y axes.

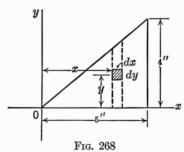

Fig. 268

Solution: The element of area is taken as $dA = dx\,dy$. In the integration y will be taken as the dependent variable and x the independent variable. Thus

$$I_{xy} = \int xy\,dA$$

$$= \int_0^5 \int_0^{\frac{4}{5}x} xy\,dy\,dx = \frac{8}{25} \int_0^5 x^3\,dx = 50 \text{ in.}^4$$

Problems

1. Determine by integration the product of inertia of a rectangle of sides b and h with respect to a pair of axes coinciding with the two adjacent sides.   *Ans.* $\pm \dfrac{b^2h^2}{4}$.

2. Determine by integration the product of inertia of a right triangle of base b and altitude h with respect to the axes coinciding with the legs of the triangle.   *Ans.* $\pm \dfrac{b^2h^2}{24}$.

3. Determine by integration the product of inertia of the triangle in Fig. 269 with respect to the centroidal axes parallel to the legs as shown.

Ans. -162 in.^{4}

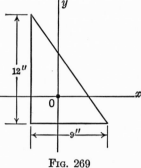

Fig. 269

Art. 54. Relation between Products of Inertia with Respect to Parallel Axes.

If the product of inertia of an area with respect to a pair of rectangular axes through its centroid is known, the product of inertia with respect to any other pair of parallel axes may be found without further integration by means of a simple relation which will now be derived.

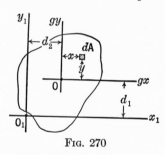

Fig. 270

In Fig. 270 is shown an area for which gx and gy are any pair of rectangular centroidal axes; x_1 and y_1 are rectangular axes parallel to the centroidal axes at distances d_1 and d_2, respectively. By definition

$$I_{x_1y_1} = \int (x + d_2)(y + d_1)\, dA$$

$$= \int xy\, dA + d_1 \int x\, dA + d_2 \int y\, dA + d_1 d_2 \int dA$$

But $\displaystyle\int xy\, dA = I_{gxy}$, $\displaystyle\int x\, dA = 0$ and $\displaystyle\int y\, dA = 0$ because x and y are measured from the centroidal axes, and $\displaystyle\int dA = A$. Thus

$$I_{x_1y_1} = I_{gxy} + A d_1 d_2$$

This relation is known as the transfer formula, or parallel axis theorem, for product of inertia and resembles in form the corresponding theorem for moment of inertia.

The distances d_1 and d_2 may be either positive or negative; hence the term Ad_1d_2 may be either positive or negative. If the centroid of the area is in the first or third quadrant formed by the x_1 and y_1 axes, then Ad_1d_2 is positive; otherwise it is negative.

If either of the centroidal axes is also an axis of symmetry, then $I_{gxy} = 0$ and $I_{x_1y_1} = Ad_1d_2$. Thus a very simple method is afforded of determining the product of inertia of an area about any pair of rectangular axes when one of these axes is parallel to an axis of symmetry.

Example

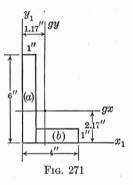

FIG. 271

Determine the product of inertia of a 6-in. by 4-in. by 1-in. angle with respect to centroidal axes parallel to the legs.

Solution: The coordinates of the centroid of the angle are obtained in the usual way and are shown in Fig. 271. The angle is divided into two rectangles (a) and (b). The products of inertia of these rectangles will be obtained separately and then added.

The centroidal axes of rectangle (a) taken alone are also axes of symmetry, for which the product of inertia is zero. Hence, for rectangle (a),

$$I_{gxy} = 0 + Ad_1d_2 = 0 + 6(-0.83)(+0.67) = -3.33 \text{ in.}^4$$

Similarly, for rectangle (b),

$$I_{gxy} = 0 + Ad_1d_2 = 0 + 3(1.67)(-1.33) = -6.67 \text{ in.}^4$$

Thus, for the entire angle,

$$I_{gxy} = (-3.33) + (-6.67) = -10.0 \text{ in.}^4$$

Problems

1. Solve Prob. 1 of Art. 53 without integration by use of symmetry and the parallel axis theorem.

2. Solve Prob. 3 of Art. 53 without integration by using the result of Prob. 2 of Art. 53 and the parallel axis theorem.

3. Determine $I_{x_1y_1}$ for the angle in Fig. 271 by the same procedure as is used in the Example of Art. 54.   *Ans.* 12.75 in.^{4}

4. Using the result of Prob. 3 and the parallel axis theorem, check the value of I_{gxy} obtained in the Example of Art. 54.

5. Determine the product of inertia of an 8-in. by 6-in. by 1-in. angle about its centroidal axes parallel to the legs.   *Ans.* 32.1 in.^{4}

Art. 55. Moment of Inertia and Product of Inertia with Respect to Inclined Axes. In Fig. 272 x and y are any pair of rectangular axes passing through point O of the area shown, and x' and y' are any other pair of rectangular axes passing through the same point and inclined at angle θ with the original pair.

The coordinates of the element of area dA are x and y with respect to the original axes, and x' and y' with respect to the inclined axes. From the geometry of the figure

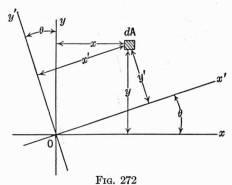

$$x' = x \cos \theta + y \sin \theta$$

$$y' = y \cos \theta - x \sin \theta$$

FIG. 272

The moment of inertia of the area with respect to the x' axis is by definition

$$I_{x'} = \int (y')^2 \, dA = \int (y \cos \theta - x \sin \theta)^2 \, dA$$

$$= \cos^2 \theta \int y^2 \, dA + \sin^2 \theta \int x^2 \, dA - 2 \sin \theta \cos \theta \int xy \, dA$$

But $\int y^2 \, dA = I_x$, $\int x^2 \, dA = I_y$, and $\int xy \, dA = I_{xy}$. Thus

$$I_{x'} = I_x \cos^2 \theta + I_y \sin^2 \theta - 2I_{xy} \sin \theta \cos \theta \tag{1}$$

or

$$I_{x'} = I_x \left(\frac{1 + \cos 2\theta}{2} \right) + I_y \left(\frac{1 - \cos 2\theta}{2} \right) - I_{xy} \sin 2\theta$$

$$I_{x'} = \frac{I_x + I_y}{2} + \frac{I_x - I_y}{2} \cos 2\theta - I_{xy} \sin 2\theta \tag{1a}$$

In similar manner, starting with $I_{y'} = \int (x')^2 \, dA$, the following relations are obtained

$$I_{y'} = I_x \sin^2 \theta + I_y \cos^2 \theta + 2I_{xy} \sin \theta \cos \theta \tag{2}$$

or

$$I_{y'} = \frac{I_x + I_y}{2} - \frac{I_x - I_y}{2} \cos 2\theta + I_{xy} \sin 2\theta \tag{2a}$$

By addition of equations (1) and (2), it is found that

$$I_{x'} + I_{y'} = I_x + I_y \tag{3}$$

This result should also be obvious from the fact that each side of the equation is equal to the moment of inertia of the area about a polar axis through point O (see Art. 49).

The product of inertia of the area about the inclined axes becomes

$$I_{x'y'} = \int x'y' \, dA$$

$$= \int (x \cos \theta + y \sin \theta)(y \cos \theta - x \sin \theta) \, dA$$

$$= \sin \theta \cos \theta \int y^2 \, dA - \sin \theta \cos \theta \int x^2 \, dA$$

$$+ (\cos^2 \theta - \sin^2 \theta) \int xy \, dA$$

$$= \frac{I_x - I_y}{2} \sin 2\theta + I_{xy} \cos 2\theta \qquad (4)$$

Problems

1. Determine $I_{x'}$, $I_{y'}$, and $I_{x'y'}$ for the rectangle shown in Fig. 273 if angle $\theta = 30°$.   *Ans.* 693 in.^{4}; 5963 in.^{4}; 43.5 in.^{4}

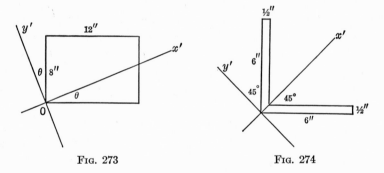

FIG. 273   FIG. 274

2. Determine $I_{x'}$, $I_{y'}$, and $I_{x'y'}$ for the 6-in. by 6-in. by $\frac{1}{2}$-in. angle section shown in Fig. 274.   *Ans.* 31.7 in.^{4}; 40.7 in.^{4}; zero.

Art. 56. Principal Axes. It has previously been stated (Art. 52) that the moment of inertia of an area is, in general, not the same for all axes passing through a given point. Those axes for which the moment of inertia has a maximum and minimum value are called the *principal axes.* A general relation will now be developed by means of which the principal axes may be located.

From equation (1a) of Art. 55 the moment of inertia about any inclined axis is

$$I_{x'} = \frac{I_x + I_y}{2} + \frac{I_x - I_y}{2} \cos 2\theta - I_{xy} \sin 2\theta$$

Differentiating with respect to θ,

$$\frac{dI_{x'}}{d\theta} = 0 - (I_x - I_y) \sin 2\theta - 2I_{xy} \cos 2\theta$$

For the maximum or minimum value of $I_{x'}$, the first derivative must equal zero; hence

$$-(I_x - I_y) \sin 2\theta - 2I_{xy} \cos 2\theta = 0 \tag{1}$$

or

$$\tan 2\theta = \frac{2I_{xy}}{I_y - I_x} \tag{2}$$

This relation determines the angle θ, for which the moment of inertia is maximum or minimum. Since for any value of tan 2θ there are two values of 2θ differing by 180°, it follows that there are two principal axes inclined at 90° with each other. About one of these axes the moment of inertia is maximum, and about the other it is minimum.

Combination of equation (1) of Art. 56 with equation (4) of Art. 55 gives $I_{x'y'} = 0$ when x' and y' are principal axes. Thus, the principal axes may also be defined as those for which the product of inertia is zero. Also, since the product of inertia is zero whenever one of the axes is an axis of symmetry, it follows that an axis of symmetry is always a principal axis.

Example

Locate the centroidal principal axes of the 6-in. by $3\frac{1}{2}$-in. by $\frac{3}{4}$-in. Z-section shown in Fig. 275.

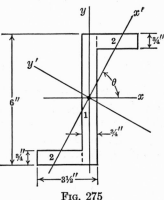

Fig. 275

Solution: The Z-section is divided into three rectangles as shown, fillets and rounded corners having been neglected. The values of I_x and I_y, determined by the usual methods or taken from a steel handbook, are $I_x = 42.1$ in.⁴ and $I_y = 15.4$ in.⁴ For rectangle 1, $I_{xy} = 0$, since x and y are axes of symmetry. For rectangle 2

$$I_{xy} = I_{gxy} + Ad_1d_2 = 0 + (2.06)(1.75)(2.625) = 9.48 \text{ in.}^4$$

For the entire section

$$I_{xy} = 0 + 2(9.48) = 18.96 \text{ in.}^4$$

$$\tan 2\theta = \frac{2I_{xy}}{I_y - I_x} = \frac{2(18.96)}{15.4 - 42.1} = -1.42$$

$$2\theta = 125.2°$$

$$\theta = 62.6°$$

Problems

1. Determine the value of angle θ for the rectangle in Fig. 273 to make x' and y' the principal axes.   *Ans.* 30.5°.

2. Locate the centroidal principal axes of the 6-in. by 4-in. by 1-in. angle section in the Example of Art. 54.   *Ans.* 22.5°.

Art. 57. Maximum and Minimum Moments of Inertia. After the principal axes through a given point have been located as explained in Art. 56, the moments of inertia of the area with respect to these axes may be found by use of the formulas for inclined axes developed in Art. 55. These values are then the maximum and minimum moments of inertia of the area with respect to axes taken through the given point. Usually the moments of inertia with respect to centroidal axes are required.

By substitution of the expression for I_{xy} from equation (2) of Art. 56 in equations (1) and (2) of Art. 55, the following simplified equations for the maximum and minimum moments of inertia may be obtained:

$$I_x' = \frac{I_x \cos^2 \theta - I_y \sin^2 \theta}{\cos 2\theta} \tag{1}$$

$$I_y' = \frac{I_y \cos^2 \theta - I_x \sin^2 \theta}{\cos 2\theta} \tag{2}$$

Example 1

Determine the maximum and minimum moments of inertia of a 6-in. by $3\frac{1}{2}$-in. by $\frac{3}{4}$-in. Z-section with respect to centroidal axes.

Solution: The centroidal principal axes of the section are inclined at an angle of 62.6° with the x and y axes, as shown in the Example of Art. 56. From equations (1) and (2) of Art. 57 the required moments of inertia are:

$$I_{x'} = \frac{42.1 \cos^2 62.6° - 15.4 \sin^2 62.6°}{\cos 125.2°} = 5.6 \text{ in.}^4 \quad \text{(min.)}$$

$$I_{y'} = \frac{15.4 \cos^2 62.6° - 42.1 \sin^2 62.6°}{\cos 125.2°} = 51.9 \text{ in.}^4 \quad \text{(max.)}$$

After determining $I_{x'}$, the value of $I_{y'}$ can also be obtained by using the relation expressed in equation (3) of Art. 55.

$$I_{x'} + I_{y'} = I_x + I_y$$

Thus

$$I_{y'} = 42.1 + 15.4 - 5.6 = 51.9 \text{ in.}^4$$

The use of equations (1) and (2) or (1a) and (2a) of Art. 55 gives the same results for $I_{x'}$ and $I_{y'}$ as were obtained above.

The maximum and minimum moments of inertia may also be obtained by use of the tables in steel handbooks. For the Z-section of this example a handbook gives the following values:

$$A = 8.63 \text{ in.}^2; I_x = 42.1 \text{ in.}^4; I_y = 15.4 \text{ in.}^4; k \text{ (min.)} = 0.81 \text{ in.}$$

Then

$$I_{x'} = Ak^2 = 8.63(0.81)^2 = 5.6 \text{ in.}^4$$

and

$$I_{y'} = I_x + I_y - I_{x'} = 42.1 + 15.4 - 5.6 = 51.9 \text{ in.}^4$$

Example 2

The cross section of a single-cell box beam from an airplane wing is shown in Fig. 276. The beam consists of four stringers (a, b, c, and d) and the connecting sheet. The areas of the stringers are 1.0, 0.6, 0.8, and 0.4 sq. in.,

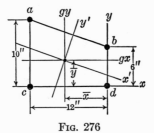

FIG. 276

respectively. Neglecting the connecting sheet, locate the centroidal principal axes of the beam section and determine the corresponding maximum and minimum moments of inertia.

Solution: For convenience a portion of the data and calculated results are arranged in tabular form as follows:

Member	Area	y	x	Ay	Ax	Ay^2	Ax^2	Axy
a	1.0	10	−12	10	−12	100	144	−120
b	0.6	6	0	3.6	0	21.6	0	0
c	0.8	0	−12	0	−9.6	0	115.2	0
d	0.4	0	0	0	0	0	0	0
Totals	2.8			13.6	−21.6	121.6	259.2	−120

$$\bar{x} = \frac{\Sigma Ax}{\Sigma A} = \frac{-21.6}{2.8} = -7.71 \text{ in.}$$

$$\bar{y} = \frac{\Sigma Ay}{\Sigma A} = \frac{13.6}{2.8} = 4.86 \text{ in.}$$

$$I_x = \Sigma Ay^2 = 121.6 \text{ in.}^4$$

$$I_y = \Sigma Ax^2 = 259.2 \text{ in.}^4$$

$$I_{xy} = \Sigma Axy = -120 \text{ in.}^4$$

$$I_{gx} = I_x - \Sigma A(\bar{y})^2 = 121.6 - 2.8(4.86)^2 = 55.4 \text{ in.}^4$$

$$I_{gy} = I_y - \Sigma A(\bar{x})^2 = 259.2 - 2.8(-7.71)^2 = 92.4 \text{ in.}^4$$

$$I_{gxy} = I_{xy} - \Sigma A(\bar{x}) \cdot (\bar{y}) = -120 - 2.8(-7.71)(4.86) = -15.0 \text{ in.}^4$$

$$\tan 2\theta = \frac{2I_{gxy}}{I_{gy} - I_{gx}} = \frac{2(-15)}{92.4 - 55.4} = -0.81$$

$$2\theta = -39° \qquad \theta = -19.5°$$

$$I_{x'} = I_{gx} \cos^2 \theta + I_{gy} \sin^2 \theta - 2I_{gxy} \sin \theta \cos \theta$$

$$= 55.4(0.941)^2 + 92.4(-0.334)^2 - 2(-15.0)(-0.334)(0.941) = 50.0 \text{ in.}^4$$

$$I_{y'} = I_{gx} \sin^2 \theta + I_{gy} \cos^2 \theta + 2I_{gxy} \sin \theta \cos \theta$$

$$= 55.4(-0.334)^2 + 92.4(0.941)^2 + 2(-15.0)(-0.334)(0.941) = 97.7 \text{ in.}^4$$

Problems

1. Using the result of Prob. 2, Art. 56, calculate the moments of inertia of a 6-in. by 4-in. by 1-in. angle section with respect to the centroidal principal axes.

$Ans.$ 35.0 in.^{4}; 6.6 in.^{4}

2. Determine the moments of inertia of a 5-in. by $3\frac{1}{4}$-in. by $\frac{1}{2}$-in. Z-section with respect to its centroidal principal axes. $Ans.$ 25.4 in.^{4}; 2.9 in.^{4}

3. A typical airplane wing leading edge box beam consisting of 3 stringers and

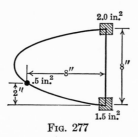

2.0 in.^{2}

$8''$

$8''$

.5 in.^{2}

$2''$

1.5 in.^{2}

Fig. 277

attached skin has cross section as shown in Fig. 277. Calculate the moments of inertia about the centroidal principal axes, neglecting the skin area.

$Ans.$ 60.4 in.^{4}; 25.4 in.^{4}

Supplementary Problems

1. Determine I_{xy} for the semicircle in Fig. 278. $Ans.$ $\frac{2}{3}r^4$.

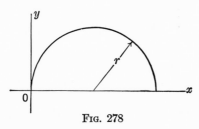

y

r

0

x

Fig. 278

2. Determine moments of inertia of the semicircle in Fig. 278 with respect to the principal axes through point O. $Ans.$ 2.21r^4; 0.149r^4.

3. Calculate the moments of inertia of an 8-in. by 8-in. by $\frac{3}{4}$-in. equal leg angle section with respect to the centroidal principal axes. Check the results by use of the value for minimum radius of gyration as given in a steel handbook.

$Ans.$ 111.2 in.^{4}; 28.2 in.^{4}

4. Calculate the moments of inertia of an 8-in. by 4-in. by $\frac{3}{4}$-in. angle section with respect to the centroidal principal axes. Check the results by use of the value for minimum radius of gyration given in a steel handbook.

$Ans.$ 58.2 in.^{4}; 6.1 in.^{4}

5. Show how equations (1) and (2) of Art. 57 are obtained.

6. Using equation (1) of Art. 55, show that the moment of inertia of a square is the same for all centroidal axes in its plane.

7. Determine the moments of inertia of a $4\frac{1}{8}$-in. by $3\frac{3}{16}$-in. by $\frac{3}{4}$-in. Z-section with respect to centroidal principal axes. Check by using the value of minimum radius of gyration given in a handbook.   *Ans.* 23.1 in.^{4}; 3.1 in.^{4}

8. Locate the principal centroidal axes of the section shown in Fig. 279 and calculate the moments of inertia with respect to these axes.

   Ans. $\bar{x}$ = 1.19; $\bar{y}$ = 1.61; θ = 28.9°; $I_{\text{max.}}$ = 11.4 in.^{4}; $I_{\text{min.}}$ = 4.0 in.^{4}

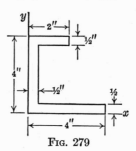

FIG. 279

9. Locate the principal centroidal axes of the box-beam section consisting of 6 stringers and connecting sheet as shown in Fig. 280. The areas of the stringers

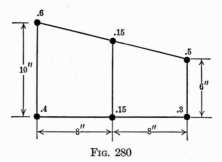

FIG. 280

are indicated; the sheet area is to be neglected. Compute the moments of inertia of the section with respect to the principal axes.

   Ans. $\bar{x}$ = 7.25; $\bar{y}$ = 4.85; θ = 11.45°; $I_{\text{max.}}$ = 117.8 in.^{4}; $I_{\text{min.}}$ = 34.4 in.^{4}

CHAPTER IX

MOMENT OF INERTIA OF MASS

Art. 58. Moment of Inertia and Radius of Gyration of Mass.
It will be shown in a subsequent chapter that a rotating body tends
to resist any change in its motion and that any such change produced
by external actions depends inversely on a property of the rotating
body known as its *moment of inertia*. Experience has shown that the
resistance offered depends on the amount of mass involved and the
square of its distance from the axis. Hence the moment of inertia
of a body is expressed in terms of mass and square of distance. For a
particle of mass dM located at distance ρ from the axis of rotation the
moment of inertia is $\rho^2\, dM$. The moment of inertia of a body is the
summation of such expressions for all elements in the body and thus
becomes the integral $\int \rho^2\, dM$ which will be represented by I.

In evaluating this integral, it is often convenient to make use of
the relation between mass, volume, and density γ. If γ is constant,

$$M = \gamma V \quad \text{and} \quad dM = \gamma \cdot dV$$

$$I = \int \rho^2\, dM = \gamma \int \rho^2\, dV$$

The *radius of gyration* of a mass, denoted by k, may be defined
as the distance from the axis at which the entire mass may be concentrated and still have the same moment of inertia as it has in its
actually distributed form. Thus

$$I = Mk^2 \quad \text{or} \quad k = \sqrt{\frac{I}{M}}$$

It will be shown later that the unit of mass used in engineering
is one possessing g units of weight, where g represents the acceleration
of gravity in feet per second per second. Thus $M = W/g$. If distances are also expressed in feet, then the units entering into moment
of inertia of mass are

$$\frac{\text{lb.}}{\text{ft./sec.}^2} \times \text{ft.}^2 = \text{lb.} \times \text{sec.}^2 \times \text{ft.}$$

In engineering the generally accepted term for W/g, or mass, is the *slug*. The unit of moment of inertia of mass is therefore slugs times feet squared or slug-ft.[2] and will so be used in this text.

Art. 59. Moment of Inertia of Mass by Integration. The algebraic expressions for the moments of inertia of some of the more frequently occurring forms of rotating mass will now be determined by means of calculus. In setting up the required integral, the differential element may be selected in various ways. Either cartesian or polar coordinates may be used, and single, double, or triple integration may result, depending on how the element is selected. The element should be selected in accordance with one of the following rules:

1. All points in the element should be equally distant from the reference axis; otherwise the distance ρ would be indefinite. Since these distances are squared, the average distance cannot be used.

2. The element is of such form and so located that its moment of inertia with respect to the reference axis is already known. The moment of inertia of the mass is then obtained by summing up the moments of inertia of all elements.

Example 1

Derive the expressions for the moment of inertia of a right prism having any shape cross section with respect to any axis perpendicular to the bases.

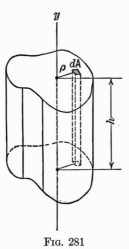

FIG. 281

Solution: The right prism of altitude h is shown in Fig. 281. The y axis is perpendicular to the bases. A differential area dA is extended from the upper to the lower base, thus forming the differential volume $dV = h \cdot dA$. The element of mass is then $\gamma \, dV = \gamma h \, dA$ and conforms to the first rule in Art. 59.

$$I_y = \int \rho^2 \, dM = \int \rho^2 \gamma h \, dA = \gamma h \int \rho^2 \, dA$$

The quantity $\int \rho^2 \, dA$ is the polar moment of inertia J of the base with respect to the y axis; hence

$$I_y = \gamma h J$$

This result holds for any right prism, and from it may be derived the expressions for any special case.

Case 1. Right circular cylinder with respect to geometric axis. Here the base of the prism is a circle of radius r whose polar moment of inertia about the axis through its center is $J = \pi r^4/2$. Hence

$$I_y = \gamma h \frac{\pi r^4}{2} = \frac{1}{2} r^2 (\gamma \pi r^2 h) = \frac{1}{2} M r^2$$

$$k_y = \sqrt{\frac{I_y}{M}} = \sqrt{\frac{1}{2} r^2} = \frac{r}{\sqrt{2}}$$

Case 2. Rectangular prism of sides a, b, and h with respect to a geometric axis parallel to side h. Here the base is a rectangle of sides a and b as shown in Fig. 282. For the base

$$J = I_x + I_z = \frac{ab^3}{12} + \frac{ba^3}{12} = \frac{ab}{12} (b^2 + a^2)$$

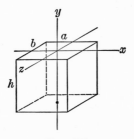

FIG. 282

For the mass

$$I_y = \gamma h J = \frac{\gamma h a b}{12} (b^2 + a^2) = \frac{1}{12} (a^2 + b^2)(\gamma a b h) = \frac{1}{12} M (a^2 + b^2)$$

$$k_y = \sqrt{\frac{I_y}{M}} = \sqrt{\frac{a^2 + b^2}{12}}$$

Example 2

Derive the expression for the moment of inertia and radius of gyration of a sphere with respect to a geometric axis.

Solution: A sphere of radius r is shown in Fig. 283, the y axis being a geometric axis. It is convenient in this example to make use of the second rule in selecting the differential element. The element is accordingly taken as a circular plate of radius x and thickness dy. From Ex. 1 the moment of inertia of the element is

$$dI_y = \frac{1}{2} dM \cdot x^2 = \frac{1}{2} \gamma \pi x^2 \, dy \cdot x^2$$

The moment of inertia of the sphere is the sum of the moments of inertia of the elements.

$$I_y = \int dI_y = \frac{1}{2} \gamma \pi \int x^4 \, dy$$

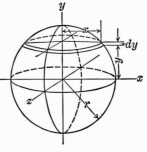

FIG. 283

Since

$$x^2 = r^2 - y^2$$

$$I_y = \frac{1}{2}\gamma\pi\int_{-r}^{+r}(r^2 - y^2)^2\,dy$$

$$I_y = \gamma\pi\int_0^r(r^4 - 2r^2y^2 + y^4)\,dy$$

$$= \frac{8}{15}\gamma\pi r^5$$

Since

$$M = \frac{4}{3}\gamma\pi r^3$$

$$I_y = \frac{2}{5}Mr^2$$

$$k_y = \sqrt{\frac{I_y}{M}} = r\sqrt{0.4}$$

Example 3

Derive the expressions for the moment of inertia and radius of gyration of a slender rod with respect to an axis normal to the rod through one end.

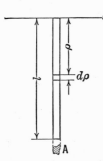

FIG. 284

Solution: A rod of length l and cross-sectional area A is shown in Fig. 284. The x axis is normal to the rod through the upper end. The mass of the differential element shown is $dM = \gamma\,dV = \gamma A\,d\rho$. It will be seen that all points in the element are not equally distant from the axis. If ρ is the distance of the center of the element from the x axis, then the distance of other points is slightly greater, particularly in elements lying near the axis. Thus the moment of inertia obtained by use of the element shown will be less than the true moment of inertia. The error involved decreases as the ratio of the length of the rod to the dimensions of the cross section increases. For a circular cylinder whose length is 10 times the diameter the error is $\frac{3}{16}$ per cent.

$$I_x = \int \rho^2\,dM = \gamma A\int_0^l \rho^2\,d\rho = \frac{\gamma A l^3}{3}$$

Since

$$M = \gamma A l$$

$$I_x = \tfrac{1}{3}Ml^2$$

$$k_x = \sqrt{\frac{I}{M}} = \frac{l}{\sqrt{3}}$$

Problems

1. Derive the expression for the moment of inertia of a right circular cone of altitude h and radius of base r with respect to its geometric axis. *Ans.* $\frac{3}{10}Mr^2$.

2. Derive the expression for the moment of inertia of a slender rod with respect to a centroidal axis normal to its length. *Ans.* $\frac{1}{12}Ml^2$.

3. Derive the expression for the moment of inertia of a slender rod with respect to an axis through one end of the rod and at angle θ with its length.
Ans. $\frac{1}{3}Ml^2 \sin^2 \theta$.

4. Derive the expression for the moment of inertia of a thin circular disk of radius r with respect to a centroidal diameter. *Ans.* $\frac{1}{4}Mr^2$.

5. Derive the expression for the moment of inertia of a hollow right circular cylinder of outside radius r_1 and inside radius r_2 with respect to its geometric axis.
Ans. $\frac{1}{2}M(r_1^2 + r_2^2)$.

Art. 60. Relation between Moments of Inertia of Mass with Respect to Parallel Axes. It is often necessary to determine the moment of inertia of a mass with respect to some axis other than that for which the moment of inertia is already known. If the two axes are parallel and one is centroidal, a simple relation may be derived making it possible to transfer the moment of inertia from one axis to the other.

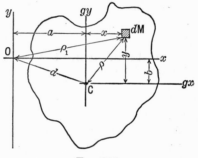

Fig. 285 represents a section through a body perpendicular to an axis through the center of

FIG. 285

gravity C. A parallel axis at distance d from the centroidal axis passes through O. Let dM be any element of mass at distances ρ_1 from O and ρ from C. By definition

$$I_O = \int \rho_1{}^2 \, dM$$

From the figure

$$\rho_1{}^2 = (x + a)^2 + (y - b)^2$$

$$= x^2 + 2ax + a^2 + y^2 - 2by + b^2$$

$$= (x^2 + y^2) + (a^2 + b^2) + 2ax - 2by$$

$$= \rho^2 + d^2 + 2ax - 2by$$

$$I_O = \int (\rho^2 + d^2 + 2ax - 2by) \, dM$$

$$= \int \rho^2\, dM + d^2 \int dM + 2a \int x\, dM - 2b \int y\, dM$$

$$= I_C + Md^2 + 2aM\bar{x} - 2bM\bar{y}$$

Since axes gx and gy are centroidal, $\bar{x} = 0$ and $\bar{y} = 0$. Thus

$$I_O = I_C + Md^2$$

It is evident from this result that the moment of inertia of a mass with respect to any axis is equal to the moment of inertia with respect to a parallel centroidal axis plus the product of the mass and the square of the distance between the two axes. This statement is known as the *transfer formula* or *parallel-axis theorem for masses.*

It will be noted from the above statement that the moment of inertia of a mass will always be less about a centroidal axis than about any other parallel axis. *It should also be noted that one of the two axes involved in the equation must be centroidal.* If it is desired to transfer the moment of inertia of a mass from one axis to another when neither axis is centroidal, the operation may be accomplished in two steps, the moment of inertia about the centroidal axis being an intermediate result.

Example

Derive the expression for the moment of inertia of a right circular cylinder of altitude h and radius of base r with respect to a diameter of the base.

Solution: The differential element is a circular disk of radius r and thickness dy as shown in Fig. 286. From Prob. 4, Art. 59, the moment of inertia of the disk about its centroidal axis gx is

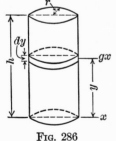

FIG. 286

$$dI_{gx} = \frac{1}{4}\, dMr^2$$

By the transfer formula the moment of inertia of the disk with respect to the parallel x axis is

$$dI_x = \frac{1}{4}\, dMr^2 + y^2\, dM$$

The moment of inertia of the cylinder with respect to the x axis is

$$I_x = \int dI_x = \frac{1}{4} r^2 \int dM + \int y^2\, dM$$

$$= \frac{1}{4} r^2 \int_0^h \gamma\pi r^2\, dy + \int_0^h y^2 \cdot \gamma\pi r^2\, dy$$

$$= M \left(\frac{r^2}{4} + \frac{h^2}{3} \right)$$

Problems

1. From the result of the preceding example determine, without further integration, the moment of inertia of the cylinder with respect to a centroidal axis parallel to the base.   *Ans.* $\frac{1}{4}M(r^2 + \frac{1}{3}h^2)$.

2. From the result of Ex. 2, Art. 59, determine, without further integration, the moment of inertia of a sphere with respect to a tangent.   *Ans.* $\frac{7}{5}Mr^2$.

3. From the result of Ex. 1, Art. 59, determine, without further integration, the moment of inertia of a right circular cylinder with respect to an element of the curved surface.   *Ans.* $\frac{3}{2}Mr^2$.

Art. 61. Computation of Moment of Inertia of Simple and Composite Masses.

As stated in Art. 58, the numerical value of the moment of inertia of a mass will be computed in terms of engineering units. All distances must therefore be expressed in feet, and the mass in slugs is obtained by dividing weight in pounds by $g = 32.2$ ft. per sec.^{2}

The moment of inertia of a composite mass about a given axis may be obtained by adding the moments of inertia of its component parts with respect to the same axis. The transfer formula should be used when needed.

Example

Determine the moment of inertia of a 6-in. diameter cast-iron governor ball with respect to an axis 8 in. from its center. Cast iron weighs 450 lb. per cu. ft.

Solution: The weight of the ball is

$$W = \tfrac{4}{3}\pi(\tfrac{3}{12})^3 \times 450 = 29.4 \text{ lb.}$$

Then

$$M = \frac{W}{g} = \frac{29.4}{32.2} = 0.915 \text{ slug}$$

By the transfer formula

$$I_O = I_C + Md^2$$

$$= \frac{2}{5}Mr^2 + Md^2 = \frac{2}{5} \times .915 \times (\tfrac{3}{12})^2 + .915 \times (\tfrac{8}{12})^2$$

$$= 0.43 \text{ slug-ft.}^2$$

Problems

(In the following problems use 450 lb. per cu. ft. as the specific weight of cast iron and 490 lb. per cu. ft. as the specific weight of steel.)

1. Compute the moment of inertia and radius of gyration of a cast-iron cylinder 2 ft. in diameter and 1 ft. long with respect to its geometric axis.   *Ans.* 22 slug-ft.^{2}; 0.707 ft.

2. Compute the moment of inertia and radius of gyration of a steel sphere 6 in. in diameter with respect to its geometric axis.   *Ans.* 0.0249 slug-ft.^{2}; 0.158 ft.

3. Compute the moment of inertia and radius of gyration of a steel rod 2 in. in diameter and 4 ft. long with respect to an axis through one end normal to the rod.
Ans. 7.08 slug-ft.^{2}; 2.31 ft.

4. A slender rod 6 ft. long and weighing 50 lb. is mounted on an axle normal to the rod and 1 ft. from an end. Compute the moment of inertia.
Ans. 10.9 slug-ft.^{2}

5. Compute the moment of inertia of a cast-iron cylinder 3 ft. in diameter and weighing 100 lb. with respect to an element of its curved surface.
Ans. 10.5 slug-ft.^{2}

6. Determine the moment of inertia of the cylinder in Prob. 5 with respect to a diameter of the base.   *Ans.* 1.75 slug-ft.^{2}

Supplementary Problems

1. Compute the moment of inertia of a hollow steel cylinder 12 in. in outside diameter, 6 in. in inside diameter, and 2 ft. long, with respect to its geometric axis.
Ans. 2.8 slug-ft.^{2}

2. Compute the moment of inertia of the hollow cylinder described in Prob. 1 with respect to an element of the inside curved surface.   *Ans.* 3.92 slug-ft.^{2}

3. A cast-iron governor ball 3 in. in diameter is attached to a steel rod 9 in. long and 1 in. in diameter. The system rotates about a vertical axis at an angle of 30° with the rod. Compute the moment of inertia with respect to the axis of rotation.   *Ans.* 0.0255 slug-ft.^{2}

4. A sector of 60°, cut out of a circular disk, is shown in Fig. 287. The weight of the sector is 30 lb. Compute its moment of inertia with respect to an axis through *O* perpendicular to the plane of the figure.   *Ans.* 0.207 slug-ft.^{2}

Fig. 287

5. Determine by the method of the example of Art. 60 the moment of inertia of a right circular cone with respect to an axis through the vertex parallel to the base.   *Ans.* $\frac{3}{5}M(\frac{1}{4}r^2 + h^2)$.

6. From the result of Prob. 5 determine, without further integration, the moment of inertia of the cone with respect to a diameter of the base.
Ans. $\frac{3}{10}M(\frac{1}{2}r^2 + \frac{1}{3}h^2)$.

7. The bases of a conical steel frustum of 8-in. altitude are 12 in. and 6 in. in diameter. A concentric hole of 4-in. diameter extends from base to base. Compute the moment of inertia of the hollow frustum with respect to its geometric axis.
Ans. 0.373 slug-ft.^{2}

8. A hemispherical cast-iron bowl of 12-in. outside radius and 10-in. inside radius rotates about its geometric axis. Compute the moment of inertia.
Ans. 7.0 slug-ft.^{2}

9. A cast-iron flywheel with solid web has dimensions as shown in Fig. 288. Compute its moment of inertia with respect to the axis of rotation.

Ans. 20.6 slug-ft.^{2}

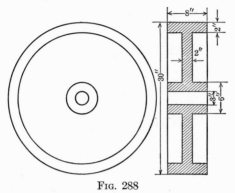

FIG. 288

10. Determine by integration the moment of inertia of the torus in Fig. 289 with respect to the x axis. *Ans.* $I = M(\frac{3}{4}r^2 + R^2)$.

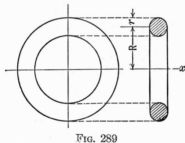

FIG. 289

PART II—KINETICS

CHAPTER X

RECTILINEAR MOTION

Art. 62. Fundamental and Derived Quantities; Dimensional Equations. A physical quantity which cannot be defined in terms of other physical quantities is called a *fundamental* quantity. In mechanics, time, space, and either force or mass are the fundamental quantities. A system of units based on time, space, and mass as fundamental quantities is known as an *absolute* system; one based on time, space, and force as fundamental quantities is known as a *gravitational* system. In either system any quantity not fundamental may be defined in terms of the fundamental quantities and is known as a *derived* quantity.

The dimensions of a physical quantity are determined by the fundamental quantities involved and the degree to which they occur. Thus velocity, which is expressed as distance per unit of time, as shown later, has the dimensions L/T or LT^{-1}, where L denotes length, and T denotes time. Moment of inertia of area has the dimensions L^4. Moment of inertia of mass has dimensions ML^2 when the absolute system is used. If each term of an equation involving physical quantities is replaced by its dimensions, the resulting equation is called a dimensional equation. Any algebraic equation involving physical quantities must be homogeneous; that is, each term must be of the same dimensions. This principle is of value in checking the correctness of equations and also in determining the units in which a result is expressed.

In subsequent articles the dimensions of each unit as defined or derived will be given in terms of mass, length, and time (M, L, T). The symbol $\approx$ will be used to denote dimensional equality. Thus,

$$I = Mk^2 \approx ML^2$$

Art. 63. Displacement. The motion of a body is *rectilinear* when it is confined to a straight-line path. The distance of the moving body from a given point of reference in the path is called the *displace-*

150

ment. Displacement may be measured in any units of length, the foot being the most common unit in kinetics.

Displacement is a vector quantity, having direction as well as magnitude, and may be represented graphically by a vector. Thus displacements may be combined to obtain a resultant displacement or may be resolved into components.

Art. 64. Velocity. *Velocity* is the time rate of change of displacement. If velocity is represented by v, displacement by s, and time by t, then

$$v = \frac{ds}{dt}$$

When velocity is constant, the above relation becomes

$$v = \frac{s}{t} \approx LT^{-1}$$

Velocity may be expressed in terms of any units of length and time, feet per second and miles per hour being the more common units. The abbreviation *ft. per sec.* or *f.p.s.* is used for *feet per second.*

Velocity, being a vector quantity, may be represented graphically by a vector. In common with other vector quantities, velocities may be combined into a resultant or resolved into components. *Speed* is a scalar quantity, representing only the magnitude of a velocity without involving any particular sense of direction.

Problems

1. A car has a velocity of 30 mi. per hr. What is its velocity in feet per second?
$Ans.$ 44 f.p.s.

2. The displacement of a ball thrown vertically upward with initial velocity of 50 ft. per sec. is given by the equation $s = 50t - 16.1t^2$, where s is in feet and t is in seconds. Derive the equation for the velocity, and determine the velocity at the end of 2 sec. $Ans.$ 14.4 f.p.s. downward.

3. If the motion of a body is described by the equation $s = \frac{1}{2} \sin 2\pi t$, determine the velocity at the end of (*a*) 1 sec.; (*b*) 2.25 sec. $Ans.$ 3.14 f.p.s.; zero.

4. A bullet traveling with a constant velocity of 1000 ft. per sec. strikes a target. The sound of striking returns to the point of firing in 0.8 sec. after firing. If the velocity of sound is 1120 ft. per sec., how far away was the target? $Ans.$ 423 ft.

Art. 65. Acceleration. *Acceleration* is the time rate of change of velocity. If acceleration is denoted by a, then

$$a = \frac{dv}{dt} = \frac{d^2s}{dt^2} \approx LT^{-2}$$

If the acceleration is constant, this relation becomes

$$a = \frac{v - v_0}{t}$$

where v = final velocity, and v_0 = initial velocity. Acceleration may be expressed in terms of any units of velocity and time. The unit most commonly employed in kinetics is the foot per second per second, written *ft. per sec. per sec.*, *ft. per sec.*^{2}, or f.p.s.^{2}

If dt is eliminated from the equations $v = ds/dt$ and $a = dv/dt$, the resulting relation is

$$v \, dv = a \, ds$$

This equation is of particular importance in problems involving variable acceleration. When the acceleration a is expressed in terms of displacement s, the above equation can be integrated.

Acceleration has direction as well as magnitude and is therefore a vector quantity. Like other vector quantities, accelerations may be represented graphically by vectors and may be combined or resolved.

Problems

1. An automobile attains a velocity of 30 mi. per hr. from a standing start in 8 sec. Determine its average acceleration in feet per second per second.
Ans. 5.5 f.p.s.^{2}

2. A train decreases its speed from 40 mi. per hr. to 25 mi. per hr. in 10 sec. Compute the average acceleration. *Ans.* −2.2 f.p.s.^{2}

3. For the motion described in Prob. 3, Art. 64, determine the acceleration at the end of (*a*) 1 sec.; (*b*) 2.25 sec. *Ans.* zero; 19.75 f.p.s.^{2}

4. The acceleration of a moving body is $a = 0.4s$. If the initial velocity was 2 ft. per sec., determine the velocity after moving 5 ft. (Note that the acceleration is variable.) *Ans.* 3.74 f.p.s.

Art. 66. Uniformly Accelerated Motion. If a body has constant acceleration, the average velocity may be expressed as

$$v_{\text{av.}} = \tfrac{1}{2}(v + v_0)$$

and its displacement may be expressed as

$$s = v_{\text{av.}} \times t = \tfrac{1}{2}(v + v_0)t \tag{1}$$

Also, from Art. 65,

$$a = \frac{v - v_0}{t} \quad \text{or} \quad v = v_0 + at \tag{2}$$

If v is eliminated from equations (1) and (2), the following relation is obtained

$$s = v_0 t + \tfrac{1}{2}at^2 \tag{3}$$

If t is eliminated from equations (1) and (2), the following relation is obtained

$$v^2 = v_0^2 + 2as \tag{4}$$

Equations (1) to (4) are known as the equations of uniformly accelerated rectilinear motion. By their use any problem involving this type of motion may be solved. These equations may also be obtained by means of calculus from the definitions of velocity and acceleration, $v = ds/dt$ and $a = dv/dt$.

Example

Two cars, A and B, accelerate from a standing start. The acceleration of A is 4 ft. per sec.^{2}, and that of B is 5 ft. per sec.^{2} If B was originally 20 ft. behind A, how long will it take B to overtake A?

Solution: Let t represent the time for each car, and x the distance traveled by A. Then the distance traveled by B will be $x + 20$. Writing the equation

$$s = v_0 t + \tfrac{1}{2}at^2$$

for each car, the resulting equations are:

For A
$$x = 0 + \tfrac{1}{2}(4)t^2$$

For B
$$x + 20 = 0 + \tfrac{1}{2}(5)t^2$$

Simultaneous solution of these equations gives

$$x = 80 \text{ ft. and } t = 6.32 \text{ sec.}$$

Problems

1. Derive equations (2), (3), and (4) of Art. 66 by calculus, starting with the definitions of velocity and acceleration, $v = ds/dt$ and $a = dv/dt$.

2. An automobile is brought to rest from a velocity of 45 mi. per hr. in a distance of 200 ft. Determine the average acceleration and the time to come to rest.
Ans. -10.9 f.p.s.^{2}; 6.06 sec.

3. A car with initial velocity of 15 mi. per hr. is accelerated at the rate of 2 ft. per sec.^{2} Determine the velocity acquired and the distance traveled in 5 sec.
Ans. 32 f.p.s.; 135 ft.

4. Two elevators in adjacent shafts approach each other, one from the top, the other from the bottom. Each starts at the same instant from rest 400 ft. apart. The top car has downward acceleration of 2 ft. per sec.^{2} The other has upward acceleration of 1 ft. per sec.^{2} When and where do they pass?
Ans. 16.3 sec.; 133 ft. from the bottom.

5. Solve Prob. 4, if the lower car starts 2 sec. after the upper one.

Ans. 17 sec.; 112 ft. from bottom.

6. Two cars moving in the same direction are 500 ft. apart when the car in front has a velocity of 10 ft. per sec. and an acceleration of 4 ft. per sec.[2] The other car has a velocity of 100 ft. per sec. and is being decelerated at 2 ft. per sec.[2] Where do they pass? Explain the answers.

Ans. 181.5 ft. in front of the initial position of the front car.

Art. 67. Motion of a Freely Falling Body.

The attraction exerted by the earth on material bodies varies, being dependent on latitude and elevation above sea level. Since, as will be shown later, acceleration is proportional to force, the acceleration of gravity varies from place to place. This variation is so slight that, for relatively small distances from the earth's surface, it may be neglected in treating the motion of falling bodies, and the acceleration of gravity may be considered as constant. If the acceleration of gravity is represented by g and vertical displacement by h, the equations of Art. 66 become:

$$h = \tfrac{1}{2}(v + v_0)t \tag{1}$$

$$v = v_0 + gt \tag{2}$$

$$h = v_0 t + \tfrac{1}{2}gt^2 \tag{3}$$

$$v^2 = v_0{}^2 + 2gh \tag{4}$$

These are known as the equations of a freely falling body. In this book the value of g will be taken as 32.2 ft. per sec.[2]

Example

A ball is dropped from rest at the top of a tower 200 ft. high. Two seconds later a second ball is thrown vertically upward from the ground with initial velocity of 100 ft. per sec. At what distance above the ground will they pass?

Solution: Let y represent the distance above the ground where the balls meet, t the time for the first ball, and $t - 2$ the time for the second. The equation of motion to be used is

$$h = v_0 t + \tfrac{1}{2}gt^2$$

Taking downward as the positive direction for the first ball, the equation becomes

$$200 - y = 0 + \tfrac{1}{2}(+32.2)t^2 \tag{1}$$

Taking upward as the positive direction for the second ball, the equation becomes

$$y = (+100)(t - 2) + \tfrac{1}{2}(-32.2)(t - 2)^2 \tag{2}$$

Simultaneous solution of equations (1) and (2) gives

$$t = 2.82 \text{ sec.} \quad \text{and} \quad y = 72 \text{ ft.}$$

Problems

1. Solve the example in Art. 67 if the two balls start at the same instant.
Ans. 2 sec.; 136 ft.

2. A body is projected vertically upward with an initial velocity of 200 ft. per sec. To what height will it rise? In what time will it return to the starting position? Determine the velocity and distance above the ground 4 sec. after it starts.
Ans. 621 ft.; 12.4 sec.; 71.2 f.p.s. upward; 542 ft.

3. From the top of a building 50 ft. high a ball is thrown vertically upward with an initial velocity of 20 ft. per sec. How long will it take to strike the ground below? With what velocity will it strike?   *Ans.* 2.49 sec.; 60.3 f.p.s.

4. A ball is projected vertically upward with an initial velocity of 60 ft. per sec. Two seconds later a second ball is projected vertically upward with the same initial velocity. Where and when do they pass?   *Ans.* 2.87 sec.; 39.7 ft.

5. A stone is dropped from a bridge into the water below. If sound has velocity of 1120 ft. per sec. and the sound of the splash is heard on the bridge 3.5 sec. after the stone was released, determine the elevation of the bridge above the water.
Ans. 180 ft.

Art. 68. Force, Mass, and Acceleration.

According to Newton's second law of motion, a body subjected to the action of an unbalanced force will experience an acceleration proportional to the force and inversely proportional to the mass of the body. This relation is expressed by the equation

$$a = \frac{F}{M} \quad \text{or} \quad F = Ma \approx MLT^{-2}$$

In order that F and a in this equation may be expressed in the customary engineering units, pounds and feet per second per second respectively, it is necessary to express the mass M in terms of the *slug*, which consists of g pounds. To avoid a possible confusion of units, it is convenient to eliminate M from the above equation. If the force acting on a body is its own weight W, then the resulting acceleration will be that of gravity g. Hence

$$W = Mg$$

If this equation is divided into the preceding one, the result is

$$\frac{F}{W} = \frac{a}{g} \quad \text{or} \quad F = \frac{Wa}{g}$$

Thus M is replaced by W/g, and the customary engineering units may be used for all quantities involved.

It should be particularly noted that the force F represents the unbalanced or resultant force acting on a body. It is often called the *effective* force, since it is that force which is effective in producing acceleration. Since the effective force for a body is the resultant of all the effective forces acting on the individual particles of mass composing the body, it must act through the center of gravity of the body.

Example

A 50-lb. horizontal force is applied to a 60-lb. block, Fig. 290, on a 30° incline for which the coefficient of friction is 0.1. Determine the resulting acceleration of the block.

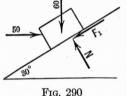

Solution: By summation of forces in the direction normal to the plane

$$N = 60 \cos 30° + 50 \sin 30° = 77 \text{ lb.}$$

then

$$F_1 = fN = 0.1 \times 77 = 7.7 \text{ lb.}$$

FIG. 290

The unbalanced or effective force parallel to the direction of motion is then

$$F = 50 \cos 30° - 7.7 - 60 \sin 30° = 5.6 \text{ lb.}$$

The resulting acceleration is thus

$$a = \frac{Fg}{W} = \frac{5.6 \times 32.2}{60} = 3 \text{ ft. per sec.}^2$$

Problems

1. A train of 20 cars, each weighing 50 tons, is hauled up a 1 per cent grade. Train resistance is 8 lb. per ton. Determine the drawbar pull required to change the velocity from 6 mi. per hr. to 24 mi. per hr. in a distance of 2000 ft.

Ans. 46,000 lb.

2. A block starts from rest and slides down a 30° plane. Compute the velocity at the end of 15 ft. Neglect friction. *Ans.* 22 f.p.s.

3. Solve Prob. 2 when the coefficient of friction is 0.2. *Ans.* 17.8 f.p.s.

4. A 1-ton elevator descending with a velocity of 10 ft. per sec. is brought to rest in a distance of 12 ft. Compute the tension in the supporting cables while the elevator comes to rest. *Ans.* 2260 lb.

5. If the coefficient of friction is 0.3 for the 150-lb. block shown in Fig. 291, determine the acceleration of the system and the tension in the cable.

Ans. T = 26.6 lb.

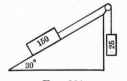

FIG. 291

Art. 69. Reversed Effective Force; D'Alembert's Principle.

Since an acceleration can be produced only by an unbalanced force, it is obvious that the system of forces acting on a body having acceleration is not in equilibrium, and the conditions of static equilibrium $\Sigma F_x = 0$, $\Sigma F_y = 0$, and $\Sigma M = 0$ cannot be applied to the system of actual forces. *However, if a force equal to the effective force Wa/g, but opposite* *in direction and collinear, were added to the actual force system, the resulting system would then be in equilibrium, and the equations of static equilibrium would then apply.* It thus results that, although the forces acting on a body possessing acceleration are not in equilibrium, static conditions may be produced by the addition of an imaginary force Wa/g acting through the center of gravity of the body and parallel but *opposite in direction to the acceleration.* This statement is known as D'Alembert's principle, and the added force is called the *reversed effective* force, the D'Alembert force, or the *inertia* force. The use of this principle is of considerable advantage in the solution of many problems involving force and acceleration.

Example 1

A 4000-lb. car is brought to rest from a speed of 30 mi. per hr. in a distance of 60 ft. by means of brakes. The center of gravity of the car is 2.5 ft. above the ground and midway between front and rear wheels, which are 10 ft. apart, center to center. Determine the normal pressure acting on the front wheels as the car is brought to rest.

Solution: The acceleration of the car is first determined:

$$a = \frac{v^2 - v_0^2}{2s} = \frac{0 - (44)^2}{2 \times 60} = -16.1 \text{ ft. per sec.}^2$$

The reversed effective force is then

$$\frac{Wa}{g} = \frac{4000 \times 16.1}{32.2} = 2000 \text{ lb.}$$

The free-body diagram of the car is shown in Fig. 292 with the addition of the reversed effective force acting through the center of gravity and opposite

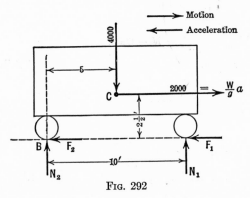

Fig. 292

in direction to the acceleration. The forces F_1 and F_2 represent the frictional forces induced by brake action on front and rear wheels, respectively.

Since static conditions now prevail, the required normal pressure N_1 on the front wheels may be obtained by moments about B:

$$\Sigma M_B = 10N_1 - 4000 \times 5 - 2000 \times 2\tfrac{1}{2} = 0$$

from which

$$N_1 = 2500 \text{ lb.}$$

This result shows that an additional pressure of 500 lb. over static conditions is produced on the front wheels in stopping the car, together with a corresponding reduction in pressure on the rear wheels.

Example 2

A 600-lb. block on a 30° incline is connected to a 150-lb. block hanging vertically by a cable running over a pulley as shown in Fig. 293 (a). The coefficient of friction between block and incline is 0.2. Neglecting the mass of the pulley and its axle friction, determine the acceleration of the system, the cable tension, and the velocity after the block has moved 20 ft. from rest.

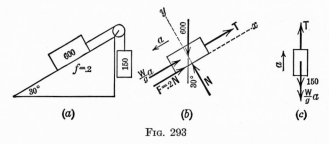

(a) (b) (c)

Fig. 293

Solution: It is seen by inspection that the only possible direction of acceleration for the 600-lb. block is down the incline. The free-body diagrams for the two blocks, including the addition of the reversed effective forces, are shown in Figs. 293 (b) and 293 (c).

In Fig. 293 (b)

$$\Sigma F_y = N - 600 \cos 30° = 0$$

$$N = 520 \text{ lb.,} \quad \text{and therefore} \quad F = 0.2N = 104 \text{ lb.}$$

$$\Sigma F_x = T + \frac{600a}{32.2} + 104 - 600 \sin 30° = 0 \tag{1}$$

In Fig. 293 (c)

$$\Sigma F_v = T - \frac{150a}{32.2} - 150 = 0 \tag{2}$$

By simultaneous solution of (1) and (2)

$$T = 159 \text{ lb.} \quad \text{and} \quad a = 1.98 \text{ ft. per sec.}^2$$

Finally

$$v^2 = v_0{}^2 + 2as = 0 + 2 \times 1.98 \times 20$$

$$v = 8.9 \text{ ft. per sec.}$$

Problems

1. A rectangular block 2 ft. square and 5 ft. long stands on end on the floor of a car with its sides parallel to those of the car. If friction is sufficient to prevent sliding, what acceleration may the car have before the block tips?

Ans. 12.9 ft. per sec.^{2}

2. Assume that the car in Ex. 1 of Art. 69 has brakes applied to the rear wheels only and that the maximum resistance that can be developed because of friction between wheel and road is one-half the corresponding normal pressure. Determine the distance in which the car can be brought to rest from a velocity of 30 mi. per hr., and the normal reaction at front wheels while the car is coming to rest.

Ans. 135 ft.; 2220 lb.

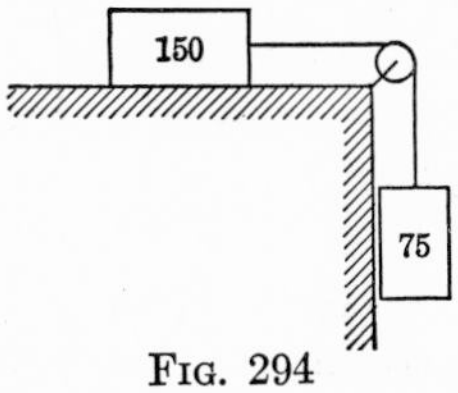

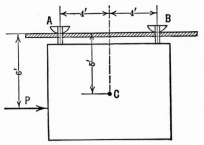

Fig. 294

3. The 150-lb. block of Fig. 294 has an initial velocity of 10 ft. per sec. directed to the left. Determine how far the weight moves before coming to rest. Compute the tension in the cord, using $f = 0.1$. *Ans. s* = 3.88 ft.

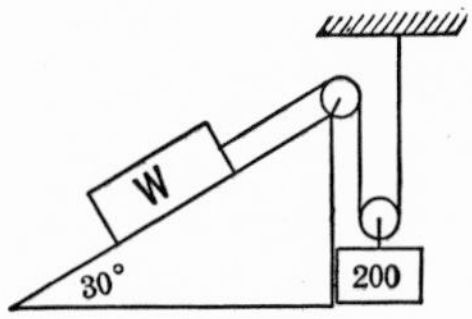

4. After the weight in Prob. 3 comes to rest, it will then move to the right. Determine its velocity and the tension in the cord after it has moved 3.88 ft. *Ans.* $T = 55.0$ lb.

5. If the coefficient of friction on the incline of Fig. 295 is 0.2, determine the weight W required to give the 200-lb. body an upward acceleration of 3 ft. per sec.^{2}

Ans. 775 lb.

Fig. 295

Supplementary Problems

1. A mine cage is rising with uniform velocity of 10 ft. per sec. When it is 200 ft. below the surface, a rock is released from rest at the top of the shaft. At what distance from the surface does the rock strike the cage? *Ans.* 168 ft.

2. Solve Prob. 1 if the cage is descending with the same velocity. *Ans.* 239 ft.

3. Two cars A and B have velocity of 60 mi. per hr. in the same direction. Car A is 250 ft. behind car B when brakes are applied to B, causing it to decelerate at the rate of 10 ft. per sec.^{2} In what time will A overtake B, and how far will each have traveled? *Ans.* 7.07 sec.; 622 ft.; 372 ft.

4. A freight car with velocity of 6 mi. per hr. is switched to a 1 per cent upgrade. If car resistance is 4 lb. per ton, how far up the grade will the car go?

Ans. 100 ft.

5. A door is hung on a track as shown in Fig. 296. The door weighs 400 lb. with its center of gravity at C. The coefficient of friction for each of the shoes A and B and the track is $\frac{1}{4}$. If the force P applied to the door is 200 lb., determine the resulting acceleration and the normal pressures at A and B.

Ans. a = 8.05 f.p.s.^{2}

6. Solve Prob. 5 if the shoe at A is replaced by a wheel which rolls freely without resistance. *Ans.* $B = 151$ lb.

Fig. 296

7. The two weights shown in Fig. 297 are released from rest. Neglecting mass of pulley and cord, compute the tension T in the cable supporting the pulley.

Ans. 106.6 lb.

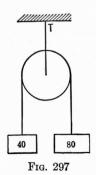

FIG. 297

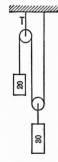

FIG. 298

8. If the weights shown in Fig. 298 are released from rest, determine the value of tension T. *Ans.* 32.8 lb.

9. The velocity of a block sliding down a 30° incline increases from 10 ft. per sec. to 20 ft. per sec. in 12 ft. Determine the value of the coefficient of friction.

Ans. 0.129.

10. A car weighing 2000 lb. is pulled by a horizontal force of 300 lb. applied 2 ft. above the track. The center of gravity of the car is 3 ft. above the track and midway between front and rear wheels, which are 10 ft. apart, center to center. Frictional resistance acting at the track on each set of wheels is one-tenth the corresponding normal pressure. Compute the acceleration of the car and the normal pressure on the front wheels. *Ans.* $N_F = 1030$ lb.

11. If the coefficient of friction under the 60-lb. block in Fig. 299 is 0.1, solve for the acceleration and the tension in the cord. *Ans.* $T = 38.1$ lb.

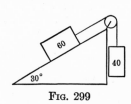

FIG. 299

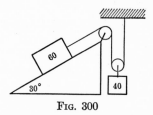

FIG. 300

12. Solve Prob. 11 if the blocks are connected as shown in Fig. 300.

Ans. $T = 20.7$ lb.

13. Determine the value of weight W in Fig. 301 which is necessary to give the two bodies on the plane an acceleration of 10 ft. per sec.² up the plane. Use $f = 0.2$. Solve for all tensions.

Ans. $W = 195$ lb.

14. The center of gravity of a 3000-lb. car is 2 ft. above the ground and midway between the front and rear wheels, which are 10 ft. apart. While the car is traveling at 60 mi. per hr., brakes are set on the rear wheels inducing a resistance at the pavement equal to

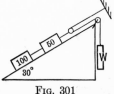

FIG. 301

the normal forces on the wheels. Compute the distance in which the car will come to rest.   *Ans.* 289 ft.

15. Two freight cars A and B, coupled together with B behind A, are coasting down a 2 per cent grade. Car A weighs 20 tons and B weighs 30 tons. Train resistance is 8 lb. per ton. When the velocity of the cars is 30 mi. per hr., brakes are set on car A, inducing an additional resistance of 200 lb. per ton. Determine the distance the cars move in coming to rest and the compression in the coupler.

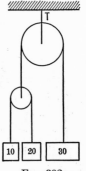

Ans. 1250 ft.; 2400 lb.

16. A train of 20 cars weighing 50 tons each reaches a 1 per cent up-grade 1 mile long with a velocity of 45 mi. per hr. If the drawbar pull is 12,000 lb. and train resistance is 6 lb. per ton, with what velocity will the train reach the top of the grade?   *Ans.* 30.2 m.p.h.

17. If the train of Prob. 16 travels on level track after reaching the top of the grade and the drawbar pull remains unchanged, in what distance will it regain its original velocity of 45 mi. per hr.?   *Ans.* 2.33 mi.

Fig. 302

18. The system of weights in Fig. 302 is released from rest. Neglecting mass of cords and pulleys, determine the tension T, supporting the system, and the velocity of each weight 2 sec. later.

Ans. $T = 56.4$ lb.; $v_{30} = 3.79$ f.p.s.

CHAPTER XI

CURVILINEAR MOTION AND ROTATION

Art. 70. Velocity and Acceleration in Curvilinear Motion. If a particle moves in a curved path, its motion is said to be *curvilinear*. Only plane curvilinear motion will be discussed in this book.

The velocity of a body moving along a curved path changes in direction from point to point and may also change in magnitude. At any given point the velocity is in the direction of the tangent to the curve at that point. In Fig. 303 (*a*), *ABCD* represents a curved

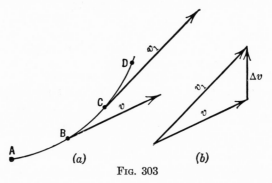

(a) (b)

FIG. 303

path; *B* and *C* are any two points in the path at which the velocities of the moving particle are v and v_1, respectively, tangent to the curve at these points. The change in velocity that has taken place in going from *B* to *C* is shown by the vector Δv in Fig. 303 (*b*).

Since the velocity in curvilinear motion necessarily changes in direction and may also change in magnitude, it follows that there is always acceleration. If the time required to travel from *B* to *C* in Fig. 303 (*a*) is denoted by Δt, then the ratio of the total change of velocity Δv to the time Δt gives the average acceleration between *B* and *C*. The limiting value of the ratio $\Delta v/\Delta t$ as Δt approaches zero becomes the instantaneous value of the acceleration.

Art. 71. Normal and Tangential Components of Acceleration. It is evident from the preceding discussion that the direction of the acceleration is usually not in the direction of the velocity of the particle. For convenience the total acceleration will be resolved into two com-

162

ponents, a_t and a_n. The component a_t, taken in the direction of the velocity, is tangent to the path of travel and is called the *tangential acceleration*. The component a_n, taken in a direction perpendicular to the velocity, is called the *normal acceleration*.

In Fig. 304 (a), B and C are consecutive points in the path at a differential distance ds apart. The time from B to C, also differential, is denoted by dt. The total change in velocity is the vector $FE = \Delta v$, shown in Fig. 304 (b). The total acceleration is the limiting value of the ratio $\Delta v / \Delta t$ as Δt approaches zero.

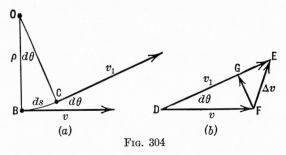

(a)   (b)

FIG. 304

In Fig. 304 (b) the velocity change Δv is resolved into its tangential component GE, parallel to the velocity at C, and its normal component GF, normal to the velocity at C. The tangential acceleration is then

$$a_t = \frac{GE}{dt} = \frac{v_1 - v \cos d\theta}{dt}$$

The limiting value of $\cos d\theta$, as $d\theta$ approaches zero, is unity. Also, as $d\theta$ approaches zero, the difference $v_1 - v$ becomes dv. Hence,

$$a_t = \frac{dv}{dt}$$

The tangential acceleration is thus the time rate of change of the magnitude of the velocity. If the velocity of a particle having curvilinear motion is constant in magnitude, the tangential acceleration will be zero.

From Fig. 304 (b), the normal acceleration is

$$a_n = \frac{GF}{dt} = \frac{v \sin d\theta}{dt} = \frac{v \, d\theta}{dt}$$

From Fig. 304 (a), $d\theta = ds/\rho$. Also, by definition, $ds/dt = v$. Therefore

$$a_n = \frac{v \, d\theta}{dt} = \frac{v \, ds}{\rho \, dt} = \frac{v^2}{\rho}$$

If the radius of curvature is constant, the normal acceleration may be written

$$a_n = \frac{v^2}{r}$$

It is apparent from these results that there will always be normal acceleration as long as the direction of velocity changes and that its direction is toward the center of curvature.

It has previously been shown (Art. 68) that the effective force acting on a body moving with acceleration is $Ma = \dfrac{Wa}{g}$. For a body having curvilinear motion there must be a tangential effective force

$$F_t = \frac{W}{g}\, a_t = \frac{W}{g}\frac{dv}{dt}$$

and a normal effective force

$$F_n = \frac{W}{g}\, a_n = \frac{W}{g}\frac{v^2}{\rho}$$

In the solution of problems involving forces acting on a body moving with curvilinear motion, the D'Alembert principle (Art. 69) may be used. This consists of adding the effective forces, reversed in direction, to the free body and then applying the conditions of static equilibrium. The normal reversed effective force, directed away from the center of curvature, is commonly called *centrifugal* force.

Art. 72. Conical Pendulum. The conical pendulum consists of a small body suspended by a cord from a support and rotating about a vertical axis through the support, as shown in Fig. 305 (a). The

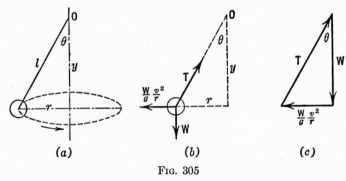

(a)   (b)   (c)

Fig. 305

free body is acted upon by the tension T in the cord and its weight W. To these is added the normal reversed effective force Wv^2/gr, directed away from the center, as shown in Fig. 305 (b). If the speed of rotation is constant, the tangential acceleration and the tangential reversed effective force are zero. If the speed of rotation is variable, the tangential reversed effective force to be added is normal to the plane of the forces shown and so does not affect the solution.

From the triangle of forces, Fig. 305 (c),

$$\tan \theta = \frac{Wv^2/gr}{W} = \frac{v^2}{gr}$$

The velocity v is obtained by writing the equation of moments with respect to point O,

$$Wr = \frac{Wv^2}{gr} \cdot y$$

$$v = r\sqrt{\frac{g}{y}}$$

The time t for one complete revolution about the axis is

$$t = \frac{s}{v} = \frac{2\pi r}{r\sqrt{\dfrac{g}{y}}} = 2\pi\sqrt{\frac{y}{g}}$$

The number of revolutions per second is

$$n = \frac{1}{t} = \frac{1}{2\pi}\sqrt{\frac{g}{y}}$$

From this relation $y = g/4\pi^2 n^2$, showing that the height y of the conical pendulum is independent of its length l and depends only on its speed of rotation.

Example

A 10-lb. weight at the end of a 20-in. cord is rotated about a vertical axis at such speed that it makes an angle of 30° with the axis. Determine the linear velocity, the tension in the cord, and the time for 1 revolution.

Solution: From the triangle of forces, Fig. 305 (c),

$$T = \frac{W}{\cos \theta} = \frac{10}{\cos 30°} = 11.5 \text{ lb.}$$

From the relation $v = r\sqrt{\dfrac{g}{y}}$,

$$v = \frac{20}{12}\sin 30° \sqrt{\frac{32.2}{\frac{20}{12}\cos 30°}} = 3.93 \text{ ft. per sec.}$$

From the relation $t = 2\pi\sqrt{\dfrac{y}{g}}$,

$$t = 2\pi\sqrt{\frac{\frac{20}{12}\cos 30°}{32.2}} = 1.33 \text{ sec.}$$

Problems

1. A conical pendulum of 10-ft. length rotates at 75° about a vertical axis. Determine its linear velocity.   *Ans.* 34 f.p.s.

2. If the conical pendulum of Prob. 1 has a linear velocity of 30 ft. per sec., determine the angle from the vertical at which it rotates.   *Ans.* 71.3°.

3. An airplane weighing 40,000 lb. is making a banked turn at an angle of 30° with the horizontal. Determine the lift force of the wing and the radius of curvature of the turn when the speed of the plane is 150 mi. per hr.

Ans. $L = 46,200$ lb.; $r = 2600$ ft.

Art. 73. Superelevation of Curved Roadways and Tracks. It is a matter of common experience that a vehicle traveling around a curve tends to skid toward the outside of the curve and to overturn. The relations between the forces acting will now be considered. In Fig. 306 is shown the free-body diagram of a car rounding a curve whose surface is horizontal and whose center is to the left. The forces consist of the weight W of the car, the normal pressures N_1 and N_2 on inner and outer wheels, the corresponding frictional forces F_1 and F_2 tending to prevent skidding outward, and the normal reversed effective force Wv^2/gr acting horizontally through the center of gravity C. If F represents the resultant of F_1 and F_2, N the resultant of N_1 and N_2, and f the coefficient of friction, then

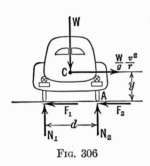

Fig. 306

$$F = F_1 + F_2 \quad \text{and} \quad N = N_1 + N_2 = W$$

$$F = fN = fW$$

By summation of forces horizontally

$$\frac{Wv^2}{gr} - fW = 0$$

$$v^2 = fgr \quad \text{and} \quad v = \sqrt{fgr}$$

This equation gives the maximum velocity with which the car may round the curve without skidding.

If the friction is sufficient to prevent skidding, it is still possible for the car to overturn. In Fig. 306, N_1 and F_1 are zero when tipping of the car impends. The equation of moments with respect to point A then gives

$$W \cdot \frac{d}{2} - \frac{Wv^2}{gr} \cdot y = 0$$

$$v = \sqrt{\frac{dgr}{2y}}$$

This equation gives the maximum velocity with which the car can round the curve without overturning.

In either of the preceding cases a higher velocity is made possible by superelevating or banking the curve. This procedure consists of sloping the surface so that the outer edge of the curve is above the level of the inner edge. In Fig. 307 (a), θ is the angle of superelevation

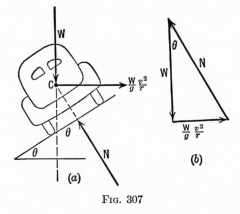

FIG. 307

required so that there will be zero side thrust on the wheels of the car for the velocity v. From the triangle of forces, Fig. 307 (b),

$$\tan \theta = \frac{v^2}{gr}$$

At velocities lower than v the car tends to slide down the slope, and a side thrust on the wheels results in the direction toward the outside. At velocities higher than v the car tends to slide outward, and a side thrust results in a direction toward the inside.

The maximum velocity with which the car can round the banked curve without skidding will now be determined. In Fig. 308 (a) the resultant of the normal and frictional forces is represented by R, in-

clined to the normal at the limiting angle of static friction $\phi = \tan^{-1} f$.
From the force triangle shown in Fig. 308 (b)

$$\tan (\theta + \phi) = \frac{v^2}{gr}$$

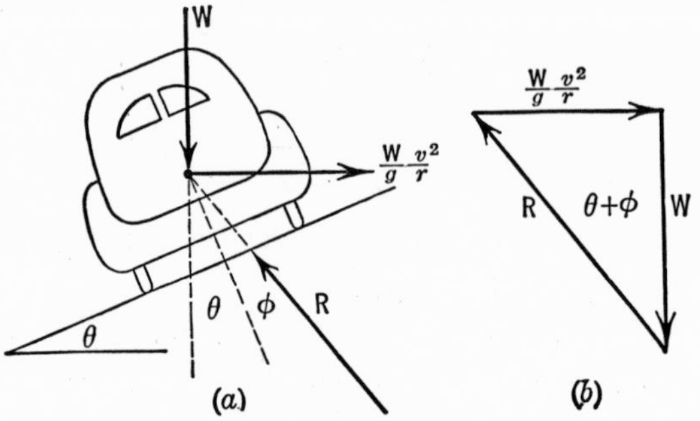

Fig. 308

The preceding method of analysis may also be applied to the super-elevation of railroad curves. In this application the side thrust is the pressure exerted by the rails on the flanges of the wheels.

Example 1

Determine the angle of superelevation for a highway curve of 600-ft. radius so that there will be no side thrust for a speed of 45 mi. per hr. At what speed will skidding impend if the coefficient of friction is 0.3?

Solution: For zero side thrust

$$\theta = \tan^{-1} \frac{v^2}{gr} = \tan^{-1} \frac{(66)^2}{32.2 \times 600} = 12.7°$$

The angle of friction is

$$\phi = \tan^{-1} 0.3 = 16.7°$$

When skidding impends,

$$\tan (\theta + \phi) = \frac{v^2}{gr}$$

$$\tan (12.7° + 16.7°) = \frac{v^2}{32.2 \times 600}$$

$$v = 104 \text{ ft. per sec.} = 71.2 \text{ mi. per hr.}$$

Example 2

Determine the superelevation of the outer rail of a track of 4.9-ft. gage (distance center to center of rails) on a curve of 3000-ft. radius so that there will be no flange pressure at a speed of 30 mi. per hr. If a 60,000-lb. car has a velocity of 45 mi. per hr. on the curve, what is the flange pressure?

Solution: The tangent of the required angle of superelevation is

$$\tan \theta = \frac{v^2}{gr} = \frac{(44)^2}{32.2 \times 3000} = 0.02$$

The amount of superelevation of the outer rail is

$$e = 4.9 \sin \theta = 4.9 \times 0.02 = 0.098 \text{ ft.} = 1.18 \text{ in.}$$

From the free-body diagram in Fig. 309,

$$\Sigma F_x = P + W \sin \theta - \frac{Wv^2}{gr} \cos \theta = 0$$

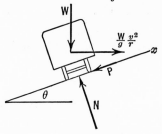

FIG. 309

Since angle θ is very small, $\sin \theta = \tan \theta = 0.02$ and $\cos \theta = 1$. The above equation then becomes

$$P + 60,000 \times 0.02 - \frac{60,000 \times (66)^2}{32.2 \times 3000} \times 1 = 0$$

$$P = 1500 \text{ lb.}$$

Problems

1. Compute the superelevation of the outer rail of a railroad track of 30,000-ft. radius for zero flange force for a velocity of 120 mi. per hr. The distance between rails is 4.9 ft.   *Ans.* 1.88 in.

2. A curve of 800-ft. radius is banked for zero side thrust at 60 mi. per hr.; compute the side thrust when a 2500-lb. car is traveling 80 mi. per hr. on this curve.   *Ans.* 556 lb.

3. If the coefficient of friction for the car of Prob. 2 is 1.0, at what speed will skidding impend?   *Ans.* 149 m.p.h.

4. Determine the maximum speed with which a car may round a flat curve of 500-ft. radius without skidding if the coefficient of friction is 0.6.   *Ans.* 67.0 m.p.h.

5. If the car of Prob. 4 has a tread of 60 in. and the center of gravity is 24 in. above the ground, determine the velocity at which tipping will impend.   *Ans.* 96.6 m.p.h.

6. Compute the flange pressure on the wheels of a 60-ton car with velocity of 45 mi. per hr. on a 4° curve superelevated for velocity of 30 mi. per hr. (A 4° curve is one in which a chord 100 ft. long subtends an angle of 4° at the center.)   *Ans.* 6300 lb.

7. Solve Prob. 6 if the velocity of the car is 15 mi. per hr.   *Ans.* −3780 lb.

Art. 74. Simple Pendulum. An ideal simple pendulum consists of a particle suspended by a weightless cord and vibrating in a vertical arc under the influence of gravity and the tension in the supporting cord. These ideal conditions are closely approximated by suspending a small, heavy body at the end of a light cord. Such an arrangement is shown in Fig. 310 (*a*), in which *B* represents any position in the arc of travel *ACD*. The free-body diagram of the body in this position is shown in Fig. 310 (*b*). The system of forces consists of the weight of the body and the cord tension, to which have been added the tangential and normal reversed effective forces. Since the tangential acceleration is always directed along the path toward *C*, the tangential reversed effective force will be directed away from *C*. The tension in the cord is determined by summation of forces in the normal direction.

$$T = W \cos \theta + \frac{Wv^2}{gl} \quad [r = l]$$

By summation of forces in the tangential direction

$$\frac{Wa_t}{g} = W \sin \theta$$

$$a_t = g \sin \theta \text{ directed toward } C$$

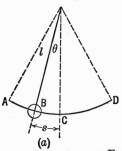

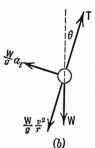

(*a*)   (*b*)

FIG. 310

From Art. 65, $v \, dv = a \, ds = -g \sin \theta \, ds$. If the motion of the pendulum is restricted to small angles, $\sin \theta$ may be replaced by θ

$$v \, dv = -g\theta \, ds = -\frac{gs}{l} \, ds$$

If displacement *s* is measured from *C* and the above equation is integrated between *C* and *B*,

$$\int_{v_c}^{v} v \, dv = -\frac{g}{l} \int_{0}^{s} s \, ds$$

$$v_C{}^2 - v^2 = \frac{g}{l} s^2$$

When the position A is reached, $v = 0$ and $s = s_A$

$$v_C{}^2 = \frac{g}{l} s_A{}^2$$

By substituting this value of v_C in the preceding equation,

$$v = \sqrt{\frac{g}{l}} \cdot \sqrt{s_A{}^2 - s^2}$$

By definition

$$v = \frac{ds}{dt}$$

$$dt = \sqrt{\frac{l}{g}} \cdot \frac{ds}{\sqrt{s_A{}^2 - s^2}}$$

If time is measured from position C, and the above equation integrated between B and C,

$$\int_0^t dt = \sqrt{\frac{l}{g}} \int_0^s \frac{ds}{\sqrt{s_A{}^2 - s^2}}$$

$$t = \sqrt{\frac{l}{g}} \sin^{-1} \frac{s}{s_A}$$

To determine the time from C to A, let $s = s_A$.   Then

$$t_A = \frac{\pi}{2} \sqrt{\frac{l}{g}}$$

The *period* T, or time required for a complete oscillation from A to D and back to A again, is obviously four times as great.   Hence

$$\boldsymbol{T = 2\pi \sqrt{\frac{l}{g}}}$$

The maximum displacement from the center of the path is known as the *amplitude*. The preceding result shows that for small amplitudes the period of vibration is independent of the amplitude, depending only on the length of the pendulum.

Problems

1. Determine the length of a simple pendulum which will make one complete vibration in 1 sec.   *Ans.* 0.815 ft.

2. Determine the period of a simple pendulum whose length is 30 in.
                                    Ans. 1.75 sec.

Art. 75. Motion of a Body in a Vertical Curved Path; Friction Neglected. In Fig. 311 (a) is shown a vertical frictionless curve AB, along which a body of weight W is moving under the influence of gravity and the normal reaction. The vertical distance of A above B is denoted by h. C is any position on the path at vertical distance y from A. The free-body diagram of the moving body at C is shown

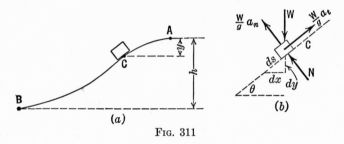

FIG. 311

in Fig. 311 (b). The normal and tangential reversed effective forces have been added. The summation of forces in the tangential direction gives

$$\frac{Wa_t}{g} = W \sin \theta \quad \text{or} \quad a_t = g \sin \theta$$

$$v \, dv = a \, ds = g \sin \theta \, ds$$

Since ds represents a differential displacement along the curve, it may be resolved into components dx and dy as shown. Then

$$\sin \theta \cdot ds = dy$$

and

$$v \, dv = g \, dy$$

This differential equation is now integrated between A and B,

$$\int_{v_A}^{v_B} v \, dv = \int_0^h g \, dy$$

$$v_B{}^2 = v_A{}^2 + 2gh$$

This equation is identical in form to the equation (4) of a freely falling body as given in Art. 67. The change in speed of a body moving along a vertical frictionless curve is therefore the same as if it fell freely through the same vertical distance.

Example

A body of weight W is attached to a slender rod whose weight is negligible. The rod is attached at its other end to a horizontal axle. If the rod and weight are held in a vertical position above the axle, as shown in Fig. 312 (a), and then released and allowed to rotate under the influence of gravity, for what position will there be no stress in the rod?

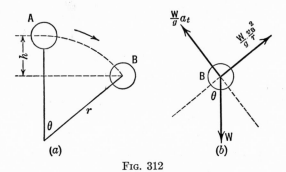

(a)   (b)

FIG. 312

Solution: The free-body diagram, including reversed effective forces, is shown in Fig. 312 (b). A summation of forces in the normal direction gives

$$\frac{W v_B{}^2}{gr} = W \cos \theta$$

$$v_B{}^2 = gr \cos \theta$$

From the equation of velocity in a vertical curve

$$v_B{}^2 = v_A{}^2 + 2gh = 0 + 2g(r - r \cos \theta)$$

If the above equations are combined,

$$gr \cos \theta = 2g(r - r \cos \theta)$$

$$\cos \theta = 2 - 2 \cos \theta$$

$$\cos \theta = \tfrac{2}{3}$$

$$\theta = 48.2°$$

Problems

1. A 10-lb. body is rotating in a vertical circle at the end of a cord 6 ft. long. Solve for the tension in the cord when the velocity at the top of the path is 20 ft. per sec.   *Ans.* 10.7 lb.

2. Compute the minimum velocity that the body in Prob. 1 must have to remain in the vertical circle.   *Ans.* 13.9 f.p.s.

3. Starting from rest at the top of the incline, a man and bicycle weighing 200 lb. move down the incline and around the loop-the-loop shown in Fig. 313. Solve for the normal force of the track on the bicycle at B.   *Ans.* 143 lb.

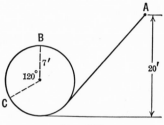

FIG. 313

4. Solve Prob. 3 when the bicycle is at C.   *Ans.* 1040 lb.
5. An airplane enters a loop of 500-ft. radius. The speed of the airplane is 150 mi. per hr. as it enters the loop. Solve for the force of the seat against the pilot if he weighs 135 lb.   *Ans.* 541 lb.

Art. 76. Motion of Projectiles; Air Resistance Neglected. The motion of a projectile is actually influenced not only by gravity but also by such other factors as air friction, wind, and rotation of the projectile due to rifling of the barrel. Air friction, in turn, depends on the velocity of the projectile, its size, and its shape. A general solution may be made by neglecting all influences except gravity; this is equivalent to considering the projectile as moving without rotation in a vacuum. The general solution may then be modified to account for any of the other influences affecting the motion.

The general solution is conveniently made by treating independently the vertical and horizontal components of the motion. In Fig. 314

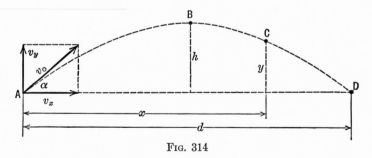

FIG. 314

is shown the path or trajectory of a projectile which starts from point A with initial velocity v_0 at angle α with the horizontal. The initial velocity v_0 is shown resolved into its vertical and horizontal components $v_y = v_0 \sin \alpha$, and $v_x = v_0 \cos \alpha$. Since no horizontal force is acting, the horizontal component of the velocity remains constant. The vertical motion is affected only by gravity and therefore is the same as that of a freely falling body. Thus for any point C in the path,

$$x = v_x t = v_0 t \cos \alpha$$

$$y = v_y t - \tfrac{1}{2} g t^2 = v_0 t \sin \alpha - \tfrac{1}{2} g t^2$$

If the time t is eliminated from these equations, the equation of the trajectory or path is obtained.

$$y = x \tan \alpha - \frac{g x^2}{2 v_0{}^2 \cos^2 \alpha}$$

This will be seen to be the equation of a parabola with vertical axis.

For the point D in the trajectory, $x = d$ and $y = 0$. If these values are substituted in the above equation of the trajectory, the horizontal range d of the projectile is obtained.

$$d = \frac{2 v_0{}^2 \cos^2 \alpha \tan \alpha}{g} = \frac{v_0{}^2 \sin 2\alpha}{g}$$

The maximum height h to which the projectile rises is obtained from the equation $v^2 = v_0{}^2 + 2gh$ for a freely falling body. Since, at the top of the path, the vertical component of the velocity is zero, $v = 0$, and

$$h = \frac{v_0{}^2 \sin^2 \alpha}{2g}$$

By considering separately the vertical and horizontal components of the motion, many projectile problems may be solved without use of the special formulas developed in this article.

Example

A projectile has an initial velocity of 1500 ft. per sec. at an angle of 30° above the horizontal. Determine (a) the maximum height; (b) the horizontal distance traveled in reaching a target at 2000-ft. height; (c) the magnitude and inclination of the velocity on striking the target; (d) the equation of the trajectory.

Solution: In the trajectory shown in Fig. 315, A is the starting point, B is the point of maximum height, and C is the target. The initial velocity at A is resolved into vertical and horizontal components, v_y and v_x.

$$v_y = 1500 \sin 30° = 750 \text{ ft. per sec.}$$

$$v_x = 1500 \cos 30° = 1300 \text{ ft. per sec.}$$

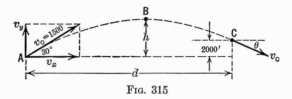

FIG. 315

a. Maximum Height. The maximum height h at B is computed from the equation of a freely falling body, $v^2 = v_0^2 + 2gh$. Since the vertical component of the velocity at B is zero, the equation becomes

$$0 = (750)^2 + 2(-32.2)h$$

$$h = 8740 \text{ ft.}$$

b. Range. To determine the range d, the time, t_{AC}, from A to C is first computed from the equation of a freely falling body, $s = v_0 t + \frac{1}{2}gt^2$. In this case $s = 2000$ ft. and the equation becomes

$$2000 = 750 t_{AC} + \frac{1}{2}(-32.2)t^2_{AC}$$

$$t_{AC} = 43.7 \text{ sec.}$$

Since the horizontal component of the initial velocity remains constant,

$$d = v_x \cdot t_{AC} = 1300 \times 43.7 = 56,800 \text{ ft.}$$

c. Velocity at C. The magnitude of the velocity at C may be obtained from the equation of velocity in a vertical curved path, Art. 75.

$$v_C^2 = v_A^2 + 2gh = (1500)^2 + 2(-32.2)(2000)$$

$$v_C = 1460 \text{ ft. per sec.}$$

Since the horizontal component of the velocity at C is the same as that at A, the angle of inclination may be found as follows:

$$\theta = \cos^{-1}\frac{v_x}{v_C} = \cos^{-1}\frac{1300}{1460} = 27°$$

d. Equation of the Trajectory. If x and y are coordinates of any point in the path and t is the time required to travel from A to this point, then

$$x = v_x t = 1300t$$

$$y = v_y t + \frac{1}{2}gt^2 = 750t + \frac{1}{2}(-32.2)t^2$$

By the elimination of t from these two equations, the equation of the trajectory is found to be

$$y = 0.577x - 0.00000953x^2$$

Problems

1. An airplane drops a bomb from a height of 10,000 ft. while traveling at 100 mi. per hr. How far in front of the point of release will the bomb strike?
Ans. 3660 ft.

2. Determine the theoretical angle at which a projectile should be fired to obtain maximum range.   *Ans.* 45°.

3. A block starts from rest at the top of a 30° plane 16 ft. long. How far out from the foot of the incline will it strike the ground 20 ft. below? Neglect friction.
Ans. 16.1 ft.

4. Solve Prob. 3 if the coefficient of friction between the block and plane is 0.2.
Ans. 13.7 ft.

5 At what angle must a ball with an initial velocity of 50 ft. per sec. be thrown from a point 5 ft. above the ground to strike an object 11.7 ft. above the ground and 15 ft. away?   *Ans.* 30°.

6. A ball is thrown from a tower 200 ft. high with an initial velocity of 100 ft. per sec. at an angle of 45° above the horizontal. When and where will it strike the ground?   *Ans.* 6.34 sec.; 448 ft.

Art. 77.   Rotation.   Motion of *rotation* is a special case of plane curvilinear motion in which the particle moves in a path of constant radius. A line through the center of the path and normal to its plane is called the axis of rotation.

The angle through which the radius vector to the particle moves as the particle changes position is called the *angular displacement.* It may be measured in any convenient angular units, such as degrees, revolutions, or radians. It is usually necessary to express the angular displacement in radians, however, when its relation to other quantities is involved. Since an angle may be expressed as the ratio of one distance to another (arc/radius), angular displacement has no dimensions. In Fig. 316, in rotating from A to B, the angular displacement of the particle is θ radians. The linear distance traveled along the arc is s. The relation between the linear and angular distances traveled is expressed by

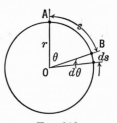

Fig. 316

$$s = r \cdot \theta$$

Angular velocity is defined as the time rate of change of angular displacement. If the angular velocity, denoted by ω, is variable, its instantaneous value is

$$\omega = \frac{d\theta}{dt} \approx T^{-1}$$

If the angular velocity is constant, then

$$\omega = \frac{\theta}{t}$$

The more common units of angular velocity are revolutions per minute (r.p.m.) and radians per second. It is usually necessary to express angular velocity in radians per second if its relation to other quantities is involved.

The relation of angular velocity to the corresponding linear velocity tangent to the path is obtained from the equation $s = r\theta$ by differentiation.

$$\frac{ds}{dt} = r\frac{d\theta}{dt}$$

$$v = r\omega$$

Since angular velocity involves both magnitude and direction, it is a vector quantity and, as such, is subject to the processes and laws governing other vector quantities. The vector representing angular velocity is parallel to the axis of rotation.

Angular acceleration is defined as the time rate of change of angular velocity. If the angular acceleration, denoted by α, is variable, its instantaneous value is

$$\alpha = \frac{d\omega}{dt} = \frac{d^2\theta}{dt^2} \approx T^{-2}$$

If the angular acceleration is constant, then

$$\alpha = \frac{\omega - \omega_0}{t}$$

Angular acceleration is usually expressed in radians per second per second (rad. per sec.²), although other units, such as revolutions per minute per second, are sometimes used. Since angular acceleration involves both magnitude and direction, it is a vector quantity and, like angular velocity, is represented by a vector parallel to the axis of rotation.

By differentiation of the equation $v = r\omega$, the relation between tangential and angular acceleration is obtained.

$$\frac{dv}{dt} = r\frac{d\omega}{dt}$$

$$a_t = r\alpha$$

From Art. 71, $a_n = v^2/r$. Since $v = r\omega$,

$$a_n = r\omega^2$$

If dt is eliminated from the equations $\omega = d\theta/dt$ and $\alpha = d\omega/dt$, the following relation results:

$$\omega\,d\omega = \alpha\,d\theta$$

This equation may be integrated if α can be expressed in terms of θ. It is therefore useful in determining the change in angular velocity in certain problems involving variable angular acceleration.

Problems

1. Make the following conversions: (a) 5 revolutions to radians; (b) 240° to radians; (c) 10 radians to revolutions; (d) $\frac{1}{3}\pi$ radians to degrees.

Ans. (a) 10π rad.; (b) $4\pi/3 = 4.19$ rad.; (c) 1.59 rev.; (d) 60°.

2. Make the following conversions: (a) 60 r.p.m. to radians per second; (b) 4.5 rad. per sec. to revolutions per minute.

Ans. (a) $2\pi = 6.28$ rad. per sec.; (b) 43.0 r.p.m.

3. A wheel 3 ft. in diameter rotates at 120 r.p.m. Determine the tangential linear velocity of a point on the rim.   Ans. 18.8 f.p.s.

4. If the speed of rotation of the wheel in Prob. 3 is increased at a uniform rate to 240 r.p.m. in 10 sec., compute: (a) the angular acceleration; (b) the tangential acceleration of a point on the rim; (c) the normal acceleration of a point on the rim for 240 r.p.m.   Ans. (a) 1.26 rad. per sec.²; (b) 1.88 f.p.s.²; (c) 948 f.p.s.²

5. Two pulleys of 12-in. and 30-in. diameters, respectively, are connected by a belt. If the linear velocity of a point on the belt is 15 ft. per sec. and the belt does not slip, determine: (a) the angular velocity of each pulley; (b) the normal acceleration of a point on the rim of each pulley.

Ans. (a) 30 rad. per sec.; 12 rad. per sec.; (b) 450 f.p.s.²; 180 f.p.s.²

6. A slender rod of length $l = 3$ ft., Fig. 317, is mounted on a horizontal axis of rotation through one end. The rod is released from rest in a vertical position above the axis and allowed to rotate under the influence of gravity alone. It may be shown (Art. 87) that its angular acceleration for any angle θ is given by the expression, $\alpha = (3g/2l)\sin\theta$. Determine the angular velocity when $\theta = 180°$. (Note that the angular acceleration is variable.)

Ans. 8.02 rad. per sec.

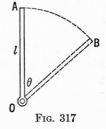

FIG. 317

Art. 78. Uniformly Accelerated Rotational Motion.

It was shown in Art. 77 that, when angular acceleration is constant or uniform,

$$\alpha = \frac{\omega - \omega_0}{t} \qquad\qquad (1)$$

Under the same conditions the average angular velocity may be expressed as

$$\omega_{av.} = \tfrac{1}{2}(\omega + \omega_0)$$

The angular displacement will then be

$$\theta = \omega_{av.}t = \tfrac{1}{2}(\omega + \omega_0)t \qquad (2)$$

If t is eliminated from equations (1) and (2), the following relation is obtained:

$$\omega^2 = \omega_0^2 + 2a\theta \qquad (3)$$

If ω is eliminated from equations (1) and (2), the resulting relation is

$$\theta = \omega_0 t + \tfrac{1}{2}at^2 \qquad (4)$$

Equations (1) to (4) are known as the equations of uniformly accelerated rotational motion. They are analogous to the equations of uniformly accelerated rectilinear motion as stated in Art. 66.

Problems

1. Derive equations (1), (3), and (4) of Art. 78 by integration of the equations $\omega = d\theta/dt$, and $\alpha = d\omega/dt$.

2. Derive equations (1) to (4) of Art. 78 from the corresponding equations of Art. 66 by use of the relations $s = r\theta$, $v = r\omega$, and $a_t = r\alpha$.

3. A flywheel is brought from rest up to a speed of 1200 r.p.m. in 3 min. with uniform acceleration. Determine the angular acceleration and the number of revolutions made in coming up to speed. *Ans.* 0.698 rad. per sec.²; 1800 rev.

4. A shaft has an initial angular velocity of 30 r.p.m. and is accelerated uniformly at the rate of 2 rev. per min. per sec. Determine the angular velocity at the end of 30 sec. and the number of revolutions made in this time.

Ans. 90 r.p.m.; 30 rev.

5. A flywheel rotating at 300 r.p.m. makes 60 revolutions in coming to rest. Determine the angular acceleration and the time to come to rest.

Ans. 1.31 rad. per sec.²; 24 sec.

Art. 79. Simple Harmonic Motion; Auxiliary Circle Method. Motion of a particle in a straight-line path with an acceleration which is proportional to the displacement from some fixed point in the path and oppositely directed is called *simple harmonic motion.* The motion is defined mathematically by the equation

$$a = -ks$$

where s denotes the displacement, k is the constant of proportionality, and the negative sign indicates that acceleration and displacement are opposite in direction. This type of motion is involved in the vibration of elastic bodies.

The development of the equations and the solution of problems in simple harmonic motion are most conveniently accomplished by the use of the auxiliary circle. This method depends on the fact that, if a point moves with constant speed in a circular path, its projection on the diameter of the circle moves with simple harmonic motion, as will now be shown. In Fig. 318, the point P moves with uniform angular velocity ω in a circular path of radius r. Its projection P' on the diameter moves back and forth across the diameter AOB. If displacements are measured from the axis Oy, the angular displacement of P is θ and the linear displacement of P' is s. Since $\theta = \omega t$,

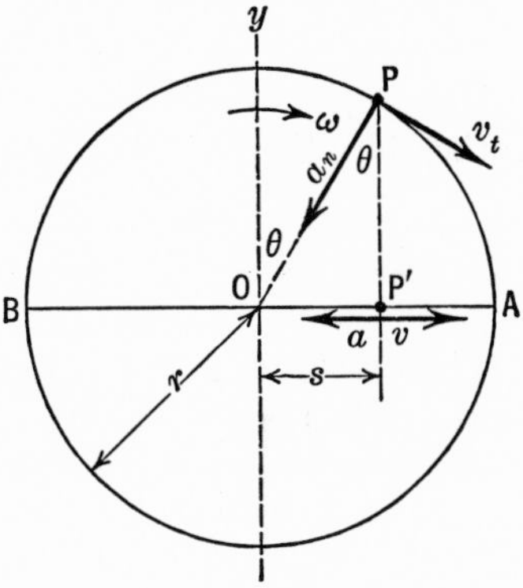

FIG. 318

$$s = r \sin \theta = r \sin \omega t$$

The linear velocity of P is tangent to the circular path and is given by

$$v_t = r\omega$$

The linear velocity of P' is

$$v = \frac{ds}{dt} = r\omega \cos \omega t$$

This will be seen from Fig. 319 (a) to be the projection of v_t upon the diameter. The linear acceleration of P is normal to the circular path and is given by

$$a_n = r\omega^2$$

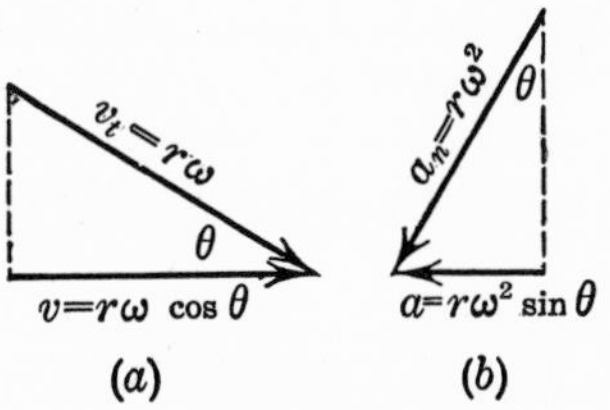

The acceleration of P' is

(a)   (b)

FIG. 319

$$a = \frac{dv}{dt} = -r\omega^2 \sin \omega t$$

This is seen from Fig. 319 (b) to be the projection of a_n upon the diameter. Since $r \sin \omega t = s$,

$$a = -\omega^2 s$$

Since ω is constant, this equation conforms to the original mathematical definition, and the motion of P' is thus shown to be simple harmonic.

From the equation $s = r \sin \omega t$, the time t to travel from O to P' is

$$t = \frac{1}{\omega} \sin^{-1} \frac{s}{r}$$

The *period* T is the time required for one complete oscillation of P'. This is obviously the same as the time required for one revolution of P. Hence

$$T = \frac{2\pi}{\omega}$$

The *frequency* n is the number of complete oscillations in 1 sec. and is therefore the reciprocal of the period.

$$n = \frac{\omega}{2\pi} = \frac{1}{T}$$

The *amplitude* is one-half the length of the path and is thus equal to the radius of the auxiliary circle.

Although simple harmonic motion is actually a rectilinear motion and might logically be treated under that heading in Chap. X, the use of the auxiliary circle and the equations of rotation simplify the treatment to such an extent as to justify its consideration as a topic in curvilinear motion.

Example 1

A particle oscillates with simple harmonic motion for which the amplitude is 3 in. and the period is $\frac{1}{3}$ sec. Determine the velocity and acceleration of the particle when its displacement from the center of the path is 1 in. Determine the time since it was at the center.

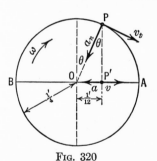

Fig. 320

Solution: The auxiliary circle with radius of 3 in. $= \frac{1}{4}$ ft. is shown in Fig. 320. P' represents the oscillating particle at 1 in. $= \frac{1}{12}$ ft. from the center O, and P is the corresponding point on the circle. The angular velocity of P is

$$\omega = \frac{2\pi}{T} = \frac{2\pi}{\frac{1}{3}} = 6\pi \text{ rad. per sec.}$$

The tangential linear velocity of P is

$$v_t = r\omega = \frac{1}{4} \times 6\pi = 4.71 \text{ ft. per sec.}$$

and its linear acceleration in the normal direction is

$$a_n = r\omega^2 = \frac{1}{4} \times (6\pi)^2 = 88.8 \text{ ft. per sec.}^2$$

The angular displacement θ is

$$\theta = \sin^{-1} \frac{\frac{1}{12}}{\frac{1}{4}} = \sin^{-1} \frac{1}{3} = 19.5°$$

The velocity and acceleration of P' are now obtained by projecting v_t and a_n upon the diameter

$$v = v_t \cos \theta = 4.71 \cos 19.5° = 4.44 \text{ ft. per sec.}$$

$$a = a_n \sin \theta = 88.8 \sin 19.5° = 29.6 \text{ ft. per sec.}^2$$

The time from O to P' is the same as that required for rotation of P through angle θ. Hence

$$t = \frac{\theta}{\omega} = \frac{19.5 \times \pi/180}{6\pi} = 0.018 \text{ sec.}$$

Example 2

A 30-lb. weight suspended from a spring whose scale is 20 lb. per in. is set into vibration. Determine the period of vibration.

Solution: Since the force required to deflect a spring (within its elastic limit) is proportional to the displacement, and since the acceleration is proportional to the force, it follows that the acceleration of the vibrating weight will be proportional to its displacement and the motion is simple harmonic.

Let O, Fig. 321, represent the equilibrium position of the suspended weight. If the spring is now deflected downward any distance r inches, the force required will be $20r$ pounds. When this force is removed, the weight will be set into vibration. At the instant of release, the weight is acted upon by an unbalanced force of $20r$ pounds and will thus have an instantaneous acceleration

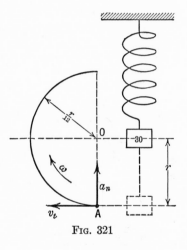

$$a = \frac{Fg}{W} = \frac{20rg}{30} \text{ ft. per sec.}^2$$

Fig. 321

This acceleration corresponds to the acceleration a_n as shown on the auxiliary circle. Since $a_n = r\omega^2$,

$$\omega^2 = \frac{a_n}{r} = \frac{20rg/30}{r/12} = 8g = 258$$

$$\omega = \sqrt{258} = 16.1 \text{ rad. per sec.}$$

$$T = \frac{2\pi}{\omega} = \frac{2\pi}{16.1} = 0.39 \text{ sec.}$$

Problems

1. The amplitude of a simple harmonic motion is 2 ft., and the period is 1 sec. Compute the maximum velocity and the maximum acceleration.
Ans. $v = 12.6$ f.p.s.

2. The amplitude of a simple harmonic motion is 10 in. and the period is 0.5 sec. Determine the position of the moving particle, its velocity, and its acceleration 0.2 sec. after leaving the end of the path.
Ans. 18.1 in. from end; 6.15 f.p.s.; 106 f.p.s.²

3. A 100-lb. weight is suspended from a spring whose scale is 50 lb. per in. and then caused to oscillate. Determine the period of oscillation. *Ans.* 0.452 sec.

4. What weight, suspended from a spring whose scale is 60 lb. per in., will oscillate with a period of 1 sec.?
Ans. 588 lb.

5. The drive wheels of a locomotive are 4 ft. in diameter and the crank radius is 1 ft. If the speed of the locomotive is 60 mi. per hr., determine the maximum velocity and the maximum acceleration of the piston with respect to the cylinder. Assume that the connecting rod is of such length that the motion of the piston may be considered as approximately simple harmonic. *Ans.* $a = 1936$ f.p.s.²

Supplementary Problems

1. At what speed in revolutions per minute will an object placed 3 ft. from the center of a horizontal rotating platform start to slide off if the coefficient of friction is 0.3?
Ans. 17.1 r.p.m.

2. Determine the length l of the arms of the conical pendulum governor shown in Fig. 322 if the angle θ is to be 30° when the speed of rotation is 90 r.p.m. Assume

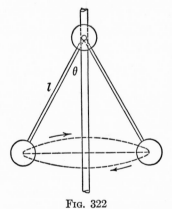

the weight of the arms to be negligible. Compute the tension in each arm if each ball weighs 20 lb.
Ans. 0.419 ft.; 23.1 lb.

3. If the length l of the arms of the governor in Prob. 2 is increased to 2 ft., determine, for the same speed of rotation, the angle θ and the tension in the arms.
Ans. 79.6°; 110 lb.

4. Determine the angle at which a highway curve of 300-ft. radius should be superelevated for a speed of 60 mi. per hr. to prevent skidding if the coefficient of friction is 0.4.
Ans. 16.8°.

5. Compute the lateral pressure on the wheels of a 3000-lb. car with velocity of 45 mi. per hr. on the curve of Prob. 4.
Ans. 425 lb.

Fig. 322

6. What is the maximum speed with which a car can travel around the curve of Prob. 4 without skidding if the surface is wet, reducing the coefficient of friction to 0.3?
Ans. 54.5 m.p.h.

7. A car starts from rest at the top of an incline and must reach the bottom with sufficient velocity to enable it to travel around a vertical loop-the-loop of 16-ft. diameter without falling. Compute the minimum height of the incline, assuming friction to be negligible.
Ans. 20 ft.

8. Compute the maximum diameter of a loop-the-loop around which a car can travel without falling after starting from rest at the top of an incline 30 ft. high. Neglect friction. *Ans.* 24 ft.

9. The airplane shown in Fig. 323 is traveling at 200 mi. per hr. while making a turn. If the weight of the plane is 12,000 lb., compute: (*a*) the lift force; (*b*) the centrifugal force; and (*c*) the radius of curvature. *Ans. r* = 4630 ft.

10. Assume the lift of the plane of Prob. 9 to be 12,000 lb. as it goes into a vertical bank while traveling at 200 mi. per hr. Compute the radius of curvature. *Ans. r* = 2670 ft.

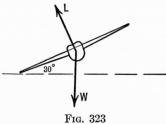

FIG. 323

11. A small block starts from rest at *A* and slides down the frictionless arc *AB* in Fig. 324. Determine the distance *d* and the magnitude and direction of the velocity of striking at *C*. *Ans. d* = 11.6 ft.

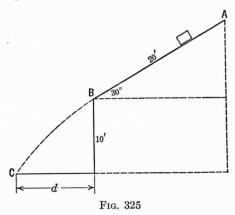

FIG. 324

12. A block with initial velocity of 10 ft. per sec. at *A* slides down the frictionless chute *AB* in Fig. 325. Compute the distance *d*. *Ans. d* = 11.2 ft.

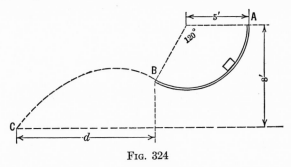

FIG. 325

13. A block starts from rest at the top of a smooth sphere. At what angle from the starting point will it leave the surface of the sphere? *Ans.* 48.2°.

14. A ball thrown horizontally from the top of a building 200 ft. high strikes the ground at 300 ft. away. Compute the velocity with which it was thrown.

Ans. 85.3 f.p.s.

15. The body shown in Fig. 326 starts from rest at A. Compute the value of angle θ when the tension in the cable is 500 lb.   *Ans.* 56.5°.

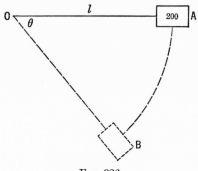

Fig. 326

16. Compute the strength of the cable of Prob. 15 if the cord breaks when angle $\theta = 75°$.   *Ans.* 580 lb.

17. A gun located in a valley fires a projectile with muzzle velocity of 1000 ft. per sec. at 45° with the horizontal. How far away on a plain at 400-ft. elevation above the valley will the projectile strike? To what height does the projectile rise?

Ans. 5.8 mi.; 7760 ft.

18. What should be the angle of firing for a projectile with muzzle velocity of 1200 ft. per sec. to strike a target 6 mi. away on the same level? *Ans.* 22.5°.

19. If the target is 2000 ft. away horizontally and 1000 ft. higher than the gun. determine the angle of elevation necessary when firing a projectile with muzzle velocity of 1500 ft. per sec.   *Ans.* 27.4°.

20. A weight of 50 lb., suspended from a spring, oscillates with a frequency of 3 vibrations per second. Compute the scale of the spring.   *Ans.* 46 lb. per in.

21. A point moves with a simple harmonic motion such that its velocity is 4 ft. per sec. when it is 3 in. from the center of its path, and 3 ft. per sec. when it is 4 in. from the center. Determine the amplitude and period. *Ans.* 5 in.; 0.523 sec.

CHAPTER XII

WORK, ENERGY, AND POWER

Art. 80. Work. When a change in the position of a body is effected in opposition to a resisting force, *work* is done. The measure of the amount of work done by or against a force is the product of the force and the displacement, provided the force is constant and acting in the direction of the displacement.

$$U = \text{work} = F \cdot s \approx ML^2T^{-2}$$

If the force and displacement are not collinear, then work is done by the component of the force in the direction of the displacement. Thus, if the force acts at angle θ with the direction of displacement,

$$U = Fs \cos \theta$$

If the force is variable, the work done during an increment of displacement may be expressed as $F \cdot ds$, and the total work is then obtained by means of an integral:

$$U = \int F \, ds$$

In order to evaluate the integral, the force must be expressed as a function of displacement. Work may be expressed in terms of any units of force and displacement. The most frequently used unit in engineering is the foot-pound (ft-lb.).

Work does not involve a sense of direction and is therefore a scalar quantity. Thus the total work done on a body or system of bodies may be obtained by algebraic addition of the work done by the various forces acting. It is customary to regard the work as positive when the force and displacement are in the same direction, and as negative when the force and displacement are oppositely directed.

Work may be represented graphically by plotting on rectangular axes the values of force and corresponding displacement. Thus in Fig. 327 (a) is shown the work diagram of a force varying inversely as the displacement. Since work is the product of force and displacement, the shaded area represents the amount of work done in a change of displacement from s_1 to s_2. The indicator card of a steam engine, shown in Fig. 327 (b), is another example of graphical representation of work. The shaded area, representing work, is determined by use of a planimeter.

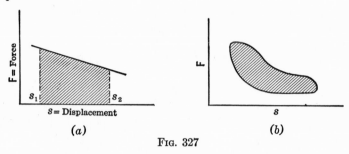

(a)   (b)

Fig. 327

In lowering or raising a body, work is done by or against gravity and is determined by the product of the weight of the body and the vertical distance the body is moved. Thus:

$$U = Wh$$

Sometimes all portions of an object are not moved the same vertical distance, and then the work is determined by summation of the amounts of work done on different parts of the body as follows,

$$U = \int h \cdot dw = W\bar{h}$$

where $\bar{h}$ is the vertical distance through which the center of gravity moves.

Example

A tank of hemispherical shape, 6 ft. in diameter, is full of water. How much work is done in emptying the tank if all the water must be pumped up over the edge of the tank?

Solution: The volume of water is:

$$V = \tfrac{2}{3}\pi r^3 = \tfrac{2}{3}\pi(3)^3 = 56.5 \text{ cu. ft.}$$

The weight of the water is

$$W = 56.5 \times 62.5 = 3530 \text{ lb.}$$

The center of gravity of the hemispherical volume is located at a distance $\bar{h}$ from the top, where

$$\bar{h} = \tfrac{3}{8}r = \tfrac{3}{8} \times 3 = 1.125 \text{ ft.}$$

The work done is thus:

$$U = W\bar{h} = 3530 \times 1.125 = 3970 \text{ ft-lb.}$$

Problems

1. Show that the work done by a constant torque of T foot-pounds which produces an angular displacement θ in radians is $T\theta$ foot-pounds.

2. A 150-ft. length of cable weighing 2 lb. per ft. is suspended from a drum. How much work is done in winding up 135 ft. of the cable on the drum?

Ans. 22,300 ft-lb.

3. The excavation for the basement of a building is 30 ft. long, 20 ft. wide, and 10 ft. deep. The first 4 ft. below the surface consists of gravel weighing 140 lb. per cu. ft.; the last 6 ft. is clay weighing 100 lb. per cu. ft. Compute the work done in lifting the excavated material to the surface.   *Ans.* 3,190,000 ft-lb.

4. A chain 100 ft. long and weighing 4 lb. per ft. passes over a pulley with 80 ft. hanging on one side and 20 ft. on the other. Compute the work done against gravity if the pulley is rotated until 50 ft. of chain hangs on each side.

Ans. 3600 ft-lb.

5. Compute the total work done by a locomotive in pulling a 50-ton car a distance of 2000 ft. up a $\frac{1}{2}$ per cent grade with uniform velocity, if train resistance is 6 lb. per ton.   *Ans.* 1,600,000 ft-lb.

6. Determine the work done in punching a $\frac{9}{16}$-in. diameter hole through a $\frac{3}{8}$-in.-thick steel plate whose ultimate shearing strength is 40,000 lb. per sq. in. Assume that during the punching operation the force exerted by the punch varies as the thickness of material remaining to be punched out.   *Ans.* 414 ft-lb.

7. A belt drives a pulley of 3-ft. diameter. If the tensions on the two sides of the belt are 400 lb. and 200 lb., respectively, determine the work done in 60 revolutions of the pulley.   *Ans.* 113,000 ft-lb.

Art. 81. Energy. *Energy* is the ability to do work and is measured by the amount of work a body is capable of doing in changing from some given condition to some standard condition. Energy is expressed in terms of work units. There are various forms of energy, but those of particular importance in mechanics are *potential* energy, due to position, and *kinetic* energy, due to motion.

A body in a position above some standard reference level is capable of doing work in falling from the higher to the lower position and is therefore said to possess potential energy. If h is the difference in elevation, the potential energy is

$$P.E. = Wh \approx ML^2T^{-2}$$

A body in motion is capable of doing work in coming to rest and is said to possess kinetic energy. Some resultant resisting force $F = Wa/g$ is necessary to bring a body having rectilinear motion to rest. The kinetic energy of the moving body is equal to the work that must be done by this force in bringing the body to rest. Therefore, the kinetic energy of translation is

$$K.E. = U = \int -F \, ds$$

$$= \int -\frac{Wa}{g}\, ds = -\frac{W}{g} \int a\, ds$$

$$= -\frac{W}{g} \int_v^0 v\, dv$$

$$K.E. = \frac{1}{2}\frac{W}{g} v^2 = \frac{1}{2} Mv^2 \approx ML^2T^{-2}$$

Problems

1. A cylindrical tank 6 ft. in diameter and 10 ft. deep is full of water. Determine the potential energy of the water with respect to a surface 12 ft. below the bottom of the tank. *Ans.* 300,000 ft-lb.

2. Compute the kinetic energy of a 2000-lb. car when its velocity is (a) 30 mi. per hr.; (b) 60 mi. per hr. *Ans.* (a) 60,100 ft-lb.

3. Water leaves a nozzle of 2-in. diameter with a velocity of 50 ft. per sec. Determine the kinetic energy of the quantity of water passing through the nozzle in 1 sec. *Ans.* 2650 ft-lb.

4. In firing an 800-lb. projectile with a muzzle velocity of 1200 ft. per sec., a 100,000-lb. gun recoils with an initial velocity of 9.6 ft. per sec. Compute the kinetic energy imparted to the gun and to the projectile by the explosion. *Ans.* 143,000 ft-lb.; 17,900,000 ft-lb.

Art. 82. Work-Energy Relations for Translation; Constant Forces.

A body in motion possesses a certain amount of kinetic energy, depending on its mass and velocity. If any forces act on the body in the direction of motion, positive work will be done, the effect of which will be to accelerate the body, thus increasing the velocity and the kinetic energy. The increase in kinetic energy must equal the positive work done. Similarly, negative work will be done by forces resisting the motion, the effect of which will be to decelerate the body, thus decreasing the velocity and the kinetic energy. The decrease in kinetic energy must equal the negative work done by these forces.

In any operation in which a moving body is acted upon simultaneously by both driving and resisting forces, the relation between the final and initial values of the kinetic energy may be expressed as follows:

Initial *K.E.* + Positive work − Negative work = Final *K.E.*

This statement will be referred to subsequently as the work-energy equation. It is particularly useful in solving problems involving force, velocity, and displacement.

Example

A 600-lb. block on a 30° incline is connected to a 150-lb. counterweight hanging vertically from a cable running over a pulley as shown in Fig. 328. The coefficient of friction between block and incline is 0.2. Neglecting the mass of the pulley and its axle friction, determine the velocity of the blocks after moving 20 ft. from rest.

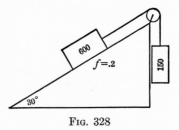

Solution: The initial kinetic energy of the system is zero. Positive work is done by gravity acting on the 600-lb. block.

Positive work $= 600 \times 20 \sin 30° = 6000$ ft-lb.

Fig. 328

Negative work is done by friction acting on the 600-lb. block and by gravity acting on the counterweight.

Negative work $= 0.2(600 \cos 30°) \times 20 + 150 \times 20 = 5080$ ft-lb.

The final kinetic energy of the system in terms of the unknown velocity v is

$$K.E. = \frac{1}{2}\frac{600}{32.2}v^2 + \frac{1}{2}\frac{150}{32.2}v^2 = \frac{1}{2}\frac{750}{32.2}v^2$$

The preceding items are now combined into the work-energy equation:

$$0 + 6000 - 5080 = \frac{1}{2}\frac{750}{32.2}v^2$$

$$v = 8.9 \text{ ft. per sec.}$$

The solution of the preceding example should be compared with its solution in Art. 69 by means of D'Alembert's principle.

Problems

1. A 500-ton train is hauled up a $1\frac{1}{2}$ per cent grade. Train resistance is 10 lb. per ton. Compute the drawbar pull required to change the speed from 10 mi. per hr. to 30 mi. per hr. in a distance of 1 mile. *Ans.* 25,000 lb.

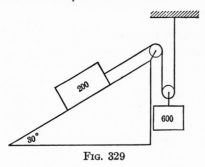

2. A block, starting from rest, slides 20 ft. down a 45° slope, then 10 ft. along a level surface, and then up a 30° incline until it comes to rest again. If the coefficient of friction is 0.15 for all three surfaces, compute the total distance traveled. *Ans.* 46.7 ft.

3. Determine the velocity of the 200-lb. block in Fig. 329 after moving 10 ft. from rest, if the coefficient of friction is 0.2. Compute the cable tension. *Ans.* 17.4 f.p.s.

Fig. 329

4. If car resistance is 8 lb. per ton for the system shown in Fig. 330, compute the value of weight W which is necessary for the car to attain a velocity of 15 mi. per hr. down the plane in a distance of 114 ft.   *Ans.* 6000 lb.

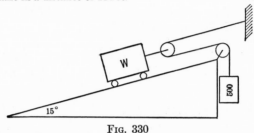

FIG. 330

5. If a 20-ton car has a velocity of 30 mi. per hr. down a $\frac{1}{2}$ per cent grade, what normal brake-shoe pressure on each of the eight wheels is required to bring the car to rest in a distance of 500 ft.? Assume that each wheel carries one-eighth of the load and that the coefficient of kinetic friction between wheel and shoe is 0.3.
     Ans. 1090 lb.

Art. 83. Work-Energy Relations for Translation; Variable Forces.
As pointed out in Art. 80, the work done by a variable force may be determined by means of the integral $\int F \, ds$, provided that the force can be expressed as a function of displacement.

The helical spring furnishes an illustration of variable force action, the force acting at any instant being proportional to the displacement as long as the elastic limit of the material is not exceeded. The scale of a spring is the force required to produce unit deflection. If C is the scale of a spring expressed in pounds per inch, as is customary, and s is the displacement in inches, then the work done in producing this displacement is

$$U = \int F \, ds = \int^s C s \, ds = \frac{Cs^2}{2} \text{ in-lb.} = \frac{Cs^2}{24} \text{ ft-lb.}$$

This expression may then be introduced into the work-energy equation.

Example

A 50-lb. block is projected up a 30° incline by means of a spring whose scale is 200 lb. per in. The coefficient of friction on the incline is 0.2. If the spring was given an initial deflection of 12 in., determine the velocity of the block after moving 30 ft. up the slope.

Solution: The initial kinetic energy of the block is zero. Positive work is done by the spring. Negative work is done by gravity and by friction. These items are shown in the following work-energy equation:

$$0 + \frac{200(12)^2}{24} - 50 \times 30 \sin 30° - 0.2(50 \cos 30°) \times 30 = \frac{1}{2} \frac{50}{32.2} v^2$$

$$v = 15.6 \text{ ft. per sec.}$$

Problems

1. A 50-ton freight car strikes a bumping post, compressing a drawbar spring 4 in. If the scale of the spring is 200,000 lb. per in., what was the velocity of the car?   *Ans.* 6.3 m.p.h.

2. A 65-lb. weight falls 15 in. upon a spring whose scale is 20 lb. per in. Compute the maximum deflection of the spring. What velocity does the weight have when the deflection of the spring is 10 in.?   *Ans.* 13.7 in.; 7.18 f.p.s.

3. If a gun weighing 25,000 lb. has an initial recoil velocity of 10 ft. per sec., what must be the scale of a set of springs which will limit the distance of recoil to 3 ft.?   *Ans.* 720 lb. per in.

4. A 30-lb. block slides 2 ft. down a 60° plane and strikes a 40-lb. spring. If the coefficient of friction on the plane is 0.25, compute the maximum deflection of the spring and the distance the block will rebound up the plane.
Ans. 5.75 in.; 1.86 ft.

5. A freight car weighing 50 tons is switched to a 2 per cent up-grade with a velocity of 15 mi. per hr. Car resistance is 9 lb. per ton. After moving 300 ft. up the grade, the car strikes a bumper. If the drawbar spring has a scale of 30,000 lb. per in., how far will it deflect?   *Ans.* 3.63 in.

Art. 84. Kinetic Energy of Rotation.

To determine the kinetic energy of a rotating body, the expression for the kinetic energy of a differential portion is integrated between proper limits so as to include the entire body. In Fig. 331 is shown a rigid body rotating with angular velocity ω about an axis through point O. The tangential linear velocity of a differential mass dM, located at distance ρ from the axis of rotation, is $v_t = \rho\omega$. The kinetic energy of the differential mass is then

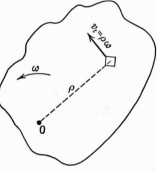

$$\frac{1}{2} dM v_t^2 = \frac{1}{2} dM \rho^2 \omega^2$$

FIG. 331

and the kinetic energy of the entire body becomes

$$\textbf{\textit{K.E.}} = \int \frac{1}{2} dM \rho^2 \omega^2 = \frac{1}{2} \omega^2 \int \rho^2 \, dM = \frac{1}{2} I_0 \omega^2$$

The work-energy equation, as used in problems of translation, also applies to rotation.

Example

A windlass with a brake to control its motion is shown in Fig. 332. The rotating parts weigh 400 lb. and have a radius of gyration of 0.75 ft. The load suspended from the windlass has a downward velocity of 15 ft. per sec. before the brake is applied. If the coefficient of friction for the brake is 0.5, and axle friction is considered negligible, what normal pressure N on the brake is required to bring the load to rest in a distance of 40 ft.?

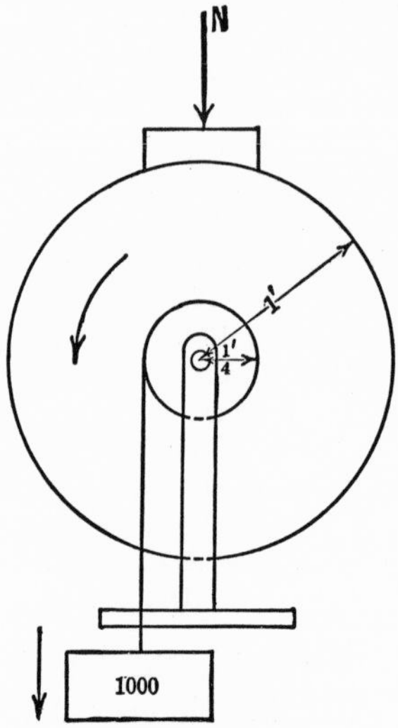

Solution: The angular velocity of the windlass is

$$\omega = \frac{v}{r} = \frac{15}{\frac{1}{4}} = 60 \text{ rad. per sec.}$$

The moment of inertia of the windlass is

$$I = \frac{W}{g} k^2 = \frac{400}{32.2} \left(\frac{3}{4}\right)^2 = \frac{225}{32.2}$$

Thus the initial kinetic energy of the windlass is

$$K.E. = \frac{1}{2} I\omega^2 = \frac{1}{2} \frac{225}{32.2} (60)^2 \text{ ft-lb.}$$

This kinetic energy, added to that of the falling load, constitutes the total initial kinetic energy of the system.

Positive work is done by gravity on the falling load. Negative work is done by the brake friction, which operates through a distance obtained by multiplying the distance traveled by the load by the ratio of the two circumferences or radii. Thus in this example, the brake friction operates through 160 ft. The final kinetic energy is zero.

The foregoing quantities are now substituted in the work-energy equation.

$$\frac{1}{2} \frac{225}{32.2} (60)^2 + \frac{1}{2} \frac{1000}{32.2} (15)^2 + 1000 \times 40 - 0.5N \times 160 = 0]$$

$$N = 701 \text{ lb.}$$

Fig. 332

Problems

1. The rotating parts of the system shown in Fig. 333 weigh 400 lb. and have a radius of gyration of 1.5 ft. If the system is released from rest, compute the angular velocity after the 100-lb. body has moved 10 ft. Use $f = 0.3$ for the 150-lb. weight and neglect journal friction.

Ans. 56 r.p.m.

2. If the 150-lb. body of Fig. 333 hangs vertically, compute the revolutions per minute of the wheel after the 100-lb. body has moved 10 ft.

Ans. 31.8 r.p.m.

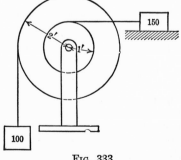

Fig. 333

3. A cylinder of 4-ft. diameter is attached to a horizontal axle through O, as shown in Fig. 334. If the cylinder is released from rest in the position indicated, with what angular velocity will it pass through a position (*a*) 90° farther on; (*b*) 180° farther on?   *Ans.* 4.64 rad. per sec.; 6.55 rad. per sec.

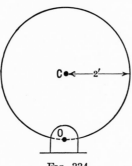

FIG. 334

4. A 1000-lb. load is suspended from a cable wrapped around a pulley of 1-ft. diameter which is attached to a flywheel as shown in Fig. 335. The total weight of the rotating parts is 500 lb., and the radius of gyration is 1.5 ft. If the load is being raised with a velocity of 20 ft. per sec., how much farther will it rise if the power is cut off? Neglect friction of bearings.   *Ans.* 34.2 ft.

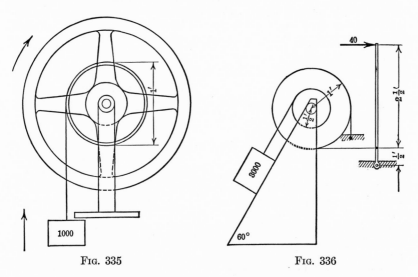

FIG. 335   FIG. 336

5. The motion of the system shown in Fig. 336 is controlled by a band brake. The weight of the rotating drum is 400 lb., and its radius of gyration is $\frac{3}{4}$ ft. The coefficient of band friction is $\frac{1}{3}$. The coefficient of kinetic friction for the incline is 0.2. If the system starts from rest, what will be the velocity of the 3000-lb. block after moving 20 ft.?   *Ans.* 12.5 f.p.s.

6. A solid-steel cylinder 4 ft. in diameter and 2 ft. long is keyed to a 6-in.-diameter shaft supported in bearings on each side of the cylinder. The coefficient of friction between axle and bearings is 0.015. If the cylinder has an angular velocity of 60 r.p.m. when power is cut off, how many revolutions will it make in coming to rest?

Ans. 52 rev.

Art. 85. Power. *Power* is the time rate of doing work. Thus

$$P = \frac{dU}{dt}$$

If power remains constant during a given operation, the preceding expression becomes

$$P = \frac{U}{t} \approx ML^2T^{-3}$$

Power is expressed in terms of work and time units, two frequently used units being the foot-pound per second and the foot-pound per minute. A larger unit commonly employed is the *horsepower* (abbreviated *hp.*), which consists of 550 ft-lb. per sec., or 33,000 ft-lb. per min.

Power may also be determined in terms of force and velocity, as shown by the following relation:

$$P = \frac{U}{t} = \frac{Fs}{t} = F \cdot v \approx ML^2T^{-3}$$

The ratio of the power output of a machine to the power input is called the efficiency of the machine.

Example 1

A turbine is driven by water supplied from a penstock of 2-ft. diameter under a head of 30 ft. Neglecting any friction losses, determine the horsepower theoretically available.

Solution: The velocity of the water leaving the penstock is given by

$$v = \sqrt{2gh} = \sqrt{2 \times 32.2 \times 30} = 44 \text{ ft. per sec.}$$

The volume of water delivered in 1 sec. is

$$Q = Av = \pi(1)^2 \times 44 = 138 \text{ cu. ft.}$$

The weight of this volume of water is

$$W = 138 \times 62.5 = 8630 \text{ lb.}$$

The energy possessed by this quantity of water may be computed either as potential energy

$$P.E. = Wh = 8630 \times 30 = 259,000 \text{ ft-lb.}$$

or as kinetic energy

$$K.E. = \frac{1}{2}\frac{W}{g}v^2 = \frac{1}{2}\frac{8630}{32.2}(44)^2 = 259,000 \text{ ft-lb.}$$

The horsepower theoretically available is then

$$hp. = \frac{U}{550t} = \frac{259,000}{550 \times 1} = 471$$

Example 2

Compute the horsepower developed by a locomotive which pulls a train of 40 cars weighing 50 tons each at a velocity of 15 mi. per hr. up a 1 per cent grade, train resistance being 10 lb. per ton.

Solution: The total drawbar pull required to overcome gravity and train resistance is

$$F = 40 \times 50 \times 2000 \times 0.01 + 40 \times 50 \times 10 = 60,000 \text{ lb.}$$

The power is then

$$hp. = \frac{Fv}{550} = 60,000 \times \frac{22}{550} = 2400$$

Problems

1. If T is the torque in foot-pounds transmitted by a shaft and n is the speed of rotation in revolutions per minute, show that the horsepower transmitted is $2\pi nT/33,000$.

2. Compute the horsepower developed by a pump which fills a 20,000-gal. water tank in 1 hr. if the water must be raised 50 ft. to an intake at the top of the tank.   *Ans.* 4.22 hp.

3. The speed of a 2000-ton train is increased from 15 mi. per hr. to 30 mi. per hr. in a distance of 1 mile up a 1 per cent grade. If train resistance is 8 lb. per ton, compute the maximum horsepower developed by the locomotive.   *Ans.* 5840 hp.

4. A turbine is driven by a 1-in.-diameter jet of water under a head of 600 ft. If the turbine has an efficiency of 90 per cent and is connected to a generator whose efficiency is 95 per cent, compute the power output of the generator in kilowatts
Ans. 46.6 kw.

5. The tensions on the two sides of a belt driving a pulley of 2-ft. diameter are 500 lb. and 200 lb. If the pulley has a speed of 300 r.p.m., what horsepower is being transmitted?   *Ans.* 17.1 hp.

6. In Fig. 337 is shown a device called the Prony brake, used to determine the power output of an engine. It consists of a type of band brake which absorbs the energy supplied by the engine and converts it into heat by means of the friction between the band brake and a flywheel or pulley driven by the engine. The force P

required to hold the brake in position is measured, and the friction F of the band is then determined from the relation, $Pl = Fr$. Show that the horsepower developed is $2\pi nPl/33,000$, if n is the speed of rotation in revolutions per minute.

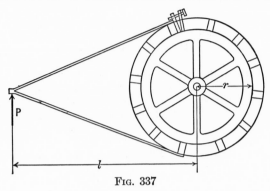

Fig. 337

Supplementary Problems

1. A water tank is cylindrical in shape with a hemispherical bottom. The cylindrical portion has a 12-ft. diameter and 5-ft. altitude. The tank is filled through its bottom, which is 40 ft. above the intake to the pump. Compute the work done by the pump in filling the tank.   *Ans.* 2,950,000 ft-lb.

2. If the pump used in filling the tank of Prob. 1 develops 2 hp., how long will it take to fill the tank?   *Ans.* 44.7 min.

3. Determine the velocity of the system of weights shown in Fig. 338 after it has been in motion for 10 sec. Use $f = 0.1$.   *Ans.* 15.5 f.p.s.

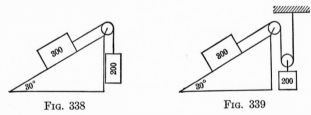

Fig. 338   Fig. 339

4. If the coefficient of friction for the 300-lb. block of Fig. 339 is 0.1, compute its velocity after it has been in motion for 20 sec. Determine the tension in the cord.   *Ans.* 44.1 f.p.s.; 103 lb.

5. An airplane weighing 6000 lb. is in steady horizontal flight. If the lift-over-drag ratio is 15 and the speed of the plane is 150 mi. per hr., compute the horsepower being developed.   *Ans.* 160 hp.

6. Compute the horsepower of a pump which takes water from a pond 10 ft. below and delivers it from a pipe 3 in. in diameter with a velocity of 120 ft. per sec.   *Ans.* 157 hp.

7. A train of 40 cars weighing 20 tons each is running at a speed of 45 mi. per hr. on a level track. If train resistance is 10 lb. per ton, determine the drawbar pull and the horsepower being developed by the locomotive.   *Ans.* 8000 lb.; 960 hp.

8. If the train in Prob. **7** arrives at a 0.5 per cent up-grade 1 mile long and the drawbar pull remains the same, with what velocity will it reach the end of the grade? *Ans.* 35.2 m.p.h.

9. If the system of bodies shown in Fig. 340 is released from rest, determine the velocity of the 60-lb. body after moving 10 ft. Compute the tension in the cord. *Ans. T* = 72 lb.

10. A 40-lb. block is projected along a horizontal surface by a 200-lb. spring whose initial deflection is 6 in. If the coefficient of friction is 0.2, what velocity will the block have after moving 20 ft.? *Ans.* 15 f.p.s.

11. What initial deflection must be given the spring of Prob. 10 in order that it may project the 40-lb. block upward to a height of 25 ft.? *Ans.* 11 in.

12. A rod 3 ft. long is attached to a horizontal axis normal to the rod through one end. If the rod is held at rest in the horizontal position and then released, with what angular velocity will it pass through a position 30° farther on? *Ans.* 4.01 rad. per sec.

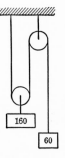

Fig. 340

13. Solve Prob. 12 if the axis goes through a point 1 ft. from the end of the rod.

14. The rotating parts of the windlass shown in Fig. 341 weigh 200 lb. and have a radius of gyration of $1\frac{1}{4}$ ft. The 800-lb. load has downward velocity of 10 ft.

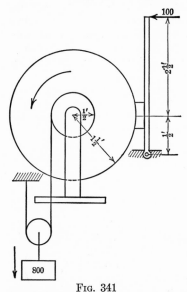

per sec. just before the brake is applied. Compute the distance the load will travel in coming to rest if the coefficient of friction for the brake on the drum is 0.4, and friction of bearings is neglected.

Ans. 14.1 ft.

15. The speed of rotation of the flywheel of a punch press decreases from 180 r.p.m. to 150 r.p.m. as the machine punches a $\frac{1}{2}$-in.-diameter hole through plate $\frac{1}{4}$ in. thick whose ultimate shearing strength is 60,000 lb. per sq. in. If 80 per cent of the energy lost by the flywheel is used in punching the hole, compute the required moment of inertia of the flywheel.

Ans. 5.64 slug-ft.^{2}

16. A Prony brake (see Fig. 337) attached to a 4-ft.-diameter flywheel has a lever arm of 5 ft. When the wheel is rotating at a speed of 250 r.p.m., the force *P* is observed to be 200 lb. Compute the horsepower being developed. *Ans.* 47.5 hp.

Fig. 341

17. The velocity of the water in a penstock of 4-ft. diameter is 8 ft. per sec. Compute the horsepower available. *Ans.* 11.3 hp.

18. A belt is in contact with half the circumference of a 2-ft.-diameter pulley which it is driving with a speed of 240 r.p.m. The coefficient of belt friction is 0.4. If the belt is transmitting 60 hp. and is on the point of slipping, compute the tension on each side. *Ans.* 1840 lb.; 522 lb.

CHAPTER XIII

DYNAMICS OF ROTATING BODIES

Art. 86.   The Effective Forces on a Rotating Body. If a rigid body
is acted upon by forces causing the body to rotate about an axis,

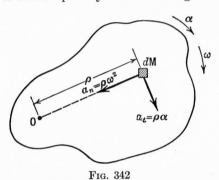

each particle in the body will
move in a plane circular path
whose center is at the axis of
rotation.   Each particle will
therefore have an acceleration
which may be represented by
its tangential and normal components.   In Fig. 342 is shown
a rigid body rotating with an
angular velocity ω and angular
acceleration α about an axis
through O.   Let dM be the

Fig. 342

mass of any particle located at radial distance ρ from O.   The tangential component of the acceleration of the particle is $a_t = \rho\alpha$, and
the normal component of the acceleration is $a_n = \rho\omega^2$.   According to
Newton's second law, the effective forces on the particle required to
produce these acceleration components are $dM\rho\alpha$ tangent to the path,

and $dM\rho\omega^2$ normal to the path
and directed toward the center,
as shown in Fig. 343.   Each
particle in the body is acted
upon by a similar pair of effective forces.   The resultant of
these effective forces for the
entire body and the moment of
the effective forces with respect
to the axis of rotation enter into
the analysis of many problems
involving rotating bodies.

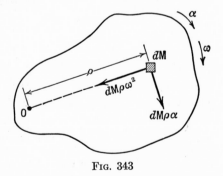

Fig. 343

Art. 87.   The Moment of the Effective Forces. The effective forces
acting on the particles of a rotating body represent the effect of the
external forces acting on the body.   The sum of their moments with

respect to the axis of rotation must therefore be equal to the sum of
the moments of the external forces on the body with respect to the
same axis. In Fig. 344, let F_1, F_2, F_3, etc., at distances r_1, r_2, r_3, etc.,
from O, represent the various external forces (including weight of the

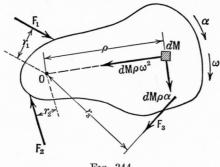

FIG. 344

body and reactions at supports) acting on the rotating body. The sum
of the moments of these external forces with respect to O is

$$F_1 r_1 + F_2 r_2 + F_3 r_3 + \text{etc.} = \Sigma Fr$$

The moment of the effective forces on the particle of mass dM with
respect to O is

$$dM\rho\omega^2 \times 0 + dM\rho\alpha \times \rho = dM\rho^2\alpha$$

The sum of the moments of the effective forces for the entire body is
$\int dM\rho^2\alpha$. Since all particles in the body have the angular acceleration α in common, the moment of the effective forces becomes

$$\alpha \int \rho^2 \, dM = I_0\alpha$$

where $I_0 = \int \rho^2 \, dM$ is the moment of inertia of the mass of the body
with respect to the axis of rotation. Equating the moment of the
external forces to the moment of the effective forces,

$$\Sigma Fr = I_0\alpha$$

This equation for rotation is analogous to the equation $F = Ma$
for rectilinear motion.

Example

The rotating parts of the windlass shown in Fig. 345 (a) weigh 300 lb. and
have a radius of gyration of 2 ft. The coefficient of friction for the brake is

0.4, and bearing friction is assumed to be negligible. Determine the angular acceleration of the windlass and the tension in the cable.

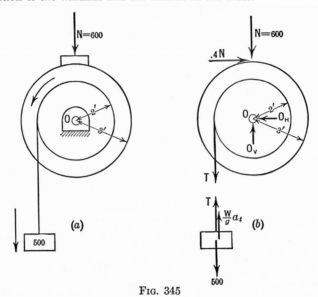

(a)

(b)

FIG. 345

Solution: The windlass and load are shown separately as free bodies in Fig. 345 (b). It may be determined by inspection that the brake friction is not sufficient to hold the load and therefore the load will accelerate downward. For the windlass,

$$I_0 = \frac{W}{g} k^2 = \frac{300}{32.2} (2)^2 = 37.3$$

By substitution in the equation $\Sigma Fr = I\alpha$

$$T \times 2 - 0.4 \times 600 \times 3 = 37.3\alpha \qquad (1)$$

By $\Sigma F_v = 0$ for the load

$$T + \frac{500a_t}{32.2} = 500 \qquad (2)$$

Also,

$$a_t = r\alpha = 2\alpha \qquad (3)$$

By simultaneous solution of equations (1) to (3)

$$T = 413 \text{ lb.}; \alpha = 2.82 \text{ rad. per sec.}^2$$

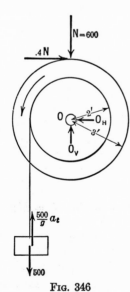

FIG. 346

A variation in the solution may be had by considering the entire system as a single free body as shown in Fig. 346. The equation $\Sigma Fr = I_0\alpha$ applied to the entire system becomes

$$500 \times 2 - \frac{500}{32.2} \times 2\alpha \times 2 - 0.4 \times 600 \times 3 = 37.3\alpha$$

$$\alpha = 2.82 \text{ rad. per sec.}^2$$

Then, using the 500-lb. load as a free body,

$$T + \frac{500(2 \times 2.82)}{32.2} = 500$$

$$T = 413 \text{ lb.}$$

Problems

1. A cast-iron cylinder 1 ft. in diameter and 2 ft. long is mounted on a shaft through its geometric axis. A 50-lb. weight is suspended from a cord wrapped around the cylinder. Neglecting journal friction, compute the linear acceleration of the weight and the tension in the cord.   *Ans.* 4 f.p.s.^{2}; 43.8 lb.

2. Solve Prob. 1 if the shaft on which the cylinder rotates has a 2-in. diameter and the coefficient of journal friction is 0.05.   *Ans.* 3.49 f.p.s.^{2}; 44.6 lb.

3. The rotating portion of the system shown in Fig. 347 weighs 150 lb. and has a radius of gyration of 1.5 ft. If the coefficient of friction for the 200-lb. block is 0.3, determine its acceleration and the tension in the attached cable.

Ans. a = 8.06 f.p.s.^{2}

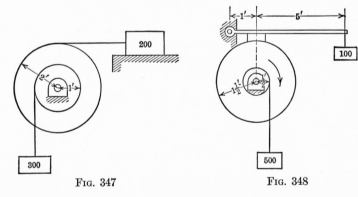

FIG. 347   FIG. 348

4. The rotating parts of the windlass shown in Fig. 348 weigh 300 lb. and have a radius of gyration of 1.25 ft. The coefficient of friction for the brake is 0.4, and axle friction is negligible. If the 500-lb. load has a downward velocity of 20 ft. per sec. just before the brake is applied, how far will it travel in coming to rest?

Ans. 67.0 ft.

5. A flywheel weighing 600 lb. has a radius of gyration of 1.75 ft. A 1500-lb. load is suspended from a cable wrapped around a pulley of 1-ft. diameter fastened to the flywheel. The load is being raised with a velocity of 15 ft. per sec. just before the power is cut off. If bearing friction is neglected, how much farther will the load continue to rise and what will be the tension in the cable while the system comes to rest?   *Ans.* 20.6 ft.; 1250 lb.

6. Solve the Example of Art. 84 by using the method of Art. 87.

Art. 88.   The Resultant of the Effective Forces.   It was shown in Art. 86 that each particle of a rigid rotating body is acted upon by an effective force whose components are $dM\rho\alpha$, acting tangent to the path in the direction of the angular acceleration, and $dM\rho\omega^2$, acting radially toward the axis of rotation.   The tangential and normal components of the resultant of these forces for the entire body will now be determined for a body possessing a plane of symmetry normal to the axis of rotation.   A body satisfying this requirement may be considered as composed of elementary rods normal to the plane of symmetry. The resultant effective forces on each rod will act at its midpoint and thus lie in the plane of symmetry, forming a coplanar system in the plane of motion of the center of gravity of the body.

In Fig. 349 is shown the plane of symmetry of such a rotating body as described.   As before, dM represents a particle located at radial

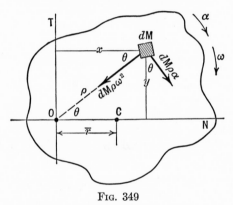

Fig. 349

distance ρ from the axis of rotation through O and acted upon by the tangential and normal components of the effective force. C represents the center of gravity of the body and $\bar{r}$ its radial distance from the axis of rotation.   Let N and T be rectangular axes selected so that N passes through the center of gravity and axis of rotation.   Let θ be the angle between the radius ρ and the N axis.

The summation of the components of the effective forces parallel to the N axis is

$$\Sigma F_N = \int dM\rho\alpha \sin\theta - \int dM\rho\omega^2 \cos\theta$$

Since $\rho \sin\theta = y$, $\rho \cos\theta = x$, and α and ω^2 are common to all particles,

$$\Sigma F_N = \alpha \int y \, dM - \omega^2 \int x \, dM = M\bar{y}\alpha - M\bar{x}\omega^2$$

However, since y is measured from the N axis, which was taken through the center of gravity, $\bar{y} = 0$ and $M\bar{y}\alpha = 0$. Also, since x is measured from the T axis and the distance of the center of gravity from that axis was originally denoted by $\bar{r}$, $\bar{x} = \bar{r}$. Thus the resultant of all effective forces on the body has a component in the N or normal direction given by

$$\Sigma F_N = M\bar{r}\omega^2$$

As shown in Fig. 349, the summation of the components of the effective forces parallel to the T axis is

$$\Sigma F_T = \int dM\rho\alpha \cos\theta + \int dM\rho\omega^2 \sin\theta$$

$$= \alpha \int x \, dM + \omega^2 \int y \, dM$$

$$= M\bar{x}\alpha + M\bar{y}\omega^2$$

Since $\bar{x} = \bar{r}$ and $\bar{y} = 0$ as already explained,

$$\Sigma F_T = M\bar{r}\alpha$$

The resultant effective force for the rotating body may now be expressed in terms of its components $M\bar{r}\omega^2$ in the N direction and $M\bar{r}\alpha$ in the T direction. The positions of these components will next be determined. The components of a force may be considered as acting together at any point on the line of action of the force; it will be convenient in this development and subsequent applications to have the components $M\bar{r}\omega^2$ and $M\bar{r}\alpha$ act at the point where their resultant intersects the N axis. The $M\bar{r}\omega^2$ component will then lie along the N axis; that is, it acts radially along the line joining the axis of rotation and center of gravity.

The $M\bar{r}\alpha$ component will be perpendicular to the N axis at some distance q from the axis of rotation. The distance q may be found by equating the sum of the moments of the resultant forces $M\bar{r}\omega^2$ and $M\bar{r}\alpha$ with respect to the axis of rotation to the sum of the moments of the effective forces acting on the elementary particles. The sum of the moments of the elementary effective forces was shown in Art. 87 to be $I_0\alpha$. Hence

$$M\bar{r}\omega^2 \cdot 0 + M\bar{r}\alpha \cdot q = I_0\alpha = Mk_0^2\alpha$$

$$q = \frac{I_0}{M\bar{r}} = \frac{k_0^2}{\bar{r}}$$

The preceding discussion may be summarized in the following statements:

1. The resultant normal effective force is $M\bar{r}\omega^2$ acting radially through the center of gravity toward the axis of rotation.

2. The resultant tangential effective force is $M\bar{r}\alpha$ acting perpendicular to the line through the center of gravity and axis of rotation at a distance $k_0^2/\bar{r}$ from the axis of rotation.

The above statements are illustrated by Fig. 350 (a), which shows the resultant normal and tangential effective forces for the entire

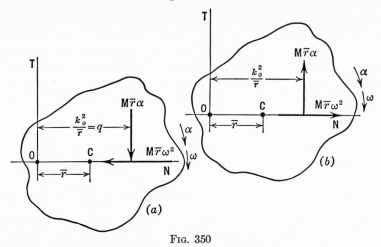

FIG. 350

body. In the solution of problems in rotation by means of D'Alembert's principle (see Art. 69) these forces are reversed in direction and applied to the free body as shown in Fig. 350 (b). They are now known as the reversed normal and tangential effective forces or the inertia forces for the rotating body. The normal reversed effective force $M\bar{r}\omega^2$ is often called the centrifugal force. The addition of the reversed effective forces to the system of forces actually acting on the rotating body forms a system of forces in equilibrium, thus reducing the problem to one of static equilibrium.

It is evident from the expressions $M\bar{r}\omega^2$ and $M\bar{r}\alpha$ that both forces reduce to zero when the axis of rotation passes through the center of gravity ($\bar{r} = 0$). It is also evident that $M\bar{r}\alpha$ is zero when the speed of rotation is constant ($\alpha = 0$). The force $M\bar{r}\omega^2$ increases in proportion to the square of the angular speed.

The results obtained above were derived for the special case of a body possessing a plane of symmetry normal to the axis of rotation. It can be shown that these results are also valid for a body possessing a line of symmetry parallel to the axis of rotation. In general, however, the resultant effective forces of rotating bodies do not necessarily lie in the plane of rotation of the center of gravity, and their exact position is usually difficult to determine. Most problems of rotation in engineering come under the special cases just described. One important exception, a slender rod inclined at any angle to its axis of rotation, is considered later. (See Prob. 4, p. 208.)

Example 1

A circular disk of radius r and weight W is attached to a horizontal axis through an element of the cylindrical surface. If the disk is held at rest with its center at 30° above the horizontal and then released and allowed to rotate under the influence of gravity alone, determine completely the reversed effective forces for the disk at the instant of release.

Solution: In Fig. 351 the disk is shown as a free body at the instant of release. In this position it is acted upon by its weight and the reaction

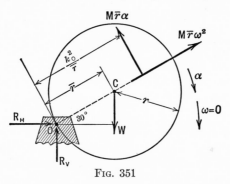

Fig. 351

components R_V and R_H at the axis of rotation. The reversed effective forces are shown in their proper positions according to the requirements determined above.

Since the angular velocity ω is zero at the instant of release,

$$M\bar{r}\omega^2 = 0$$

The angular acceleration for this position is found by means of the equation

$$\Sigma Fr = I_0\alpha$$

$$I_0 = \frac{3}{2}Mr^2 \text{ by transfer from } C$$

$$W \times \bar{r}\cos 30° = \frac{3}{2}\frac{W}{g}r^2\alpha$$

$$\alpha = \frac{2}{3}\frac{g}{r}\cos 30°$$

$$M\bar{r}\alpha = \frac{W}{g}\cdot r\cdot\frac{2}{3}\frac{g}{r}\cos 30° = \frac{2}{3}W\cos 30° = 0.577W$$

$$\frac{k_0{}^2}{\bar{r}} = \frac{I_0}{M\bar{r}} = \frac{\tfrac{3}{2}M\bar{r}^2}{M\bar{r}} = \frac{3}{2}r$$

The magnitude of the force $M\bar{r}\alpha$ may also be determined by an alternative method in which the distance $k_0{}^2/\bar{r}$ is first computed and then the equation $\Sigma M_0 = 0$ gives

$$M\bar{r}\alpha \times \frac{3}{2}r - W \times r\cos 30° = 0$$

$$M\bar{r}\alpha = \frac{2}{3}W\cos 30° = 0.577W$$

Example 2

If the diameter of the disk in Ex. 1 is 1 ft. and its weight is 50 lb., determine completely the reversed effective forces when it is rotated at a constant speed of 150 r.p.m. about the same axis.

Solution: Since the angular acceleration α is zero when the speed of rotation is constant,

$$M\bar{r}\alpha = 0$$

$$M\bar{r}\omega^2 = \frac{50}{32.2} \times \frac{1}{2} \times \left[\frac{150}{60} \times 2\pi\right]^2 = 192 \text{ lb.}$$

Problems

1. Solve Ex. 1 if the center C is horizontally opposite the axis of rotation at the instant of release.   *Ans. $M\bar{r}\alpha = \frac{2}{3}W$.*

2. Solve Prob. 1 if the axis of rotation passes through the disk midway between the center and the outside edge.   *Ans. $M\bar{r}\alpha = \frac{1}{3}W$; $k_0{}^2/\bar{r} = \frac{3}{2}r$.*

3. A flywheel weighing 1000 lb. rotates at 300 r.p.m. about an axis which is 0.05 in. off center. Compute the normal reversed effective force. *Ans.* 128 lb.

4. Show that the resultant normal effective force for a slender prismatic rod rotating about a vertical axis through one end is $M\bar{r}\omega^2$ and acts radially through a point in the rod at two-thirds the length from the point of support.

5. A steel rod 2 in. in diameter and 30 in. long is fastened to a vertical axis through one end so that the rod is inclined at 30° with the vertical. Compute the normal effective force for the rod when its speed of rotation is 60 r.p.m.

Ans. 20.5 lb.

Art. 89. Kinetic Reactions. If the resultant normal and tangential effective forces for a rotating body are zero, the reactions at the supports of the body are the same as when the body is at rest. If, however, the nature of the rotating body is such that either one or both of the effective forces is not zero, additional components will be introduced into the reactions at the supports. Furthermore, these additional components of the reactions vary in both magnitude and direction as the position of the rotating body and its speed of rotation change. Those components of the reactions at the supports of a rotating body which vary in magnitude and direction as the body rotates are known as the *kinetic components*, whereas those components which remain constant are known as the *static components*. In order to determine the reactions at the supports of a rotating body the free-body diagram is drawn, including both known and unknown forces acting upon the body, the normal and tangential effective forces are determined and added in the reversed direction, after which the necessary equations of static equilibrium are applied to complete the solution.

Example 1

A slender prismatic rod, 6 ft. long and weighing 50 lb., is held at rest in a vertical position with its center directly above a horizontal axis through the lower end. If the rod is released from this position and allowed to rotate under the influence of gravity alone, determine the normal and tangential components of the reaction at the support as the rod passes through a position 30° below the horizontal.

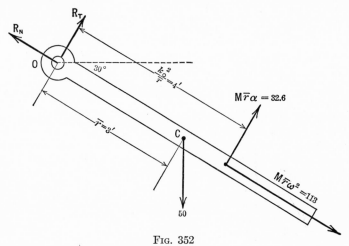

Fig. 352

Solution: The free-body diagram of the rod as it rotates through the designated position is shown in Fig. 352.

$$I_0 = \frac{1}{3}\frac{W}{g}l^2 = \frac{1}{3}\frac{50}{32.2}(6)^2 = 18.6$$

$$k_0{}^2 = \frac{1}{3}l^2 = \frac{1}{3}(6)^2 = 12$$

$$\frac{k_0{}^2}{\bar{r}} = \frac{12}{3} = 4 \text{ ft.}$$

The angular acceleration α is determined by applying $\Sigma Fr = I_0\alpha$,

$$50 \times 3 \cos 30° = 18.6\alpha$$

$$\alpha = 7.00 \text{ rad. per sec.}^2$$

$$M\bar{r}\alpha = \frac{50}{32.2} \times 3 \times 7 = 32.6 \text{ lb.}$$

$M\bar{r}\alpha$ may also be determined by applying $\Sigma M_0 = 0$,

$$M\bar{r}\alpha \times 4 - 50 \times 3 \cos 30° = 0$$

$$M\bar{r}\alpha = 32.6 \text{ lb.}$$

The angular velocity ω is found by equating the work of gravity to the increase in kinetic energy, or $W\bar{h} = \frac{1}{2}I_0\omega^2$. The center of gravity of the rod has been lowered a total distance $\bar{h} = 4.5$ ft. from its initial position; and so

$$50 \times 4.5 = \frac{1}{2} \times 18.6\omega^2$$

$$\omega^2 = 24.2$$

$$M\bar{r}\omega^2 = 113 \text{ lb.}$$

If the reversed effective forces as computed are applied to the free body, it will be in a state of static equilibrium, and the normal and tangential components, R_N and R_T, of the reaction at O, may be determined. In Fig. 352,

$$\Sigma F_N = R_N - 113 - 50 \sin 30° = 0 \qquad R_N = 138 \text{ lb.}$$

$$\Sigma F_T = R_T + 32.6 - 50 \cos 30° = 0 \qquad R_T = 10.7 \text{ lb.}$$

Example 2

The rod of Ex. 1 rotates with constant speed of 30 r.p.m. about a vertical axis through one end. Determine the angle at which the rod will stand out from the axis, and the vertical and horizontal components of the reaction at the support.

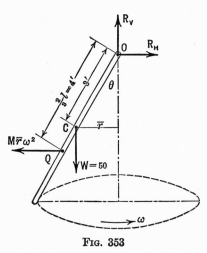

Fig. 353

Solution: The free-body diagram of the rod is shown in Fig. 353. Since the speed of rotation is constant, $\alpha = 0$, and $M\bar{r}\alpha = 0$. Since the normal effective forces on the particles of this rotating body constitute a series of parallel forces acting radially through the axis of rotation and increasing in magnitude in proportion to the distances of the consecutive particles from the axis, their resultant will be $M\bar{r}\omega^2$, acting through point Q at two-thirds the length of the rod from the support O. (See

Prob. 4, Art. 88.) If this force is reversed in direction and applied to the free body as shown, the system is in equilibrium, and the equation $\Sigma M_O = 0$ gives

$$\frac{W}{g}\bar{r}\omega^2 \cdot \frac{2}{3}l\cos\theta - W\bar{r} = 0$$

$$\cos\theta = \frac{3g}{2\omega^2 l} = \frac{3 \times 32.2}{2(\frac{30}{60} \times 2\pi)^2 \times 6} = 0.815$$

$$\theta = 35.4°$$

$$\bar{r} = 3\sin\theta = 1.73 \text{ ft.}$$

$$M\bar{r}\omega^2 = \frac{50}{32.2} \times 1.73 \times \pi^2 = 26.5 \text{ lb.}$$

$$\Sigma F_V = R_V - 50 = 0 \qquad\qquad R_V = 50 \text{ lb.}$$

$$\Sigma F_H = R_H - 26.5 = 0 \qquad\qquad R_H = 26.5 \text{ lb.}$$

Problems

1. Solve for the vertical and horizontal components of the reaction of the support in Ex. 1 as the rod passes through the horizontal position.

Ans. $R_V = 12.5$ lb.; $R_H = 75.0$ lb.

2. Solve for the vertical and horizontal components of the reaction of the support in Ex. 1 as the rod passes through the vertical position with its center directly below the axis. *Ans.* $R_V = 200$ lb.; $R_H = 0$.

3. Solve for the speed of rotation required to make the rod in Ex. 2 stand at 60° with the vertical axis. *Ans.* 38.3 r.p.m.

4. A cast-iron sphere 6 in. in diameter is connected by a stiff rod to a horizontal axis 2 ft. from the center of the sphere. If the sphere is released from rest with its center vertically above the axis and allowed to rotate under the influence of gravity alone, compute the vertical and horizontal components of the reaction at the support when the angular displacement of the system is 60°. Neglect the weight of the arm. *Ans.* $R_V = 7.13$ lb.; $R_H = 12.7$ lb.

5. A 1500-lb. flywheel rotates at 1800 r.p.m. about a horizontal axis 0.05 in. off center. If the wheel is midway between bearings, compute the maximum and minimum values of the bearing reactions.

Ans. 4200 lb.; −2700 lb.

6. The 40-lb. weight of Fig. 354 rotates about the vertical axis AB with a speed of 30 r.p.m. Compute the components of the reactions at A and B.

Ans. $B_x = 29.9$ lb.

7. A steel rod, 2 in. in diameter and 8 ft. long, is released from rest in a horizontal position and allowed to rotate, under the influence of gravity alone, about a horizontal axis normal to the rod through a point 2 ft. from its end. Compute the vertical and horizontal components of the reaction at the support as the rod passes through a position 60° below the horizontal.

Ans. $R_V = 131$ lb.; $R_H = 47.5$ lb.

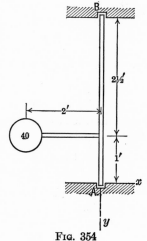

FIG. 354

Art. 90. Balancing of Rotating Bodies. It was shown in Art. 89 that the reactions at the supports of rotating bodies often include kinetic components which vary in magnitude and direction as the body rotates. As a result of these kinetic reactions injurious effects, such as vibration and undue wear of bearings, may occur. It is therefore desirable to eliminate such reactions. Balancing may be defined as the addition or removal of such rotating parts as will cause the effective forces for the entire system to be in equilibrium and thus induce no kinetic reactions.

A rotating body may be in static balance or dynamic balance. If a body has no tendency to rotate regardless of the position in which

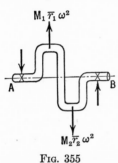

FIG. 355

it is placed, it is said to be in *static balance*. If no kinetic reactions are induced when the body rotates, it is said to be in *dynamic balance*. It is possible for a body to be statically balanced and yet not dynamically balanced. The crank shaft of a two-cylinder engine, shown in Fig. 355, serves as an example. If the two eccentric portions are identical, the shaft will not rotate when placed in frictionless bearings at A and B, regardless of its position, and is therefore in static balance. However, when the shaft rotates, it exerts upon the bearings a centrifugal couple composed of the forces $M_1\bar{r}_1\omega^2$ and $M_2\bar{r}_2\omega^2$, and kinetic reactions are induced at A and B. The shaft is thus not in dynamic balance. It is necessary to add counterweights to the shaft to balance it completely.

The following discussion will be limited to rotation at constant speed, so that only normal effective forces need be considered.

Art. 91. Balancing in a Single Transverse Plane. If a rotating system contains a part, of weight W_1, at radial distance $\bar{r}_1$ from the axis of rotation and exerting a centrifugal pull $\dfrac{W_1}{g}\bar{r}_1\omega^2$, balancing may be accomplished by addition of another part, of weight W_2, placed diametrically opposite in the same plane of rotation and at such distance r_2 from the axis that

$$\frac{W_1}{g}\bar{r}_1\omega^2 = \frac{W_2}{g}\bar{r}_2\omega^2$$

The balanced system is shown in Fig. 356. Since g and ω are common factors, the above requirement for balance may be expressed as

$$W_1\bar{r}_1 = W_2\bar{r}_2$$

This is also the requirement for static balance. In practice, dynamic balance, for rotating bodies in which the bulk of the material lies approximately in a single plane of rotation, may be accomplished by adding or removing material until static balance is obtained.

If the rotating system contains several unbalanced parts in the same transverse plane, each part may be individually balanced by adding a balancing weight diametrically opposite in the same plane, thus introducing as many balancing weights as there are unbalanced parts.

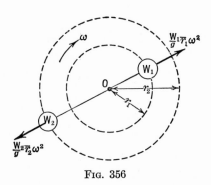

FIG. 356

However, since it has previously been shown that the balancing operation reduces to one of balancing forces, and since the system of forces is concurrent, it is evident that only one balancing weight W, so placed that its centrifugal pull $\dfrac{W}{g} \bar{r}\omega^2$ will hold in equilibrium the centrifugal pulls of the parts to be balanced, will be sufficient. As previously pointed out, the $W\bar{r}$ products may be used instead of the actual forces. The required balancing weight and its position may be determined graphically by means of the vector polygon of the $W\bar{r}$ products, or algebraically by summation of the $W\bar{r}$ products in each of two directions. Either W or $\bar{r}$ for the balancing weight may be assumed and the other computed.

Example

The system of three rotating bodies shown in Fig. 357 is to be balanced by a weight W at 12 in. from the axis of rotation. Determine W and the angle θ at which it must be placed.

Solution: The summation of $W\bar{r}$ products in the x direction gives

$$W \times 12 \cos \theta + 20 \times 10 \sin 60° - 50 \times 6 = 0$$

$$W \cos \theta = 10.6 \qquad (1)$$

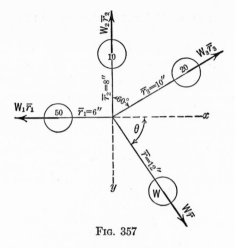

FIG. 357

The summation of $W\bar{r}$ products in the y direction gives

$$20 \times 10 \sin 30° + 10 \times 8 - W \times 12 \sin \theta = 0$$

$$W \sin \theta = 15.0 \qquad (2)$$

Simultaneous solution of equations (1) and (2) gives

$$W = 18.4 \text{ lb.}; \theta = 54.7°$$

Problems

1. In Fig. 357, let $W_1 = 60$ lb., $\bar{r}_1 = 8$ in., $W_2 = 0$, $W_3 = 45$ lb., and $\bar{r}_3 = 6$ in. If $\bar{r} = 10$ in., determine W and θ.   *Ans.* $W = 28$ lb.; $\theta = 28.8°$.

2. A steel disk 2 ft. in diameter and 1 in. thick rotates about an axis $\frac{1}{16}$ in. from its geometric axis. At what distance from the axis of rotation should a 2-in.-diameter hole be drilled to balance the disk?   *Ans.* 9 in.

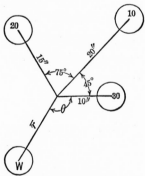

FIG. 358

3. If the balancing weight W for the system shown in Fig. 358 is to be 50 lb., determine $\bar{r}$ and θ.   *Ans.* 9.92 in.; 126°.

4. Solve Prob. 3 when the 10-lb. weight is removed.   *Ans.* $\bar{r} = 6.0$ in.

Art. 92. Balancing in Different Transverse Planes. The balancing weight for a rotating body cannot always be placed in the plane of rotation of the body. The crank shaft of Fig. 355 is an example of this situation. When the balancing weight cannot be placed in the same transverse plane as the rotating body, balancing can be accomplished by the addition of two balancing weights in different planes normal to the axis. Thus in Fig. 359 the weight W_1 at distance r_1 from the axis AB may be balanced by addition of weights W_A and W_B in the same axial plane but in different transverse planes through A and B and at distances l_A and l_B from the plane of weight W_1. The necessary conditions for balance are obtained from the equations:

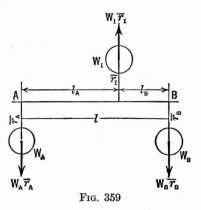

Fig. 359

$$\Sigma M_A = W_1 \bar{r}_1 l_A - W_B \bar{r}_B l = 0$$

$$\Sigma M_B = W_1 \bar{r}_1 l_B - W_A \bar{r}_A l = 0$$

If the same shaft carries additional unbalanced parts W_2, W_3, etc., each of the additional parts can be balanced by the addition of a balancing weight in plane A and one in plane B. Finally, all the balancing weights in the transverse plane A can be replaced by a single weight, and those in the transverse plane B can likewise be replaced by a single weight.

Example

The rotating system shown in Fig. 360 is to be balanced by the addition of a weight W_A to be placed in the normal plane at A and a weight W_E to be

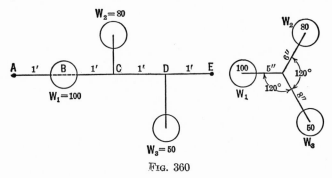

Fig. 360

placed in the normal plane at E, each at 6 in. from the axis of rotation. Determine the required values of W_A and W_E and their angular positions.

Solution: The system is projected into coordinate planes as shown in Fig. 361. The true values of the $W\bar{r}$ products are shown in Fig. 361 (c). The projected values of these products are given in Fig. 361 (a) and (b).

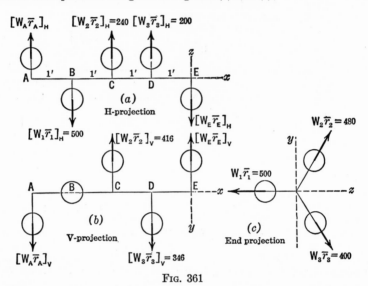

FIG. 361

In the projected system of Fig. 361 (a) the equation $\Sigma M_A = 0$ gives

$$(W_E\bar{r}_E)_H \times 4 = 200 \times 3 + 240 \times 2 - 500 \times 1$$

$$(W_E\bar{r}_E)_H = 145$$

Similarly, from the equation $\Sigma M_E = 0$

$$(W_A\bar{r}_A)_H = 205$$

In the projected system of Fig. 361 (b) the equations $\Sigma M_A = 0$ and $\Sigma M_E = 0$ give

$$(W_E\bar{r}_E)_V = 52.0$$

$$(W_A\bar{r}_A)_V = 122$$

The $W\bar{r}$ components in plane A are shown in Fig. 362 (a), and those for plane E in Fig. 362 (b). By combination of the components in plane A

$$W_A\bar{r}_A = \sqrt{(205)^2 + (122)^2} = 238$$

$$W_A = \frac{238}{6} = 39.7 \text{ lb.}$$

$$\theta_A = \tan^{-1}\frac{122}{205} = 30.8°$$

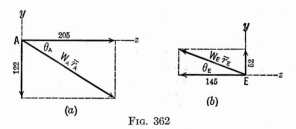

(a) (b)

FIG. 362

By combination of the components in plane E

$$W_E \bar{r}_E = \sqrt{(52)^2 + (145)^2} = 154$$

$$W_E = \tfrac{154}{6} = 25.7 \text{ lb.}$$

$$\theta_E = \tan^{-1} \tfrac{52}{145} = 19.7°$$

Problems

1. The crank shaft of a single-cylinder gas engine is 3 ft. long between bearings. The plane of rotation of the crank is 1 ft. from the left bearing. The crank arms and pin are equivalent to a weight of 60 lb. at a radial distance of 8 in. from the axis of rotation. The crank is to be balanced by weights at 6-in. radial distance in each of two planes 6 in. from the bearings. Determinine the balancing weights required. *Ans.* 60 lb. at left; 20 lb. at right.

2. A two-cylinder engine has a crank shaft like the one described in Prob. 1 except that a second crank, similar to the first, rotates in a plane at 1 ft. from the right bearing and 180° back of the first crank. Determine the balancing weights to be placed in the same normal planes and at the same radial distance as before. *Ans.* 40 lb. at left; 40 lb. at right.

3. The rotating system shown in Fig. 363 is to be balanced by a weight at 5 in. from the axis of rotation in the normal plane A and a weight at 3 in. from the axis

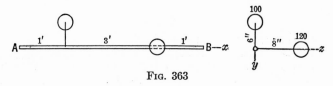

FIG. 363

in the normal plane B. Determine the balancing weights required and their location in their respective planes.

Ans. $W_A = 103$ lb.; $\theta = 248°$; $W_B = 259$ lb.; $\theta = 189°$.

Art. 93. Circumferential Tension in Flywheels. When a flywheel rotates, the centrifugal action exerted on the rim causes a circumferential or "hoop" tension to be developed in the rim. This stress increases as the square of the velocity, as will be shown, and may become quite important at high speeds. If the tension in the spokes is neglected, the tension in the rim may be determined.

In Fig. 364 is shown half of the rim of a flywheel. If the thickness of the rim is small compared to the mean radius r, the center of gravity C of the half-rim coincides very nearly with the centroid of the semi-circular arc of radius r. Thus $\bar{r} = 2r/\pi$. Now, if W represents the weight of the half-rim, the normal reversed effective force becomes

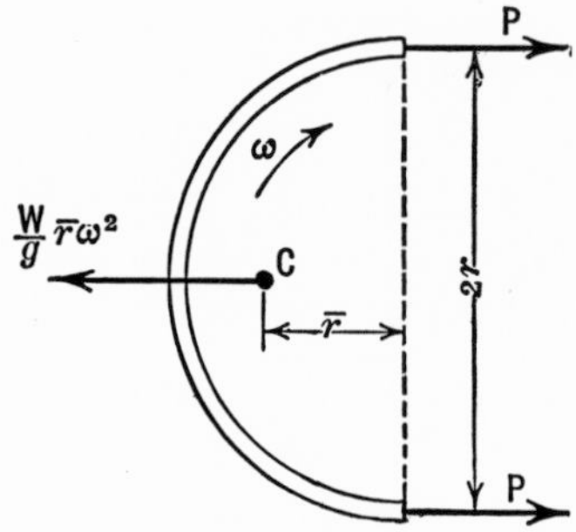

Fig. 364

$$\frac{W}{g}\,\bar{r}\omega^2 = \frac{2Wr\omega^2}{\pi g}$$

This force is in equilibrium with the induced tensile forces P, P in the rim. Thus

$$2P = \frac{2Wr\omega^2}{\pi g} \quad \text{or} \quad P = \frac{Wr\omega^2}{\pi g}$$

The unit stress S in the rim is P/A, so

$$S = \frac{Wr\omega^2}{\pi g A}$$

Since $W = \pi r A \gamma$, where γ = weight per unit volume,

$$S = \frac{r^2\omega^2\gamma}{g} = \frac{\gamma v^2}{g} \approx ML^{-1}T^{-2}$$

When γ is in pounds per cubic foot, v in feet per second, and g in feet per second per second, S will be in pounds per square foot.

Problems

1. A cast-iron flywheel 8 ft. in diameter outside has a rim 4 in. thick. Compute the unit tensile stress in the rim when the speed of rotation is 300 r.p.m. Neglect the tension in the spokes.   *Ans.* 1410 p.s.i.

2. If the allowable tensile stress for cast iron is 3000 lb. per sq. in., compute the maximum safe speed in revolutions per minute for a cast-iron flywheel of 10-ft. outside diameter and 2-in. rim thickness.   *Ans.* 342 r.p.m.

3. The two halves of a 2500-lb. flywheel are cast separately and then fastened together by 6 rivets of 1-in. diameter each. If the mean diameter of the rim is 10 ft. and the wheel rotates at 180 r.p.m., compute the unit tensile stress in the rivets.   *Ans.* 9320 p.s.i.

Art. 94.   The Loaded Conical Pendulum Governor. It was shown in Art. 72 that the height h of a conical pendulum depends only on the angular speed and is not affected by the weight of the rotating mass or the length of its arm. By means of a suitable mechanism the change in height of the pendulum due to a variation in speed may be made to actuate a valve and thereby control the speed of the engine by which it is being rotated. Such a device, known as a simple conical pendulum governor, is shown in Fig. 365.

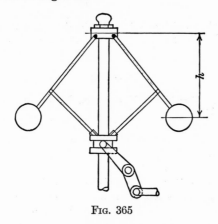

FIG. 365

It may be seen that in this type of governor the change in height h for a given change in speed is greater at low speed than at high speed. In order to make the governor more sensitive at high speed, the height h may be increased by loading. In Fig. 366 (a) is shown such a loaded governor.

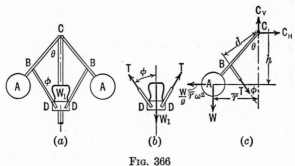

FIG. 366

The load W_1 on the governor is shown as a free body in Fig. 366 (b). Equation $\Sigma F_v = 0$ gives

$$T = \frac{W_1}{2 \cos \phi}$$

One of the rotating spheres is shown as a free body in Fig. 366 (c). Since the weight of the arm is usually small compared to the weight of the sphere, it may be neglected without appreciable error. The equation $\Sigma M_C = 0$ gives

$$W \cdot \bar{r} + T \cdot d = \frac{W}{g} \bar{r}\omega^2 \cdot h$$

The relations between the weights involved, the angles, and the speed of rotation may be determined from the two equations above.

Problems

1. If $AB = 6$ in., $BC = 12$ in., $W = 30$ lb., $W_1 = 150$ lb., and $\theta = \phi = 45°$ for the governor of Fig. 366 when it is at rest, at what speed will it begin to act?
Ans. 109 r.p.m.

2. What load W_1 on the governor of Prob. 1 will cause it to begin to act at a speed of 100 r.p.m.?   *Ans.* 118 lb.

Art. 95. Center of Percussion. If an impulsive force or blow F is applied to a body suspended from an axis O, as shown in Fig. 367,

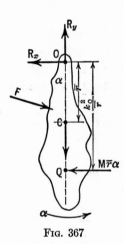

an angular acceleration will result. As shown in Art. 88, the resultant tangential effective force $M\bar{r}\alpha$ acts at point Q, at distance $k_0^2/\bar{r}$ from the axis O. With this force applied in the reversed direction, the body is in equilibrium. From the equation $\Sigma M_Q = 0$, it is seen that a tangential reaction R_x will be induced at O whose direction is to the left when the blow F is struck above Q and to the right when the blow is struck below Q. It is evident that, if the blow were struck at Q, the tangential reaction R_x must be zero regardless of the magnitude of force F. The point Q, at which the body may be struck without producing a tangential reaction at the support, is called the *center of percussion*.

Fig. 367

Problems

1. A uniform slender rod 6 ft. long is suspended from a horizontal axis passing through the rod at 1 ft. from the end. Locate the center of percussion with respect to the lower end of the rod. If a force of 20 lb. is applied horizontally at the center of gravity of the rod, determine the tangential reaction at the support.
Ans. 1.5 ft.; 8.57 lb.

2. A cylindrical disk of 3-ft. diameter is suspended from a horizontal axis parallel to its geometric axis and 1 ft. from it. If a 50-lb. horizontal force is applied to the disk at the center, what tangential reaction at the support will result?
Ans. 26.4 lb.

Art. 96. Compound Pendulum. Any rigid body free to rotate under the influence of gravity about a horizontal axis not passing through the center of gravity is called a *compound pendulum*. In Fig. 368 is shown a compound pendulum, suspended from an axis through O, and having center of gravity at C. With the reversed effective forces added as shown, the body is in equilibrium, and the equation $\Sigma M_O = 0$ gives

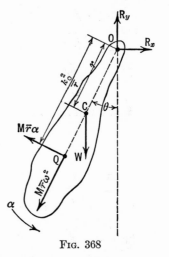

Fig. 368

$$W \cdot \bar{r} \sin \theta = \frac{W}{g} \bar{r} \alpha \cdot \frac{k_0{}^2}{\bar{r}}$$

$$\alpha = \frac{\bar{r}}{k_0{}^2} g \sin \theta$$

The tangential acceleration of point Q is

$$a_t = r\alpha = \frac{k_0{}^2}{\bar{r}} \times \frac{\bar{r}}{k_0{}^2} g \sin \theta = g \sin \theta$$

This is identical with the acceleration of a simple circular pendulum as shown in Art. 74. Therefore the compound pendulum has the same motion as a simple circular pendulum whose length l equals the distance $k_0{}^2/\bar{r}$, and will oscillate with the same period.

Since the period of the simple pendulum has been shown to be

$$T = 2\pi \sqrt{\frac{l}{g}}$$

the period of the compound pendulum becomes

$$T = 2\pi \sqrt{\frac{k_0{}^2}{g\bar{r}}}$$

The distance $k_0{}^2/\bar{r}$ is called the length of the compound pendulum and the point Q is called the *center of oscillation*. By referring to Art. 95, it is seen that the center of oscillation coincides with the center of percussion.

It may further be shown that the center of oscillation and point of suspension are interchangeable. In Fig. 368

$$CQ = \frac{k_0{}^2}{\bar{r}} - \bar{r}$$

Since

$$k_0{}^2 = k_C{}^2 + \bar{r}^2$$

$$CQ = \frac{k_C{}^2 + \bar{r}^2}{\bar{r}} - \bar{r} = \frac{k_C{}^2}{\bar{r}}$$

Now let Q be made the point of suspension. The new center of oscillation O' will be at distance CO' from the center of gravity. By analogy from the preceding equation

$$CO' = \frac{k_C{}^2}{\bar{r}}$$

The new $\bar{r}$ will now be the distance CQ. Thus

$$CO' = \frac{k_C{}^2}{CQ} = \frac{k_C{}^2}{\dfrac{k_C{}^2}{\bar{r}}} = \bar{r}$$

Therefore O' must coincide with O, and what was formerly the point of suspension is now the center of oscillation.

The moment of inertia of a body of irregular shape which might be difficult, if not impossible, to compute, may be found experimentally by suspending the body from a horizontal axis and allowing it to oscillate as a compound pendulum. From the equation for the period of a compound pendulum, as stated above,

$$k_0{}^2 = \frac{T^2}{4\pi^2} g\bar{r}$$

$$I_0 = \frac{W}{g} k_0{}^2 = \frac{W T^2 \bar{r}}{4\pi^2}$$

T may be found by observation of the period of oscillation, and $\bar{r}$ may be found by balancing. The moment of inertia I_0 with respect to the axis of suspension may then be computed.

Problems

1. A slender rod 6 ft. long is suspended from a horizontal axis through one end. Compute the period of oscillation. At what distance from the end may it be suspended and still have the same period?   *Ans.* 2.21 sec.; 2 ft.

2. Determine the length of a slender rod which, when suspended from an axis through one end, will have a period of oscillation of 2 sec.   *Ans.* 4.89 ft.

3. A compound pendulum consists of a circular steel disk of 12-in. diameter and 1-in. thickness at the end of a steel rod 36 in. long, 4 in. wide, and 1 in. thick, suspended from a horizontal axis through its end, as shown in Fig. 369. Compute the period of oscillation.   *Ans.* 1.91 sec.

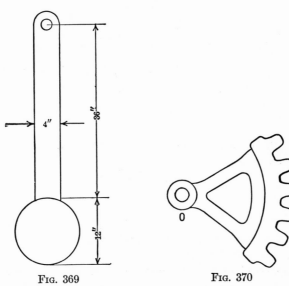

Fɪɢ. 369

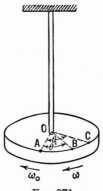

Fɪɢ. 370

4. The gear sector shown in Fig. 370 weighs 180 lb., and the distance of the center of gravity from the axis *O* is found by balancing to be 21 in. When allowed to oscillate as a compound pendulum about a horizontal axis through *O*, it is observed to make 30 complete oscillations per minute. Compute the moment of inertia of the gear sector with respect to its axis of rotation. *Ans.* 32.0 slug-ft.²

Art. 97. Torsion Pendulum.

A body suspended by an elastic wire or slender rod and allowed to oscillate about the axis of the wire, as shown in Fig. 371, is known as a *torsion pendulum.* The wire is rigidly attached to a support at its upper end, and the body is so attached that its center of gravity lies on the axis of the wire. As long as the elastic limit of the wire in shear is not exceeded, the angular displacement θ is proportional to the restoring torque in the opposite direction. Since the angular acceleration α is proportional to the torque, it follows that

$$\alpha = -k\theta$$

where k is the constant of proportionality. Let ω_0 be the angular velocity of the system as it passes

Fɪɢ. 371

through the midposition OA, and ω the angular velocity as it passes through any other position OB for which the angular displacement is θ. Since

$$\omega\, d\omega = \alpha\, d\theta$$

$$\frac{\omega\, d\omega}{d\theta} = \alpha = -k\theta$$

$$\int_{\omega_0}^{\omega} \omega\, d\omega = -k \int_0^{\theta} \theta\, d\theta$$

$$\omega = \sqrt{\omega_0{}^2 - k\theta^2}$$

If θ_1 represents the maximum displacement, the corresponding angular velocity is zero. Hence

$$0 = \sqrt{\omega_0{}^2 - k\theta_1{}^2}$$

$$\omega_0 = \sqrt{k}\cdot\theta_1$$

$$\omega = \sqrt{k(\theta_1{}^2 - \theta^2)}$$

Since $\omega = d\theta/dt$, this equation becomes

$$dt = \frac{d\theta}{\sqrt{k(\theta_1{}^2 - \theta^2)}}$$

Now, if the time is measured from the midposition,

$$\int_0^t dt = \int_0^{\theta} \frac{d\theta}{\sqrt{k(\theta_1{}^2 - \theta^2)}}$$

$$t = \frac{1}{\sqrt{k}} \sin^{-1} \frac{\theta}{\theta_1}$$

The time from midposition to the position of maximum displacement θ_1 is

$$t_1 = \frac{1}{\sqrt{k}} \sin^{-1} \frac{\theta_1}{\theta_1} = \frac{\pi}{2\sqrt{k}}$$

Since this represents the time for one-quarter of an oscillation, the period T of a complete oscillation becomes

$$T = \frac{2\pi}{\sqrt{k}}$$

If the torque required to produce the angular displacement θ_1 is denoted by C_1, and the moment of inertia of the body with respect to the axis of rotation by I, then

$$C_1 = -I\alpha = Ik\theta_1$$

$$k = \frac{C_1}{I\theta_1}$$

The period T thus becomes

$$T = 2\pi\sqrt{\frac{I\theta_1}{C_1}}$$

The moment of inertia of a body of irregular shape may be determined experimentally by means of the torsion pendulum. The apparatus for this purpose consists of two disks firmly connected as shown in Fig. 372, with the upper disk rigidly fastened to the wire and the lower disk supporting the object whose moment of inertia is required, so placed that its center of gravity is at the axis of the wire. If I_1 represents the moment of inertia of the apparatus alone and T_1 its period, then

$$T_1 = 2\pi\sqrt{\frac{I_1\theta_1}{C_1}}$$

Since the ratio θ_1/C_1 is a constant for the wire within its elastic limit,

$$T_1 = K\sqrt{I_1} \qquad\qquad (1)$$

FIG. 372

where K is a constant.

Similarly, if I represents the moment of inertia of the body and T the period of body and apparatus together,

$$T = K\sqrt{I_1 + I} \qquad\qquad (2)$$

By combining equations (1) and (2), the following relations are obtained:

$$\frac{T_1}{T} = \sqrt{\frac{I_1}{I_1 + I}}$$

$$I = I_1\left[\frac{T^2}{T_1^2} - 1\right]$$

If the value θ_1/C_1 can be determined, I_1 may be obtained from equation (1) after observing the period of oscillation of the apparatus alone.   If the apparatus is of such form that its moment of inertia I_1 can be computed directly, it will not be necessary to determine the value θ_1/C_1.

Problems

1. A torsion pendulum consists of a cast-iron plate 1 ft. square and 1 in. thick, suspended at its center by a steel wire 5 ft. long and $\frac{1}{8}$ in. in diameter.   What torque is required to produce a displacement of 30°?   Compute the period of oscillation. Modulus of elasticity in shear, $E = 12,000,000$ lb. per sq. in.

Ans. 0.209 ft-lb.; 4.38 sec.

2. The disks of the torsion pendulum shown in Fig. 372 have a diameter of 2 ft. and a combined weight of 120 lb.   The unloaded pendulum is observed to make 25 oscillations in 1 min.   A connecting rod whose moment of inertia is required is placed on the lower disk with its center of gravity at the axis of the wire and the combination is now observed to make 15 oscillations in 1 min.   Compute the moment of inertia of the connecting rod with respect to its centroidal axis. (Assume the weight of the vertical rods between the disks to be negligible.)

Ans. 3.32 slug-ft.^{2}

Supplementary Problems

1. The rotating parts of the hoist shown in Fig. 373 weigh 600 lb. and have a radius of gyration of 1.8 ft.   The loaded car has a velocity of 22 ft. per sec. down the incline just before the band brake is applied.   Car resistance is 8 lb. per ton,

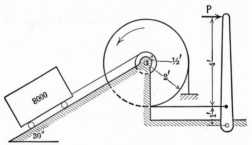

Fig. 373

and the coefficient of friction for the band brake is 0.35.   What force P on the brake lever is required to decelerate the car at the rate of 2 ft. per sec.^{2}?   Neglect the bearing friction.

Ans. 59.0 lb.

2. The rim of a cast-iron flywheel has 6-ft. diameter outside, 5-ft. diameter inside, and 1-ft. width.   The axle has 4-in. diameter and rotates in bearings for which the coefficient of friction is 0.015.   Neglecting the mass of hub and spokes, in what time will the flywheel come to rest from a speed of 200 r.p.m. under the action of friction alone?

Ans. 33.1 min.

3. Two cast-iron balls, each 12 in. in diameter, are connected by a stiff rod and rotate about a vertical axis midway between them as shown in Fig. 374.   Neglecting bearing friction and the mass of rod and axle, what weight W will give the spheres an angular velocity of 600 r.p.m. in 20 sec., starting from rest?   *Ans.* 228 lb.

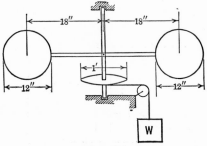

FIG. 374

4. A circular steel disk of 3-ft. diameter and 2-in. thickness is mounted on a horizontal axis through an element of its curved surface. It is held at rest with its center vertically above the axis, then released, and allowed to rotate under the influence of gravity alone. Compute the normal and tangential components of the reaction at the support as the disk passes through (*a*) a position 120° from the starting position; (*b*) a position 180° from the starting position.

Ans. (*a*) $R_n = 1440$ lb., $R_t = 167$ lb.; (*b*) $R_n = 2110$ lb., $R_t = 0$.

5. The disk of Prob. 4 is cut into two equal semicircular portions. One of these is mounted on a horizontal axis coinciding with its geometric axis. It is held at rest with its center of gravity vertically above the axis, then released, and allowed to rotate under the influence of gravity alone. Compute the normal and tangential components of the reaction at the support as the disk passes through a position (*a*) 90° from the starting position; (*b*) 180° from the starting position.

Ans. (*a*) $R_n = 208$ lb., $R_t = 185$ lb.; (*b*) $R_n = 705$ lb., $R_t = 0$ lb.

6. Determine the period of oscillation of the semicircular disk described in Prob. 5.   *Ans.* 1.47 sec.

7. Show that for a slender rod of length l, suspended from a vertical axis through its upper end, the limiting speed of rotation in revolutions per minute for which lifting impends is given by $n = \dfrac{15}{\pi}\sqrt{\dfrac{6g}{l}}$.

8. If the rod described in Prob. 7 is rotated at a speed twice that for which lifting impends, to what angle with the vertical will it rise?   *Ans.* 75.5°.

9. What are the speed of rotation about the vertical axis and the tension in the supporting cables of the swing shown in Fig. 375 when the angle θ is 75°?

Ans. 29.4 r.p.m.; 3.87W lb.

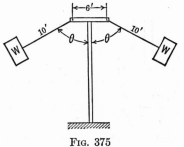

FIG. 375

10. A cast-iron flywheel whose rim is 12 in. wide, 4 in. thick, and 10 ft. in outside diameter is ruptured while rotating at a speed of 900 r.p.m. Compute the maximum tensile strength. Neglect the tension in the spokes.   *Ans.* 20,100 p.s.i.

11. If the allowable tensile strength of cast iron is 3,000 lb. per sq. in., determine the limiting speed for a flywheel 12 ft. in diameter. *Ans.* 280 r.p.m.

12. If the allowable tensile stress for cast iron is 3000 lb. per sq. in., what is the limiting diameter of cast-iron flywheels rotating at 600 r.p.m., assuming tension in spokes to be neglected? *Ans.* 5.6 ft.

13. In the weighted conical pendulum governor shown in Fig. 376, $W_1 = 60$ lb. and $W = 20$ lb. What is the speed of rotation for the position shown? *Ans.* 137 r.p.m.

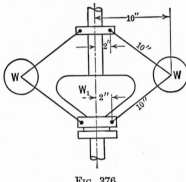

Fig. 376

14. A compound pendulum consists of a semicircular steel disk of 6-in. diameter and 1-in. thickness attached to a circular steel rod 18 in. long and 1 in. in diameter suspended from a horizontal axis through its upper end, as shown in Fig. 377. Compute the distance of the center of oscillation from the support, and the period of oscillation.

Ans. 17 in.; 1.32 sec.

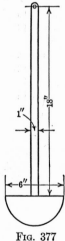

15. The connecting rod of a locomotive weighs 600 lb., and the distance of its center of gravity from the center of the crank pin is found to be 3 ft. Upon suspending the connecting rod from the crank pin and allowing it to oscillate as a compound pendulum, it is observed to make 25 complete vibrations in 60 sec. Compute the moment of inertia of the connecting rod with respect to the axis of the crank pin and also with respect to the parallel centroidal axis. *Ans.* 263 slug-ft.^{2}; 95 slug-ft.^{2}

16. A shaft 8 ft. long carries at 2 ft. from the left end a steel disk 18 in. in diameter and 3 in. thick, keyed to the shaft and 6 in. eccentric. At 2 ft. from the right end is keyed a similar disk at 90° behind the first. The system is to be balanced by placing counterweights at 12-in. radial distance in planes at the ends of the shaft. Determine the balancing weights required and their angular position. *Ans.* 85.4 lb.; 162°; 108°.

Fig. 377

CHAPTER XIV

PLANE MOTION

Art. 98. Plane Motion. When a body moves in such a manner that all points in the body describe paths lying in parallel planes, the motion is known as plane motion. The plane in which the center of gravity moves is usually taken as the reference plane. Such motion in general consists of a combination of translation and rotation, as is evident in a rolling wheel or the connecting rod of an engine. If the motion of some point of reference within a body having plane motion is known, the motion of any other point in the body may be determined by the principle of relative motion, as discussed in Art. 99. It can also be shown that any plane motion at a given instant may be reduced to one of rotation only about an axis known as the *instantaneous axis*. The use of the instantaneous axis in determining the motion of any point in the body will be discussed in Art. 100.

Art. 99. Relative Motion. The motion of a body referred to a point fixed in space is known as its absolute motion. The motion of a body referred to a point which is itself in motion is known as its motion relative to the given moving point. Thus, the displacement, velocity, or acceleration of a body may be absolute or relative. Although the earth is in motion through space, it is customary, in dealing with objects moving on the earth, to regard points on the earth's surface as fixed. The motion of a body with respect to a point fixed on the earth is then regarded as absolute.

If the velocity of a point B relative to a moving point A be added vectorially to the absolute velocity of A, the vector sum will be the absolute velocity of B.

Absolute velocity of A +> Velocity of B relative to A =

Absolute velocity of B

The same proposition is equally true when displacement or acceleration is substituted for velocity. It should be particularly noted that the addition indicated must be performed vectorially. The principle of relative motion may be used to advantage in many problems involving motion of two or more objects.

229

Example

In Fig. 378 (*a*), *A* is the cross head, *B* the crank pin, *AB* the connecting rod, and *O* the center of the flywheel of a reciprocating engine. The connecting rod is 3 ft. long, and the crank radius is 1 ft. Determine the absolute velocity of the cross head *A* when the speed of rotation of the flywheel is 120 r.p.m. and the crank pin *B* is 60° from dead center, as shown.

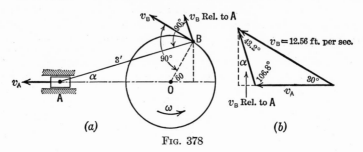

(*a*)   (*b*)

FIG. 378

Solution: The absolute velocity of the crank pin *B* is at 90° with the crank radius *OB*. It is therefore at 30° with the horizontal, and its magnitude is

$$v_B = r\omega = 1 \cdot \left(\frac{120}{60}\right) \times 2\pi = 12.56 \text{ ft. per sec.}$$

The cross head *A* is forced to move between horizontal guides, and therefore the direction of the absolute velocity of *A* is known to be horizontal.

The crank pin *B* is always at a fixed distance of 3 ft. from *A*. Therefore the direction of the velocity of *B* relative to *A* must be at 90° with *AB* and consequently at angle α with the vertical. From Fig. 378 (*a*)

$$\alpha = \sin^{-1}\frac{1 \sin 60°}{3} = \sin^{-1} 0.289 = 16.8°$$

The directions of all three of the velocities involved are now known, together with the magnitude of one of them; the vector triangle is thus determined as shown in Fig. 378 (*b*). The value of v_A may be determined graphically from the triangle, or trigonometrically, by the sine law, as follows:

$$\frac{v_A}{\sin 43.2°} = \frac{12.56}{\sin 106.8°}$$

$$v_A = 8.98 \text{ ft. per sec.}$$

Problems

1. A boat which can develop a speed of 20 mi. per hr. in still water is directed straight across a river 3000 ft. wide whose velocity is 3 mi. per hr. How long will it take to cross the river? Where, and with what velocity, will it strike the opposite bank?   *Ans.* 450 ft. downstream.

2. At what angle must the boat in Prob. 1 be directed upstream in order to land directly across the river?   *Ans.* 8.62°.

3. Solve Prob. 1 if the boat is directed 30° upstream.   *Ans.* 1210 ft. upstream.

4. An iceboat is to attain a velocity of 60 mi. per hr. due east when the wind from the north has a velocity of 30 mi. per hr. At what angle with the direction of the boat must the sail be placed to make this possible? Assume friction to be negligible.
                                                              Ans. 26.6°.

5. Solve the Example of Art. 99 if the crank angle is 120° instead of 60°.
                                                              Ans. 12.8 f.p.s.

6. An airplane is headed east with a speed of 120 mi. per hr. There is a 60-mi.-per-hr. northeast wind. Compute (*a*) the ground speed; (*b*) the drift.
                                                              Ans. 88.3 m.p.h.; 28.6°.

7. The water-driven turbine shown in Fig. 379 is rotating at 382 r.p.m. The water enters with a velocity of 80 ft. per sec. at an angle of 60° with the radius

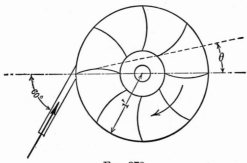

FIG. 379

extended. If the outside radius of the wheel is 1 ft., at what angle θ should the blade be curved at the outer edge for smooth entrance?   *Ans.* 36.2°.

Art. 100. Instantaneous Center.

It was pointed out in Art. 98 that any plane motion of a body can be reduced to one of rotation only about an axis called the instantaneous axis. The intersection of the instantaneous axis with the plane of reference is called the *instantaneous center*. If the direction of the absolute velocities of any two points in the body is known, the location of the instantaneous center may be found. Let v_A and v_B, Fig. 380, represent the respective velocities of points A and B in a rigid body having plane motion. If the motion of the body can be reduced to one of rotation only, the center about which A rotates must lie on a line through A normal to the direction of the velocity v_A. Likewise, the center about which B rotates must lie on a line through B normal to the direction of the velocity v_B. The intersection I of these two lines must therefore be the instantaneous center of rotation for the body. This point does not in general remain fixed in position with respect to the body or to space.

If the angular velocity of the body with respect to the instantaneous axis is denoted by ω, then $v_A = r_A \omega$ and $v_B = r_B \omega$.

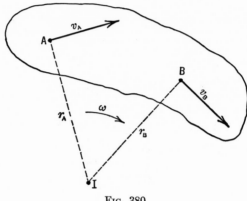

FIG. 380

Example

Solve the Example of Art. 99, making use of the instantaneous center.

Solution: The instantaneous center of rotation for the connecting rod AB, Fig. 381, is located at I, the intersection of the normals to the absolute velocities of points A and B.

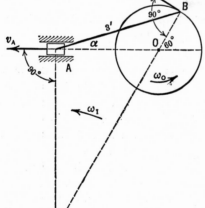

FIG. 381

In the triangle AOB, the angle α is 16.8°, as previously determined. Angle ABO is thus 43.2°, and angle AIB is 30°. Now, applying the sine law to triangle ABI,

$$\frac{AI}{\sin 43.2°} = \frac{3}{\sin 30°} = \frac{BI}{\sin 106.8°}$$

$$AI = 4.11 \text{ ft.}; \; BI = 5.74 \text{ ft.}$$

The absolute linear velocity of B is 12.56 ft. per sec., as previously determined. Hence the angular velocity of B with respect to the instantaneous center is

$$\omega_I = \frac{v_B}{BI} = \frac{12.56}{5.74} = 2.18 \text{ rad. per sec.}$$

This is also the angular velocity of the body. Hence the absolute linear velocity of A is

$$v_A = AI \cdot \omega_I = 4.11 \times 2.18 = 8.98 \text{ ft. per sec.}$$

Problems

1. Solve the Example of Art. 100 if the crank angle is 120° instead of 60°.
Ans. 12.8 f.p.s.

2. Figure 382 shows the absolute velocity of various points on the rim of a wheel in plane motion. If the wheel is 4 ft. in diameter and has a linear speed of 20 ft. per sec., compute the absolute velocities at points A, B, and D.
Ans. $V_A = 0$; $V_D = 28.3$ f.p.s.

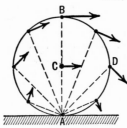

Fig. 382

3. In the mechanism shown in Fig. 383 the wheel A rotates at 450 r.p.m. Determine the absolute velocity of point C and the angular velocity of link CD when in the position shown. *Ans.* 16.6 f.p.s.; 11.1 rad. per sec.

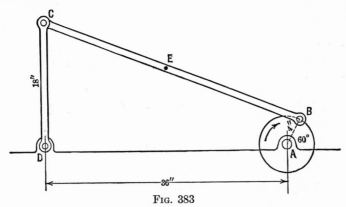

Fig. 383

4. Compute the absolute velocity of the center of gravity E of the link BC shown in Fig. 383 if $CE = 20$ in. *Ans.* 15.6 f.p.s.

Art. 101. Equations of Plane Motion.

In Fig. 384 is shown a rigid body, with center of gravity at C, rotating about an axis through any point O with angular velocity ω and angular acceleration α, the axis of rotation itself having motion of translation with velocity v and acceleration a. A particle of mass dM at radial distance ρ from O is shown. Because of the rotation of the body, the particle will have a tangential acceleration $\rho\alpha$ and a normal acceleration $\rho\omega^2$. Because of the translation of the body, the particle will have an acceleration a, parallel to the direction of translation. The effective forces acting on the particle to produce these accelerations are $dM\rho\alpha$ in the tangential direction, $dM\rho\omega^2$ in the normal direction, and dMa in the direction of

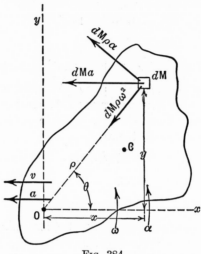

Fig. 384

the translation. The point O is taken as the origin of coordinates with the x axis in the direction of translation. The following equations are then obtained:

$$\Sigma F_x = \int dMa + \int dM\rho\alpha \sin\theta + \int dM\rho\omega^2 \cos\theta \qquad (1)$$

$$\Sigma F_y = \int dM\rho\alpha \cos\theta - \int dM\rho\omega^2 \sin\theta \qquad (2)$$

$$\Sigma M_o = \int dMa \cdot \rho \sin\theta + \int dM\rho\alpha \cdot \rho \qquad (3)$$

Since a, α, and ω are common to all points in the body, and since $\rho \sin\theta = y$, and $\rho \cos\theta = x$, equations (1) to (3) become:

$$\Sigma F_x = a \int dM + \alpha \int y \, dM + \omega^2 \int x \, dM \qquad (4)$$

$$\Sigma F_y = \alpha \int x \, dM - \omega^2 \int y \, dM \qquad (5)$$

$$\Sigma M_o = a \int y \, dM + \alpha \int \rho^2 \, dM \qquad (6)$$

Now, $\int dM = M$, $\int y\, dM = M\bar{y}$, $\int x\, dM = M\bar{x}$, and $\int \rho^2\, dM$
$= I_0$, so that the equations now become:

$$\Sigma F_x = Ma + M\bar{y}\alpha + M\bar{x}\omega^2 \tag{7}$$

$$\Sigma F_y = M\bar{x}\alpha - M\bar{y}\omega^2 \tag{8}$$

$$\Sigma M_0 = M\bar{y}a + I_0\alpha \tag{9}$$

Equations (7) to (9) are the general equations for plane motion.

Art. 102. Rolling Bodies. Equations (7) to (9) of Art. 101 may be further simplified if the axis of rotation is taken through the center of gravity. When this is done, $\bar{x} = 0$, $\bar{y} = 0$, a becomes $\bar{a}$, I_0 becomes I_C, and the equations of motion become

$$\Sigma F_x = M\bar{a} \tag{1}$$

$$\Sigma F_y = 0 \tag{2}$$

$$\Sigma M_C = I_C\alpha \tag{3}$$

Equations (1) to (3) may be applied to any rolling body, provided the axis of reference is taken through the center of gravity. Their application will now be shown.

Example 1

A solid cylinder 3 ft. in diameter and weighing 400 lb. is pulled up a 30° incline by a force $P = 300$ lb., as shown in Fig. 385. Assuming that the cylinder

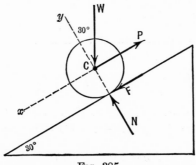

FIG. 385

rolls freely (without slipping), determine the linear acceleration of the center of gravity of the cylinder and the static frictional force F developed between cylinder and incline.

Solution· The cylinder will be considered as rotating about an axis through its center, which in turn will have a linear acceleration directed up the slope

The x axis is taken parallel to the line of motion, and equations (1) to (3) of Art. 102 are applied:

$$\Sigma F_x = 300 - 400 \sin 30° - F = \frac{400}{32.2}\, a$$

$$\Sigma F_y = N - 400 \cos 30° = 0$$

$$\Sigma M_C = F \times 1.5 = \frac{1}{2}\frac{400}{32.2}\,(1.5)^2\alpha$$

Also:

$$a = r\alpha = 1.5\alpha$$

Simultaneous solution of these equations gives

$$a = 5.37 \text{ ft. per sec.}^2;\, F = 33.3 \text{ lb.}$$

Example 2

A solid cylinder rolls down a plane inclined at angle θ with the horizontal. Show that $f = \frac{1}{3}\tan\theta$ is the minimum value of the coefficient of friction which will prevent slipping.

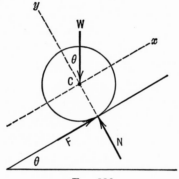

Fig. 386

Solution: The forces acting on the cylinder are shown in Fig. 386. The equations of plane motion become

$$\Sigma F_x = W \sin\theta - F = \frac{Wa}{g} \tag{1}$$

$$\Sigma F_y = N - W \cos\theta = 0 \tag{2}$$

$$\Sigma M_C = F\cdot r = \frac{1}{2}\frac{W}{g}r^2\alpha \tag{3}$$

Also

$$a = r\alpha \tag{4}$$

and

$$F = fN \tag{5}$$

Simultaneous solution of these equations gives $f = \frac{1}{3}\tan\theta$. For smaller values of f, partial slipping will occur.

Example 3

The roller in Fig. 387 weighs 200 lb. and has a radius of gyration of $\frac{3}{4}$ ft. If the roller is released from rest and rolls freely, compute the linear velocity of its center of gravity after it has moved 10 ft.

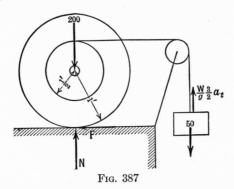

Fig. 387

Solution: Letting T represent the unknown cable tension and a the unknown linear acceleration of the center of gravity, the equations of plane motion for the roller become

$$\Sigma F_x = T - F = \frac{200}{32.2}\, a \tag{1}$$

$$\Sigma F_y = N - 200 = 0 \tag{2}$$

$$\Sigma M_C = T \times \frac{1}{2} + F \times 1 = \left[\frac{200}{32.2} \left(\frac{3}{4} \right)^2 \right] \alpha \tag{3}$$

Also

$$a = r\alpha = 1 \cdot \alpha = \alpha \tag{4}$$

The acceleration of the 50-lb. counterweight will, by inspection or by use of the instantaneous center, be $1\frac{1}{2}$ times that of the center of the roller. If the reversed effective force is added to this body, a vertical summation of forces gives

$$T + \frac{50(\frac{3}{2}a)}{32.2} = 50 \tag{5}$$

Simultaneous solution of equations (1) to (5) gives

$$F = 1.5 \text{ lb.;} \; T = 36.8 \text{ lb.;} \; a = 5.69 \text{ ft. per sec.}^2$$

Finally

$$v^2 = v_0^2 + 2as$$

$$v^2 = 0 + 2(5.69)(10) = 113.8$$

$$v = 10.7 \text{ ft. per sec.}$$

Problems

1. A cylinder starts from rest and rolls freely down a 30° plane. How far will it roll in 2 sec.?   *Ans.* 21.5 ft.

2. Solve Prob. 1 if the cylinder is replaced by a sphere.   *Ans.* 23 ft.

3. Solve for the velocity of the cylinder shown in Fig. 388 after it has rolled 10 ft. from rest. Compute the friction force. The weight of the cylinder is 100 lb. Assume the cylinder to be solid in determining the moment of inertia.

Ans. 4.62 f.p.s.

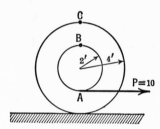

FIG. 388

4. Solve Prob. 3 if the force is horizontal and applied at *B*.   *Ans.* 8.02 f.p.s.

5. Solve Prob. 3 if the force is applied at *C*.

6. A cylinder starts up a 20° incline with a velocity of 15 ft. per sec. Assuming that no slipping occurs, how far will the cylinder roll?   *Ans.* 15.3 ft.

7. The roller shown in Fig. 389 weighs 50 lb. and has a radius of gyration of 1.5 ft. If it starts from rest and rolls freely, determine its angular velocity at the end of 20 sec. and the frictional force.   *Ans.* 99.0 rad. per sec.; 17.3 lb.

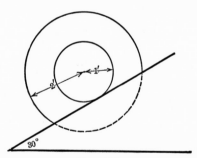

FIG. 389

8. A 100-lb. cylinder of 2-ft. diameter starts from rest on a 45° incline. The coefficient of kinetic friction is 0.2; the coefficient of static friction is 0.22. Compute the force of friction, the linear velocity of the center, and angular velocity of the cylinder, after it has traveled 15 ft.   *Ans.* 14.1 lb.; 23.3 f.p.s.; 11.6 rad. per sec.

9. A solid sphere rolls down a plane inclined at angle θ with the horizontal. Determine the minimum value of the coefficient of friction which will prevent slipping.   *Ans.* $f = \frac{2}{7} \tan \theta$.

10. Solve Ex. 3 if the rope comes off the lower side of the drum attached to the roller.   *Ans.* 7.03 f.p.s.

11. The roller in Fig. 390 is a solid cylinder weighing 600 lb. with the rope wrapped around it. Assuming that no slipping occurs, compute the cable tension,

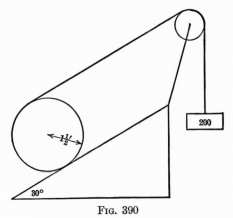

Fig. 390

the friction, and the linear velocity of the center of the roller after moving 20 ft. from rest.   *Ans.* 177 lb.; 159 lb.; 8.7 f.p.s.

Art. 103. Kinetic Energy of Plane Motion. A rigid body having plane motion is shown in Fig. 391 (*a*). The motion consists of rotation with angular velocity ω about an axis through point O combined with translation of the axis with linear velocity v_0. Any particle of mass dM within the body will have two component velocities, $v_t = \rho\omega$ in the tangential direction, and v_0 parallel and equal to the velocity of O.

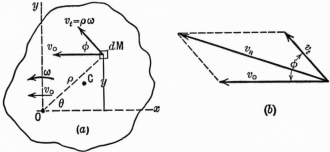

Fig. 391

The resultant velocity of dM is the vector sum of these two components, or v_R as shown in Fig. 391 (*b*). By the cosine law

$$v_R{}^2 = v_0{}^2 + v_t{}^2 + 2v_0 \cdot v_t \cdot \cos\phi$$

$$= v_0{}^2 + \rho^2\omega^2 + 2v_0 \cdot \rho\omega \cdot \sin\theta$$

$$= v_0{}^2 + \rho^2\omega^2 + 2v_0\omega \cdot y$$

Since the kinetic energy of the particle is $\frac{1}{2} dMv_R{}^2$, the total kinetic energy of the body is

$$K.E. = \int \tfrac{1}{2} dMv_R{}^2$$

$$K.E. = \int \tfrac{1}{2} dMv_0{}^2 + \int \tfrac{1}{2} dM\rho^2\omega^2 + \int dMv_0\omega y$$

Since v_0 and ω are common to all particles, the preceding equation becomes

$$K.E. = \tfrac{1}{2}v_0{}^2 \int dM + \tfrac{1}{2}\omega^2 \int \rho^2 \, dM + v_0\omega \int y \, dM$$

$$= \tfrac{1}{2}Mv_0{}^2 + \tfrac{1}{2}I_0\omega^2 + v_0\omega M\bar{y}$$

Now, if the axis of rotation is taken through the center of gravity C, $\bar{y} = 0$ and the total kinetic energy becomes

$$\boldsymbol{K.E. = \tfrac{1}{2}M\bar{v}^2 + \tfrac{1}{2}I_C\omega^2}$$

Thus, the total kinetic energy of a body having plane motion may be considered as the sum of its kinetic energy of translation and its kinetic energy of rotation about an axis through its center of gravity.

The work-energy equation as previously applied to rectilinear motion and to motion of rotation may also be applied to plane motion.

Example 1

A sphere starts from rest and rolls freely down a 30° incline 40 ft. long. Determine the linear velocity of its center of gravity as it reaches the foot of the slope.

Solution: The initial kinetic energy of the sphere is zero. Positive work is done by gravity. No negative work is done since the frictional force necessary to prevent slipping is static and produces no displacement. The final kinetic energy is the sum of the energies of translation and rotation. The work-energy equation thus becomes:

$$0 + W \cdot 40 \sin 30° - 0 = \frac{1}{2} \frac{W}{32.2} v^2 + \frac{1}{2} \left[\frac{2}{5} \frac{W}{32.2} r^2 \right] \left(\frac{v}{r} \right)^2$$

$$v = 30.3 \text{ ft. per sec.}$$

Example 2

The roller in Fig. 392 weighs 200 lb. and has a radius of gyration of $\frac{3}{4}$ ft. If the roller is released from rest and rolls freely, compute the linear velocity of its center after it has moved 10 ft.

Solution: The initial kinetic energy of the system is zero. Positive work is done by gravity on the 50-lb. counterweight. No negative work is done.

The final kinetic energy of the system includes the energy of translation of the roller, the energy of rotation of the roller, and the energy of translation of the counterweight.

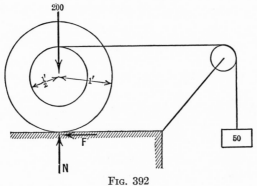

FIG. 392

By inspection it is seen that the displacement and velocity of the counterweight will each be $1\frac{1}{2}$ times that of the roller. The resulting work-energy equation is then:

$$0 + 50 \times 15 - 0 = \frac{1}{2}\frac{200}{32.2}v^2 + \frac{1}{2}\left[\frac{200}{32.2}\left(\frac{3}{4}\right)^2\right]\left(\frac{v}{1}\right)^2 + \frac{1}{2}\frac{50}{32.2}(1.5v)^2$$

$$v = 10.7 \text{ ft. per sec.}$$

This solution should be compared with that of Ex. 3, Art. 102.

Problems

1. Solve Prob. 3, Art. 102, by the work-energy method.

2. Solve for the angular velocity of the roller in Prob. 7, Art. 102, by the work-energy method.

3. Solve for the velocity of the roller in Prob. 11, Art. 102, by the work-energy method.

4. A sphere of 8-in. diameter is given an initial linear velocity of 15 ft. per sec. along a horizontal surface. If the coefficient of rolling resistance is 0.1 in., how far will the sphere roll? *Ans.* 196 ft.

5. Solve Prob. 6, Art. 102, by the work-energy method.

6. Determine the angle of inclination of force P in Fig. 388, so that the cylinder will slide without rolling. *Ans.* 60° with the horizontal.

Supplementary Problems

1. It is desired to fly an airplane due north. The air speed is 120 mi. per hr., and there is a 60-mi.-per-hr. wind coming from the northeast, 70° from north. Determine the proper heading and the ground speed. *Ans.* 28.1°; 85.5 m.p.h.

2. The drive wheel of a locomotive is 6 ft. in diameter, and the crank radius is 15 in. If the locomotive is running at a speed of 60 mi. per hr., determine the absolute velocity of the crank pin (a) when it is horizontally in front of the center of the wheel; (b) when it is directly below the center of the wheel; (c) when it is behind and 30° above the center of the wheel.

Ans. (c) 111 f.p.s. at 16.6° above the horizontal.

3. Steam with a velocity of 2500 ft. per sec. enters a turbine through a nozzle placed at 20° with the plane of the rotor as shown in Fig. 393. If the bucket speed

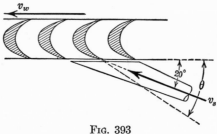

Fig. 393

is 500 ft. per sec., at what angle θ should the buckets be curved at the outer edge for smooth entrance?   Ans. 24.8°.

4. In the quick-return shaper mechanism shown in Fig. 394, B is a block which is pinned to the wheel D and slides within the slotted arm AC, causing it to oscillate

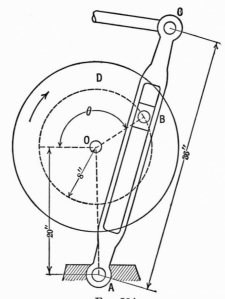

Fig. 394

about the fixed center A as the wheel rotates. If the wheel D rotates at 30 r.p.m., determine the velocity of B relative to the arm AC, and the absolute velocity of C, when the angle θ is 150°.

Ans. 1.45 f.p.s. toward A; 2.16 f.p.s. at 16.1° with horizontal.

5. Solve for the absolute velocity of C in Prob. 4 (a) when θ = 90°; (b) when θ = 270°.   Ans. 2.69 f.p.s.; 6.28 f.p.s.

6. The connecting rod in Fig. 395 is 20 in. long, and the radius of the crank is 8 in. If the flywheel is rotating at 150 r.p.m., determine the velocity of the cross

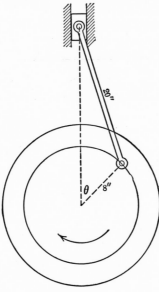

FIG. 395

head when $\theta = 45°$. Solve by use of relative motion and check by use of the instantaneous center.   *Ans.* 9.58 f.p.s.

7. A cylinder 1 ft. in diameter and weighing 60 lb. has a cord wrapped around it and attached to a support above, as shown in Fig. 396. If the cylinder is released from rest and allowed to fall, determine the linear acceleration and the tension in the cord. From the acceleration determine the linear velocity of the center of gravity after it has fallen 5 ft. Check the velocity by the work-energy method.
                Ans. 21.5 f.p.s.^{2}; 20.0 lb.; 14.6 f.p.s.

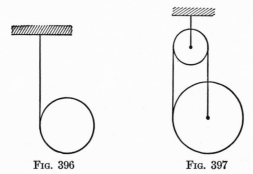

FIG. 396   FIG. 397

8. Solve Prob. 7 if the cord passes around a pulley at the top and returns to the center of the cylinder as shown in Fig. 397. Neglect the mass of the pulley.
                Ans. 10.7 f.p.s.^{2}; 20 lb.; 10.3 f.p.s.

9. A wheel and its axle weigh 400 lb. and have a radius of gyration of 1.5 ft. The wheel is placed with the projecting parts of the axles resting on tracks inclined to 30° with the horizontal as shown in Fig. 398. What friction force is required

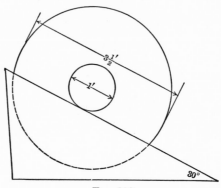

FIG. 398

to prevent slipping as the wheel rolls down the track? Assuming that no slipping occurs, determine the angular velocity of the wheel after rolling 10 ft.

Ans. 180 lb.; 108 r.p.m.

10. The wheel described in Prob. 9 is pulled up the inclined track by a force P applied at the center of the wheel and acting parallel to the track. Determine the force P required to give the center of the wheel a linear acceleration of 0.5 ft. per sec.[2] Assuming that no slipping occurs, determine the friction at the rolling surface.

Ans. 262 lb.; 56 lb.

11. A 20-lb. block is suspended from a cord wrapped around a cylinder which rolls on a horizontal track as shown in Fig. 399. The cylinder has a 2-ft. diameter and weighs 200 lb. If the cylinder starts from rest and rolls without slipping, compute its angular velocity after it has rolled 10 ft. *Ans.* 58.7 r.p.m.

12. A hollow cylinder having 18-in. outside diameter and 15-in. inside diameter starts from rest and rolls freely down a 15° slope 20 ft. long. With what velocity and in what time will it reach the foot of the slope? Solve by means of the equations of plane motion and check by means of work-energy.

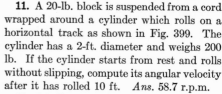

FIG. 399

Ans. 13.4 f.p.s.

13. Solve Prob. 12 if rolling resistance is taken into consideration, the coefficient being 0.05 in. *Ans.* 13.3 f.p.s.

14. How far along a horizontal surface will the hollow cylinder of Prob. 13 continue to roll after reaching the foot of the slope? *Ans.* 915 ft.

CHAPTER XV

IMPULSE, MOMENTUM, AND IMPACT

Art. 104. Linear Impulse and Momentum. The effect of forces on the motion of bodies has been determined thus far by the force, mass, and acceleration method (Chap. X) and by the work-energy method (Chap. XII). A third method, utilizing impulse and momentum, is of advantage in certain problems and will now be considered.

The *impulse* of a force is the product of the force and the time during which it acts. Thus, if a force F is constant in magnitude and direction during time t, its impulse is given by the statement:

$$\text{Linear impulse} = F \cdot t \approx MLT^{-1}$$

If the force is variable in magnitude, the impulse may be taken for a differential time dt and then integrated to determine the total impulse $\int_0^t F \, dt$. Impulse is a vector quantity and subject to the laws governing vectors in general. The direction of the impulse vector is the same as that of the force involved. There is no special name for the unit of impulse, and it is therefore expressed in terms of the force and time units in use. Thus the customary unit in engineering work is the pound-second.

The linear *momentum* of a body is the product of its mass and velocity. Thus

$$\text{Linear momentum} = Mv \approx MLT^{-1}$$

Momentum is a vector quantity also, the direction being the same as that of the change of velocity involved. There is no special name for the unit of momentum; but, since linear momentum has the same dimensions as linear impulse, it may be expressed in the same units. As stated above, the customary unit is the pound-second.

The relation between the impulse of a force acting upon a body and the change of momentum of the body is based on Newton's second law of motion, the mathematical expression of which, as stated in Chap. X, is $F = Ma$, where F represents the resultant or unbalanced force acting on the body and a the acceleration produced. Let both sides of the equation be multiplied by dt. Then

$$F\,dt = Ma\,dt$$

Since $a = dv/dt$ by definition, the above equation becomes

$$F\,dt = M\,dv$$

Let the limits be 0 and t for time and v_0 and v for velocity. Then, if the mass is constant,

$$\int_0^t F\,dt = M \int_{v_0}^v dv = Mv - Mv_0$$

If the force is constant,

$$\boldsymbol{Ft = Mv - Mv_0}$$

It is thus seen that the linear impulse of a force acting upon a body is equal to the change of linear momentum. If a body is acted upon by several forces, the change of momentum is equal to the vector sum of the separate impulses received.

The above relation is particularly useful in problems where force, mass, velocity, and time are involved. It is also valuable in analyzing situations involving impulsive forces, that is, forces acting for infinitesimal or indefinitely small intervals of time.

Example 1

Determine the drawbar pull required to increase the velocity of a 50-ton car on a 1 per cent grade from 30 mi. per hr. to 60 mi. per hr. in 2 min. if the train resistance is 8 lb. per ton.

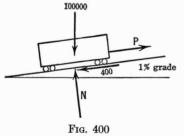

Solution: The forces acting on the car, including the total train resistance of 400 lb. and the unknown drawbar pull P, are shown in Fig. 400. The resultant force in the direction of motion is

$$F = P - 400 - 1000 = P - 1400$$

Since

$$Ft = Mv - Mv_0$$

Fig. 400

$$(P - 1400)120 = \frac{100,000}{32.2} \times 88 - \frac{100,000}{32.2} \times 44$$

$$P = 2540 \text{ lb.}$$

Example 2

Water, under a head of 100 ft., issues from a nozzle of 1-in. diameter and impinges normally upon a flat vane which is moving with a velocity of 25 ft. per sec. in a direction away from the nozzle. Neglecting any losses, compute the impulsive force of the jet upon the vane.

Solution: The velocity of the water as it leaves the nozzle is

$$v_w = \sqrt{2gh} = \sqrt{2 \times g \times 100} = 80.2 \text{ ft. per sec.}$$

The force exerted on the vane is equal and opposite to the force F exerted by the plate on the stream of water, Fig. 401. Since this force remains constant as long as the original conditions prevail, any length of time may be assumed. It is convenient to assume the time interval as 1 sec.

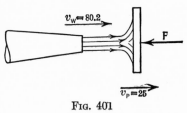

FIG. 401

The weight of water striking the moving vane in 1 sec. is

$$W = 62.5Q = 62.5A(v_w - v_p)$$

$$W = 62.5 \times \frac{\pi}{4}\left(\frac{1}{12}\right)^2 \times (80.2 - 25) = 18.8 \text{ lb. per sec.}$$

Since

$$Ft = Mv - Mv_0$$

$$-F \times 1 = \frac{18.8}{32.2}(25 - 80.2)$$

$$F = 32.2 \text{ lb.}$$

Problems

1. If the system shown in Fig. 402 starts from rest and the coefficient of friction is 0.3, determine the velocity after 8 sec. and the tension in the cord.

Ans. 66.2 f.p.s.

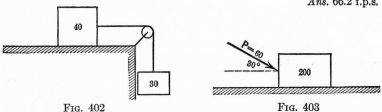

FIG. 402   FIG. 403

2. If the coefficient of friction for the block in Fig. 403 is 0.2, determine the velocity of the block 15 sec. after it starts from rest.   *Ans.* 14.5 f.p.s.

3. If the force P acting on the block described in Prob. 2 is replaced by a variable horizontal force $P = 50 + t^3$, determine the velocity of the block 3 sec. after it starts from rest.   *Ans.* 8.09 f.p.s.

4. A machine gun fires 450 bullets per minute. If each bullet weighs 0.1 lb. and the muzzle velocity is 3000 ft. per sec., compute the average recoil force exerted by the gun.   *Ans.* 69.8 lb.

5. A 2-in.-diameter stream of water with a velocity of 120 ft. per sec. impinges normally upon a stationary flat vane. Compute the impulsive force exerted by the water upon the vane.   *Ans.* 610 lb.

6. If the vane in Prob. 5 has a velocity of 30 ft. per sec. toward the nozzle, compute the force.   *Ans.* 952 lb.

7. Solve Prob. 5 if the vane has a velocity of 30 ft. per sec. away from the nozzle.
                                                       Ans. 344 lb.

8. If the stream of water in Prob. 5 impinges tangentially on a stationary curved vane which changes the direction of the water by 90°, compute the resultant force exerted on the vane.   *Ans.* 862 lb. at 45°.

9. Solve Prob. 8 if the vane is curved through an angle of 120°. *Ans.* 1050 lb.

Art. 105. Conservation of Linear Momentum. If the vector sum of the various separate impulses received by a body or system of bodies is zero, the change of momentum of the system must be zero. This situation exists when two bodies or two parts of the same body interact on each other. By Newton's third law of motion the forces exerted by each body on the other are equal and opposite, and since the time of interaction must necessarily be the same, the impulses of the forces are equal but opposite in direction. Then, if no other external forces are acting during the period of contact, the resultant impulse received by the system is zero, and the total momentum of the system remains constant. If M_1 and M_2 represent the masses of two bodies, v_1 and v_2 their velocities before contact, v_1' and v_2' their velocities after contact, the foregoing statement may be expressed algebraically as follows:

$$M_1 v_1 + M_2 v_2 = M_1 v_1' + M_2 v_2'$$

In using this equation, the algebraic sign of each known velocity must be taken as positive or negative according to some previously chosen convention. A velocity unknown in direction is assumed to be positive, and the sign of the result then determines the correct direction.

It is important to recognize the fact that, although there is no loss of momentum in the interaction of two bodies, there is always a loss of kinetic energy due to generation of heat.

Example

A gun weighing 100,000 lb. fires a projectile weighing 800 lb. with a muzzle velocity of 1200 ft. per sec. Neglecting the effect of the powder charge, compute the initial recoil velocity of the gun, the kinetic energy of the projectile and the kinetic energy of the gun.

Solution: Before the shot is fired, the momentum is zero for the gun and also for the projectile. The conservation of momentum equation thus becomes

$$0 + 0 = \frac{100,000}{32.2} v_1' - \frac{800}{32.2} \times 1200$$

$$v_1' = 9.6 \text{ ft. per sec.}$$

The kinetic energy of the projectile is

$$\frac{1}{2} \frac{W}{g} v^2 = \frac{1}{2} \frac{800}{32.2} (1200)^2 = 17,900,000 \text{ ft-lb.}$$

The kinetic energy of the gun is

$$\frac{1}{2} \frac{W}{g} v^2 = \frac{1}{2} \times \frac{100,000}{32.2} (9.6)^2 = 143,000 \text{ ft-lb.}$$

These results show that, although the gun and projectile have equal momentum, the kinetic energy of the projectile is about 125 times as great as that of the gun.

Problems

1. Solve the Example of Art. 105 if the powder charge weighs 400 lb. and is assumed to have half the velocity of the projectile.
Ans. 12.0 f.p.s.; 17,900,000 ft-lb.; 224,000 ft-lb.

2. A 50,000-lb. freight car with velocity of 6 mi. per hr. collides with another car weighing 80,000 lb. and having a velocity of 2 mi. per hr. in the opposite direction. During the collision the cars are automatically coupled together. Compute their common velocity after the collision and the change of kinetic energy for each car. *Ans.* 1.08 m.p.h.

3. A 250,000-lb. gun fires a 1000-lb. projectile with a muzzle velocity of 2000 ft. per sec. Compute the initial recoil velocity of the gun. If the gun recoils a distance of 4 ft. against a constant force, determine the force.
Ans. 8 f.p.s.; 62,100 lb.

4. A 0.1-lb. bullet is fired horizontally into a 20-lb. block of wood resting on a horizontal surface for which the coefficient of friction is 0.3. If the block is moved a distance of 15 in. along the surface, what was the velocity of the bullet before striking? *Ans.* 989 f.p.s.

5. The ballistic pendulum, consisting of a block of wood suspended by a light cord as shown in Fig. 404, is a device used at one time for measuring the velocity of small projectiles. The bullet is fired horizontally so as to strike the block at its center of percussion and is embedded in the block. (If the length of the cord is large compared to the depth of the block, the center of percussion will very nearly coincide with the geometric center of the block.) The angle θ to which the block swings after being struck is measured. If the bullet weighs 0.1 lb., the block weighs 24 lb., the center of the block is 10 ft. from the point of suspension, and the block swings 45° from the vertical, what was the velocity of the bullet? *Ans.* 3310 f.p.s.

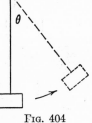

Fig. 404

Art. 106. Impact. The impulse of a force which acts during a very short interval of time (impulsive force) is sometimes called an *impact*. Since the forces exerted by two bodies on each other during collision are impulsive, the act of collision is commonly known as impact. Usually the effect of the impulsive forces on the motion of the bodies is so large in comparison with that of other external forces that the effect of these other forces may be neglected for the duration of the impact. Although the distance traveled during impact, the forces acting, and the time interval may all be unknown, it is possible by means of the principles of momentum to determine the changes of velocity.

Impact between two bodies may be direct or oblique, and central or eccentric. If the mass centers of the bodies, as they approach each other, move along the same straight line, the impact is direct; otherwise the impact is oblique. If the pressures exerted are along the line of mass centers, the impact is central; otherwise the impact is eccentric. Direct central impact will be considered first.

It has already been shown that the total momentum of the system remains constant during impact, as represented by the following equation:

$$M_1 v_1 + M_2 v_2 = M_1 v_1' + M_2 v_2' \qquad (1)$$

A solution of problems in impact is possible by use of this equation alone if the two bodies have the same velocity after impact, that is, if $v_1' = v_2'$. In general, however, this is not the case, and another relation between the velocities is required to complete the solution. This may be had from a consideration of the relative velocities of the two bodies during approach and during separation.

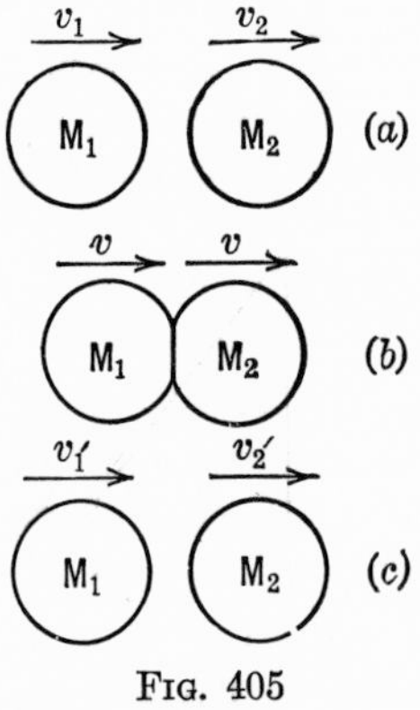

Fig. 405

If the two bodies were perfectly elastic, the relative velocity of separation would be equal to the relative velocity of approach. If the bodies were inelastic, no separation would occur and the relative velocity of separation would be zero. For partly elastic bodies the relative velocity of separation is somewhat less than that of approach. Newton proved that the relative velocity of separation is directly proportional to the relative velocity of approach. The constant of proportionality depends on the materials and is called the *coefficient of restitution*. In Fig. 405 (a) the two bodies are approaching each other and have velocities v_1 and v_2 just before impact. The relative velocity of approach is $v_1 - v_2$. In

Fig. 405 (b) the bodies are in contact and have the same velocity. In Fig. 405 (c) the bodies have just separated and have velocities v_1' and v_2'. The relative velocity of separation is $v_2' - v_1'$. According to the definition stated above, the coefficient of restitution, denoted by e, is:

$$e = \frac{v_2' - v_1'}{v_1 - v_2}$$

This may also be written

$$v_2' - v_1' = e(v_1 - v_2) \tag{2}$$

For perfectly elastic bodies the value of e is unity; for inelastic bodies it is zero. For partly elastic bodies its value may be found by experiment. A few values thus obtained are 0.95 for glass; 0.89 for ivory; 0.55 for steel; 0.50 for cast iron; and 0.15 for lead. Equations (1) and (2) are then sufficient to complete the solution. As previously explained, known velocities should be substituted into these equations as positive or negative according to some predetermined convention; the signs obtained for the unknown velocities in the final solution indicate the directions of these velocities.

The kinetic energy lost because of impact is the difference between the kinetic energy of the system before impact and the kinetic energy of the system after impact.

In oblique impact the velocities of approach may be resolved into components along the line of centers and normal to the line of centers. The normal components remain unchanged by impact. The components along the line of centers are then treated as in direct central impact, and the final components are then combined to obtain the final velocities.

Example

A 20-lb. body with velocity of 15 ft. per sec. collides with a 50-lb. body moving in the opposite direction with velocity of 5 ft. per sec. If the coefficient of restitution is 0.8, determine the magnitude and direction of the velocities after impact and the loss in kinetic energy.

Solution: The two bodies just before impact are shown in Fig. 406 (a). Velocity toward the right is taken as positive.

$$M_1v_1 + M_2v_2 = M_1v_1' + M_2v_2'$$

$$20 \times 15 - 50 \times 5 = 20v_1' + 50v_2' \tag{1}$$

$$v_2' - v_1' = e(v_1 - v_2)$$

$$v_2' - v_1' = 0.8[15 - (-5)] \tag{2}$$

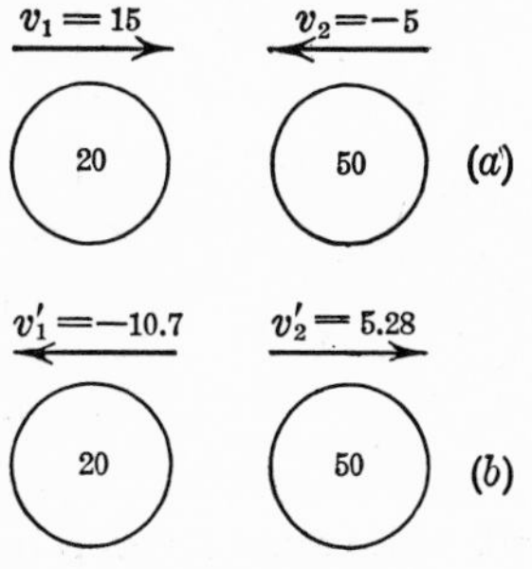

$v_1 = 15$ $v_2 = -5$

20   50   (a)

$v_1' = -10.7$ $v_2' = 5.28$

20   50   (b)

FIG. 406

Simultaneous solution of equations (1) and (2) gives

$$v_1' = -10.7 \text{ ft. per sec.}; \; v_2' = +5.28 \text{ ft. per sec.}$$

In Fig. 406 (b) these velocities are shown in the directions corresponding to their respective signs.

The kinetic energy before impact is

$$K.E. = \frac{1}{2}\frac{20}{32.2}(15)^2 + \frac{1}{2}\frac{50}{32.2}(5)^2 = 89.4 \text{ ft-lb.}$$

The kinetic energy after impact is

$$K.E. = \frac{1}{2}\frac{20}{32.2}(10.7)^2 + \frac{1}{2}\frac{50}{32.2}(5.28)^2 = 57.4 \text{ ft-lb.}$$

The loss in kinetic energy is $89.4 - 57.4 = 32.0$ ft-lb.

Problems

1. A 10-lb. body with a velocity of 20 ft. per sec. strikes a 35-lb. body at rest. If the coefficient of restitution is 0.5, compute the velocities after impact and the loss in kinetic energy.   *Ans.* −3.33 f.p.s.; 6.67 f.p.s.; 36.2 ft-lb.

2. With what velocity must a 12-lb. body strike a 10-lb. body at rest to give the 10-lb. body a velocity of 50 ft. per sec. if the coefficient of restitution is 0.8?
                                                                                          Ans. 51 f.p.s.

3. If the coefficient of restitution is 0.9, from what height must a ball be dropped upon a stationary slab if it is to rebound to a height of 20 ft.? *Ans.* 24.7 ft.

4. A ball is thrown horizontally with an initial velocity of 100 ft. per sec. from a point 5 ft. above the ground and 70 ft. from a vertical wall. How high above the ground will the ball strike the wall if the coefficient of restitution is 0.8?
                                                                                          Ans. 1.72 ft.

5. The 30-lb. ball in Fig. 407 is released from rest in position A and allowed to strike the 40-lb. ball. If the coefficient of restitution is 0.5, to what angle θ with the vertical will the 40-lb. ball swing?   *Ans.* 28.7°.

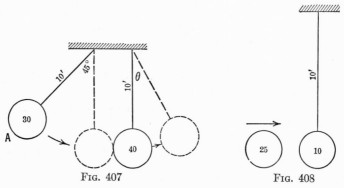

FIG. 407   FIG. 408

6. If the coefficient of restitution is 0.8, with what velocity must the 25-lb. body in Fig. 408 strike the 10-lb. body in order to cause it to swing through an arc of 60°?
                                                                                          Ans. 13.9 f.p.s.

Art. 107. Angular Impulse and Momentum; Plane Motion. The *angular impulse* of a force F with respect to a given axis is the moment of its linear impulse. Thus, if a constant force F at distance r from an axis acts during time t, the linear impulse of the force is Ft and the moment of this linear impulse is

$$\textbf{Angular impulse} = \textbf{\textit{Ftr}} \approx ML^2T^{-1}$$

If the force is variable, the angular impulse may be taken for a differential interval dt and then integrated to obtain the total angular impulse, $\displaystyle\int Fr\,dt$. The unit of angular impulse is the foot-pound-second.

The *angular momentum* of a particle with respect to a given axis is the moment of its linear momentum. The angular momentum of a rotating body is the summation of the moments of momentum of all particles in the body. Thus in Fig. 409 dM is the mass of any particle at distance ρ from the axis O, about which the body is rotating with angular velocity ω. The tangential velocity of the particle is $\rho\omega$, and its linear momentum is $dM\rho\omega$ as indicated. The moment of momentum of the particle is $dM\rho^2\omega$. The summation of these elementary moments of momentum for the entire body is the angular momentum of the body.

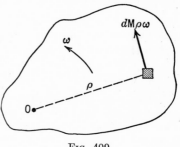

Fig. 409

$$\int dM\rho^2\omega = \omega\int \rho^2\,dM = I_0\omega$$

$$\textbf{Angular momentum} = \textbf{\textit{I}}_0\boldsymbol{\omega} \approx ML^2T^{-1}$$

Since the dimensions of angular momentum are the same as for angular impulse, the same unit, the foot-pound-second, is used for each.

The relation between the angular impulse of the forces acting on a rotating body and the change of angular momentum is obtained from the equation $Fr = I\alpha$ (Art. 87). Let both sides of this equation be multiplied by dt.

$$Fr\,dt = I\alpha\,dt$$

Since $\alpha = d\omega/dt$ by definition, the equation becomes,

$$Fr\,dt = I\,d\omega$$

This equation may now be integrated between limits 0 and t for time and ω_0 and ω for angular velocity.

$$\int_0^t Fr\, dt = I \int_{\omega_0}^{\omega} d\omega = I\omega - I\omega_0$$

If the force F is constant, this equation becomes

$$Ftr = I\omega - I\omega_0$$

It is thus seen that the angular impulse received by a rotating body is equal to the change in angular momentum of the body. This principle may be applied to advantage in the solution of problems in rotation involving force, time, and angular velocity.

Angular impulse and angular momentum are both vector quantities and may be resolved into components or combined into resultants as desired. The vector, representing graphically either angular impulse or angular momentum, is parallel to the axis of rotation and so directed that, if the rotation appears clockwise to an observer looking along the axis, the vector points away. For the counterclockwise rotation shown in Fig. 409, the vectors would be perpendicular to the plane of the figure and toward the observer. This convention may be described as the right-hand screw rule, since the direction of the vector bears the same relation to the direction of rotation as the advance of a right-hand screw to its direction of rotation.

Impulse and momentum methods are also applicable in the analysis of problems in plane motion. As explained in Art. 101, any plane motion may be considered as a motion of rotation, about an axis through the center of gravity of the body, combined with a linear motion of translation of the center of gravity. The equation $Ft = Mv - Mv_0$ is then applied to the motion of translation, and the equation $Ftr = I\omega - I\omega_0$ is applied to the motion of rotation. In the latter case, both angular impulse and angular momentum must be taken with respect to the axis through the center of gravity.

Example 1

A 50-lb. body is suspended from a cable which wraps around a 100-lb. cylinder 3 ft. in diameter and free to rotate about its geometric axis as shown in Fig. 410. If the system is released from rest, determine the angular velocity of the cylinder at the end of 2 sec., and the tension in the cable.

Solution: The system is separated into two parts, one having motion of rotation as shown in Fig. 411 (a), and the other having motion of translation as shown in Fig. 411 (b). The unknown cable tension is represented by T.

The linear impulse of this force is $T \times t = 2T$ and is represented as a vector in the figure.

A procedure involving the use of a principle similar to the D'Alembert principle (Art. 69) is of advantage in many problems of impulse and momentum. The procedure consists of applying the momentum of the body in the reversed direction and then considering the impulse and the reversed momentum as a system in equilibrium. Accordingly, the momentum Mv of the 50-lb. body is

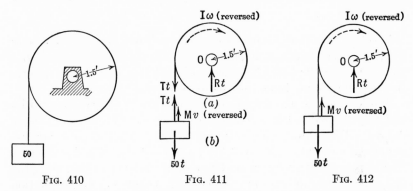

FIG. 410   FIG. 411   FIG. 412

shown reversed in direction in Fig. 411 (b). The vector representing the angular momentum $I_0\omega$ of the rotating part is actually normal to the plane of the figure and parallel to the axis of rotation and thus would not appear in the figure. In order to indicate the direction of the reversed angular momentum, the dotted arrow is used.

The moment of inertia of the cylinder is

$$I_0 = \frac{1}{2}\frac{100}{32.2}(1.5)^2 = 3.50$$

The angular impulse for the cylinder is $T \times 2 \times 1.5$.

$$T \times 2 \times 1.5 - 3.5\omega = 0 \tag{1}$$

For the 50-lb. body

$$T \times 2 + \frac{50}{32.2} \times v - 50 \times 2 = 0 \tag{2}$$

also

$$v = r\omega = 1.5\omega \tag{3}$$

Simultaneous solution of equations (1), (2), and (3) gives

$$T = 25 \text{ lb.}; \ \omega = 21.4 \text{ rad. per sec.} = 204 \text{ r.p.m.}$$

An alternative solution by means of which ω may be determined in a single step consists of taking the two parts together as a single system as shown in Fig. 412. By moments about O

$$50 \times 2 \times 1.5 - \frac{50}{32.2} \times v \times 1.5 - 3.5\omega = 0$$

By substitution of $v = r\omega = 1.5\omega$ and solving

$$\omega = 21.4 \text{ rad. per sec.} = 204 \text{ r.p.m.}$$

The cable tension T may now be determined by considering the 50-lb. body alone.

Example 2

A solid sphere starts from rest and rolls freely down a 30° inclined plane. Compute the linear velocity of the center of the sphere at the end of 2 sec.

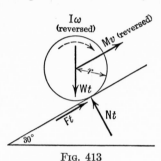

Fig. 413

Solution: Let the weight of the sphere be represented by W, the radius by r, and the static friction preventing slipping by F. The moment of inertia of the sphere with respect to an axis through its center of gravity is

$$I_C = \frac{2}{5}\frac{W}{g}r^2.$$

This is an example of plane motion and may be solved by considering the motion as one of rotation about the center of gravity C, combined with translation of C. The reversed linear momentum Mv and the reversed angular momentum $I_C\omega$ are in the directions indicated in Fig. 413. The various external impulses are also shown. By summation parallel to the incline

$$(W \times 2)\sin 30° - F \times 2 - \frac{W}{32.2}v = 0 \tag{1}$$

By summation of moments about C

$$(F \times 2) \times r - \frac{2}{5}\frac{W}{32.2}r^2 \cdot \omega = 0 \tag{2}$$

Also

$$v = r\omega \tag{3}$$

Simultaneous solution of equations (1), (2), and (3) gives

$$v = 23.0 \text{ ft. per sec.}$$

Problems

1. A 1200-lb. flywheel with a radius of gyration of 1.75 ft. is keyed to a 4-in. diameter shaft which turns in bearings for which the coefficient of friction is 0.05. If the power is cut off when the wheel is rotating at 200 r.p.m., how long will it take to come to rest under the action of friction alone?   *Ans.* 3.98 min.

2. A cylinder 4 ft. in diameter starts up a 15° incline with an angular velocity of 90 r.p.m. If no slipping occurs, how long will it continue to move up the slope?   *Ans.* 3.39 sec.

3. The roller in Fig. 414 weighs 200 lb. and has a radius of gyration of 5 in. If the system starts from rest and no slipping occurs, what will be the angular velocity of the roller at the end of 3 sec.?   *Ans.* 103 r.p.m.

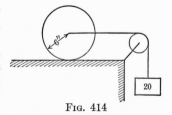

Fig. 414

4. Solve Prob. 3 if the cable is wrapped around the roller and comes off the top in a horizontal direction toward the pulley.   *Ans.* 176 r.p.m.

Art. 108. Conservation of Angular Momentum. If mutual inter-action takes place between rotating bodies or parts of the same rotating body, the action and reaction exerted between any pair are equal and opposite. If no external angular impulse is applied to the system during this time, the resultant angular impulse is zero, and there will be no change in the angular momentum of the system. For instance, let the two wheels shown in Fig. 415 rotate independently of each other

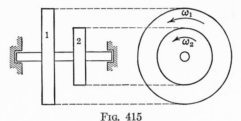

Fig. 415

about the same axis with angular velocities ω_1 and ω_2. If by means of a clutch or other device the wheels are now connected, the angular velocity of each is changed, but the total angular momentum of the system must remain constant, since no external angular impulse has been applied. Thus, if the new angular velocities are ω_1' and ω_2',

$$I_1\omega_1 + I_2\omega_2 = I_1\omega_1' + I_2\omega_2'$$

If no separation occurs after the wheels are connected, the final angular velocities ω_1' and ω_2' are identical, and the above relation becomes

$$I_1\omega_1 + I_2\omega_2 = (I_1 + I_2)\omega$$

Problems

1. Two pulleys similar in all respects to each other are rotating in the same direction on the same shaft with angular velocities of 30 r.p.m. and 60 r.p.m. If the two pulleys are suddenly connected by means of a clutch, what will be their common angular velocity?   *Ans.* 45 r.p.m.

2. In Fig. 415, wheel 1 is a solid cylinder of 2-ft. diameter and weighing 150 lb.; wheel 2 is a solid cylinder of 1.5-ft. diameter and weighing 80 lb. Wheel 1 is rotating at 120 r.p.m., and wheel 2 is at rest. If the two wheels are suddenly connected and forced to rotate together, determine the resulting angular velocity and the loss in kinetic energy.   *Ans.* 92.4 r.p.m.; 42.2 ft-lb.

Art. 109. Impact of Translating Body with Rotating Body. In Fig. 416 is shown a body of mass M_1 and weight W_1, which has linear velocity v_1, just before direct impact with a body of mass M_2 and weight

W_2, which has angular velocity ω_2 about a fixed horizontal axis through O. The linear momentum of the mass M_1 before impact is M_1v_1;

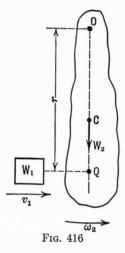

the angular momentum of M_1 with respect to the axis through O is the moment of the linear momentum and is thus M_1v_1r. The angular momentum of the rotating body is $I_2\omega_2$. Thus the total angular momentum of the system before impact is $M_1v_1r + I_2\omega_2$.

If the linear velocity of M_1 after impact is v_1' and the angular velocity of M_2 is ω_2', then the total angular momentum of the system after impact is $M_1v_1'r + I_2\omega_2'$.

During impact the two bodies act on each other with equal and opposite forces; hence the angular impulses received are equal and opposite. The resultant angular impulse is thus zero, and there can be no change in angular momentum of the system. The total momentum of the system before impact may then be equated to the total momentum after impact.

Fig. 416

$$M_1v_1r + I_2\omega_2 = M_1v_1'r + I_2\omega_2' \qquad (1)$$

If the two bodies do not separate after impact, the above equation alone is sufficient to determine the velocity after impact. If separation occurs, a second equation involving the coefficient of restitution may be used. From Art. 106

$$v_2' - v_1' = e(v_1 - v_2)$$

Since $v_2' = r\omega_2'$ and $v_2 = r\omega_2$, the above equation becomes

$$r\omega_2' - v_1' = e(v_1 - r\omega_2) \qquad (2)$$

Equations (1) and (2) together are now sufficient to determine the velocities after impact.

Example

In Fig. 416, let $W_1 = 0.1$ lb. be the weight of a bullet fired with a velocity of 1600 ft. per sec. directly at the center of percussion Q of a timber 6 ft. long of uniform cross section whose weight W_2 is 40 lb., and which is hanging at rest from a horizontal axis O at the upper end. If the bullet remains embedded in the wood, determine the angular velocity of the timber just after the impact.

Solution: The timber may, with very little error, be considered as a slender rod.

$$I_0 = \frac{1}{3}\frac{W}{g}l^2 = \frac{1}{3}\frac{40}{32.2}(6)^2 = 14.9$$

The distance r from O to the center of percussion is

$$r = \frac{k_0{}^2}{\bar{r}} = \frac{\frac{1}{3}l^2}{l/2} = \tfrac{2}{3}l = 4 \text{ ft.}$$

Substituting in equation (1),

$$\frac{0.1}{32.2} \times 1600 \times 4 + 14.9 \times 0 = \frac{0.1}{32.2} \times 4\omega_2' \times 4 + 14.9\omega_2'$$

$$\omega_2' = 1.33 \text{ rad. per sec.}$$

Problems

1. Figure 417 shows a cylinder of 1.5-ft. diameter and weighing 150 lb. from which is suspended a 50-lb. block. If the block is lifted upwards a distance of 2 ft. and

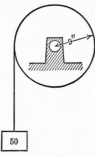

FIG. 417

then dropped, compute the angular velocity of the cylinder immediately after the cable becomes taut.   *Ans.* 57.7 r.p.m.

2. If the timber described in the Example of Art. 109 swings 30° from the vertical, compute the velocity of the bullet before impact.   *Ans.* 1770 f.p.s.

Art. 110. Gyroscopic Action.

Any rotating body is found to resist a change in the direction of its axis of rotation, the effect being particularly noticeable in bodies having relatively large moments of inertia or high speed of rotation. This effect, called *gyroscopic action*, is utilized in such devices as gyroscopic stabilizers, the gyroscopic compass, and gyroscopic steering mechanisms. A complete discussion of gyroscopic action is beyond the scope of this book, and this article will be limited to a consideration of gyroscopic action where the spin axis, torque axis, and precession axis are mutually rectangular.

The principles of angular impulse and momentum may be used in the analysis of gyroscopic motion. In Fig. 418 (*a*) is shown a wheel rotating with angular velocity ω about the horizontal axis AB, henceforth known as the spin axis. The angular momentum of the wheel is $I\omega$, which may be represented by a vector parallel to the axis of rotation as explained in Art. 107, the direction of the vector being from A toward B according to the right-hand screw rule. The angular momentum about the spin axis is thus represented by the vector OM in Fig. 418 (b). Now let a torque T be applied, tending to rotate the body and spin axis about the z axis in the clockwise direction. During a differential time dt, the angular impulse is $T\,dt$, which produces an equal change in angular momentum, represented by the vector ON.

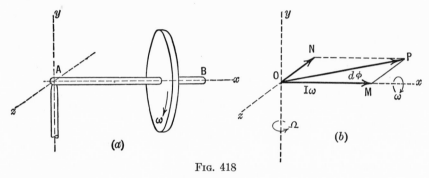

FIG. 418

The resultant of the two angular momentum vectors is OP, at angle $d\phi$ with the original direction of the spin axis. The spin axis thus must rotate about the y axis to the new position OP. As long as the torque continues to act, the spin axis continues to rotate. This rotation of the spin axis is called *precession*. Thus, whenever a torque about an axis normal to the spin axis is applied to a rotating body, the body will not rotate about the torque axis but will rotate or precess about a third axis normal to the two.

The angular velocity of precession will now be determined. From Fig. 418 (b)

$$ON = OM \cdot d\phi$$

$$T\,dt = I\omega \cdot d\phi$$

$$T = I\omega \frac{d\phi}{dt}$$

The quantity $d\phi/dt$, is the rate of change of the angular position of the spin axis and is thus the angular velocity of precession, denoted by Ω. Hence,

$$T = I\omega\Omega$$

As long as the torque and the angular velocity of spin remain unchanged, the velocity of precession will be constant.

A forced precession about an axis perpendicular to the spin axis causes a torque about a third rectangular axis. Thus the wheels of a car going around a curve are forced to precess about a vertical axis through the center of the curve. A torque is thereby produced about an axis tangent to the curve making the road pressure on the outer wheels more and on the inner wheels less than it would be on a straight road. This effect is in addition to that produced by centrifugal action.

Example

A car rounds a curve of 200-ft. radius at 40 mi. per hr. Each wheel and tire has outside diameter of 2 ft., weighs 50 lb., and has radius of gyration of 10 in. Determine the additional road pressure on an outside wheel due to gyroscopic action if the tread is 5 ft.

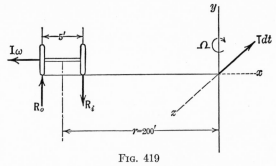

FIG. 419

Solution: In Fig. 419, a pair of wheels and connecting axle are shown as the car recedes from the observer. For the two wheels

$$I = \frac{W}{g} k^2 = \frac{100}{32.2} \left(\frac{10}{12}\right)^2 = 2.16$$

$$v = 40 \text{ mi. per hr.} = 58.7 \text{ ft. per sec.}$$

$$\omega = \frac{v}{r'} = \frac{58.7}{1} = 58.7 \text{ rad. per sec.}$$

$$\Omega = \frac{v}{r} = \frac{58.7}{200} = 0.294 \text{ rad. per sec.}$$

The vector representing the angular momentum $I\omega$ about the spin axis is shown in Fig. 419. The forced precession takes place about the y axis as indicated. The corresponding change in angular momentum must be produced by an equal angular impulse $T\, dt$ in the z direction as shown. The torque T required to produce the angular impulse is given by $T = I\omega\Omega$. The torque is due to an increased pressure R_o on the outer wheel and an equally decreased pressure R_i on the inner wheel and is therefore $R_o \times 5$. Hence

$$T = R_o \times 5 = I\omega\Omega$$

$$R_o = \frac{2.16 \times 58.7 \times 0.294}{5} = 7.46 \text{ lb.}$$

Problems

1. Determine the gyroscopic effect on a side-wheel steamer when it makes a sharp turn to the left.   *Ans.* Left side is tilted upward.

2. Determine the gyroscopic effect on a ship with a screw propeller when a wave strikes it from the front, tending to lift the bow. Assume that the rotation of the propeller is clockwise when viewed from behind.

Ans. Ship turns to the right.

3. Solve the Example of Art. 110 if the velocity of the car is increased to 60 mi. per hr.   *Ans.* 16.7 lb.

4. The wheel of a gyroscope weighs 60 lb. and has a radius of gyration of 2 ft. The wheel spins at 300 r.p.m. about a horizontal axle supported on a pivot 3 ft. along the axle from the wheel. Determine the velocity of precession due to the gravity torque.   *Ans.* 7.35 r.p.m.

5. Show that an airplane, with the propeller and engine rotating clockwise as viewed from the rear, can be turned to the right by elevating a horizontal rudder at the stern.

Supplementary Problems

1. A cylindrical stream of water 2 in. in diameter with a velocity of 50 ft. per sec. impinges normally upon a flat vane moving with velocity of 20 ft. per sec. in the same direction as the water. Compute the force exerted on the vane and the horsepower developed by the vane.   *Ans.* 38.1 lb.; 1.39 hp.

2. If the stream of water described in Prob. 1 impinges tangentially upon a stationary curved vane which changes the direction of the water by 180°, compute the resultant force exerted on the vane.   *Ans.* 212 lb.

3. A stream of water impinges normally upon a flat vane moving in the same direction as the water. Show that the vane develops maximum power when its velocity is one-third the velocity of the stream of water. (Suggestion: Develop the expression for the power in terms of the area of the stream, its velocity, the density of water, and the velocity of the vane. Then apply the customary mathematical procedure for determining a maximum.)

4. Two cubic feet per second of water impinges tangentially on a series of vanes curved through an angle of 120°. The jet velocity is 100 ft. per sec., and the

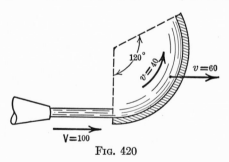

Fig. 420

vane velocity is 60 ft. per sec. parallel to the jet velocity. Compute the absolute exit velocity and the horsepower developed by the vanes. See Fig. 420.

Ans. 53.0 f.p.s.; 25.3 hp.

5. The hammer of a pile driver descends vertically between fixed guides. If the weight of the hammer is 2000 lb. and the friction of the guides is 100 lb., how long will it take the hammer, starting from rest, to acquire a velocity of 75 ft. per sec.? The hammer, after striking, is drawn back up with a velocity of 10 ft. per sec. If this velocity is to be acquired in 2 sec., what cable pull is needed?

Ans. 2.45 sec.; 2410 lb.

6. A 750-lb. projectile is fired with a muzzle velocity of 1800 ft. per sec. from a gun weighing 150,000 lb. Neglecting the reaction due to the discharged gases, what must be the scale of a set of springs to limit the recoil of the gun to a distance of 3 ft.? *Ans.* 3500 lb. per in.

7. A bullet weighing $\frac{1}{2}$ oz. and moving horizontally with a velocity of 2000 ft. per sec. strikes centrally a block of wood weighing 10 lb. which is suspended by a cord from a point 4 ft. above the center of the block. To what angle from the vertical will the block and embedded bullet swing? *Ans.* 31.7°

8. A 170,000-lb. cannon fires a 1500-lb. projectile with a velocity of 1000 ft. per sec. If the recoil velocity is 10 ft. per sec., compute the weight of the powder charge. Assume that the velocity of the powder charge is one-half the velocity of the projectile. *Ans.* 400 lb.

9. A body weighing 100 lb. and having a velocity of 10 ft. per sec. to the right collides with an 80-lb. body having a velocity of 5 ft. per sec. to the left. If the coefficient of restitution is 0.5, solve for the velocities of the bodies after impact and the loss in kinetic energy. *Ans.* Loss = 116 ft-lb.

10. The rotating parts of the windlass shown in Fig. 421 weigh 120 lb. and have a radius of gyration of 1 ft. The 400-lb. body is falling with a velocity of 20 ft. per sec. just before the brake is applied. If the coefficient of friction for the brake

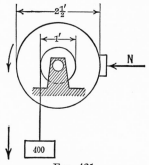

Fig. 421

is 0.5 and friction at the bearing is neglected, in what time will the brake bring the system to rest when applied with a force $N = 400$ lb.? Determine the tension in the cable while the brake is acting. *Ans.* 5.46 sec.; 445 lb.

11. A sphere of 1.5-ft. diameter and weighing 120 lb. starts from rest and rolls down a 30° inclined plane without slipping. Determine the friction at the surface required to prevent slipping and the linear velocity of the sphere after 10 sec.

Ans. 17.2 lb.

12. Replace the sphere of Prob. 11 with a cylinder and solve.

Ans. 20 lb.; 107 f.p.s.

13. A ball is dropped from a height of 20 ft. upon a stationary slab. If the coefficient of restitution is 0.4, how high will the ball rebound? *Ans.* 3.2 ft.

14. If a ball is dropped from a height of h feet upon a stationary slab and rebounds to a height of h' feet, show that the coefficient of restitution is given by $e = \sqrt{h'/h}$.

15. Two cast-iron spheres 6 in. in diameter are mounted on a slender rod with their centers 2 ft. apart. The system rotates at a speed of 30 r.p.m. in a horizontal plane about a vertical axis through the middle of the rod. If, by means of a spring, the spheres are brought into contact at the center, determine the new speed of rotation.   *Ans.* 352 r.p.m.

16. A pair of drive wheels and connecting axle of a locomotive have weight of 4000 lb., a diameter of 64 in., and a radius of gyration of 20 in. Determine the added pressure on the outer wheel due to gyroscopic action when the locomotive rounds a curve of 1000-ft. radius at a speed of 60 mi. per hr. The distance between centers of rails is 4.9 ft.   *Ans.* 205 lb.

17. A rotary airplane engine having a weight of 325 lb. and radius of gyration of 14 in. makes 1300 r.p.m. when the plane has a speed of 150 mi. per hr. Compute the gyroscopic torque exerted on the plane when making a turn of 200-ft. radius. If the distance from the center of pressure of the tail to the center of gravity of the plane is 15 ft., compute the force acting on the tail.   *Ans.* 2060 ft-lb.; 137 lb.

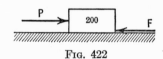

Fig. 422

18. The block shown in Fig. 422 has the driving force $P = (10 + t^3)$ and the resisting force $F = (6 - t^2)$. Solve for the velocity of the block 2 sec. after it has started from rest.   *Ans.* 2.36 f.p.s.

INDEX

(Numbers refer to pages)